Teacher Edition

Eureka Math®
Grade 4
Module 6

Special thanks go to the Gordon A. Cain Center and to the Department of Mathematics at Louisiana State University for their support in the development of *Eureka Math*.

For a free *Eureka Math* Teacher
Resource Pack, Parent Tip
Sheets, and more please visit
https://eurekamath.greatminds.org/teacher-resource-pack

Published by Great Minds.

Copyright © 2015 Great Minds®. No part of this work may be reproduced, sold, or commercialized, in whole or in part, without written permission from Great Minds. Non-commercial use is licensed pursuant to a Creative Commons Attribution-NonCommercial-ShareAlike 4.0 license; for more information, go to http://greatminds.net/maps/math/copyright. "Great Minds" and "Eureka Math" are registered trademarks of Great Minds.

Printed in the U.S.A.
This book may be purchased from the publisher at eureka-math.org
BAB 10 9 8 7 6 5 4 3 2
ISBN 978-1-63255-375-1

Eureka Math: A Story of Units® Contributors

Katrina Abdussalaam, Curriculum Writer
Tiah Alphonso, Program Manager—Curriculum Production
Kelly Alsup, Lead Writer / Editor, Grade 4
Catriona Anderson, Program Manager—Implementation Support
Debbie Andorka-Aceves, Curriculum Writer
Eric Angel, Curriculum Writer
Leslie Arceneaux, Lead Writer / Editor, Grade 5
Kate McGill Austin, Lead Writer / Editor, Grades PreK–K
Adam Baker, Lead Writer / Editor, Grade 5
Scott Baldridge, Lead Mathematician and Lead Curriculum Writer
Beth Barnes, Curriculum Writer
Bonnie Bergstresser, Math Auditor
Bill Davidson, Fluency Specialist
Jill Diniz, Program Director
Nancy Diorio, Curriculum Writer
Nancy Doorey, Assessment Advisor
Lacy Endo-Peery, Lead Writer / Editor, Grades PreK–K
Ana Estela, Curriculum Writer
Lessa Faltermann, Math Auditor
Janice Fan, Curriculum Writer
Ellen Fort, Math Auditor
Peggy Golden, Curriculum Writer
Maria Gomes, Pre-Kindergarten Practitioner
Pam Goodner, Curriculum Writer
Greg Gorman, Curriculum Writer
Melanie Gutierrez, Curriculum Writer
Bob Hollister, Math Auditor
Kelley Isinger, Curriculum Writer
Nuhad Jamal, Curriculum Writer
Mary Jones, Lead Writer / Editor, Grade 4
Halle Kananak, Curriculum Writer
Susan Lee, Lead Writer / Editor, Grade 3
Jennifer Loftin, Program Manager—Professional Development
Soo Jin Lu, Curriculum Writer
Nell McAnelly, Project Director

Ben McCarty, Lead Mathematician / Editor, PreK–5
Stacie McClintock, Document Production Manager
Cristina Metcalf, Lead Writer / Editor, Grade 3
Susan Midlarsky, Curriculum Writer
Pat Mohr, Curriculum Writer
Sarah Oyler, Document Coordinator
Victoria Peacock, Curriculum Writer
Jenny Petrosino, Curriculum Writer
Terrie Poehl, Math Auditor
Robin Ramos, Lead Curriculum Writer / Editor, PreK–5
Kristen Riedel, Math Audit Team Lead
Cecilia Rudzitis, Curriculum Writer
Tricia Salerno, Curriculum Writer
Chris Sarlo, Curriculum Writer
Ann Rose Sentoro, Curriculum Writer
Colleen Sheeron, Lead Writer / Editor, Grade 2
Gail Smith, Curriculum Writer
Shelley Snow, Curriculum Writer
Robyn Sorenson, Math Auditor
Kelly Spinks, Curriculum Writer
Marianne Strayton, Lead Writer / Editor, Grade 1
Theresa Streeter, Math Auditor
Lily Talcott, Curriculum Writer
Kevin Tougher, Curriculum Writer
Saffron VanGalder, Lead Writer / Editor, Grade 3
Lisa Watts-Lawton, Lead Writer / Editor, Grade 2
Erin Wheeler, Curriculum Writer
MaryJo Wieland, Curriculum Writer
Allison Witcraft, Math Auditor
Jessa Woods, Curriculum Writer
Hae Jung Yang, Lead Writer / Editor, Grade 1

Board of Trustees

Lynne Munson, President and Executive Director of Great Minds
Nell McAnelly, Chairman, Co-Director Emeritus of the Gordon A. Cain Center for STEM Literacy at Louisiana State University
William Kelly, Treasurer, Co-Founder and CEO at ReelDx
Jason Griffiths, Secretary, Director of Programs at the National Academy of Advanced Teacher Education
Pascal Forgione, Former Executive Director of the Center on K-12 Assessment and Performance Management at ETS
Lorraine Griffith, Title I Reading Specialist at West Buncombe Elementary School in Asheville, North Carolina
Bill Honig, President of the Consortium on Reading Excellence (CORE)
Richard Kessler, Executive Dean of Mannes College the New School for Music
Chi Kim, Former Superintendent, Ross School District
Karen LeFever, Executive Vice President and Chief Development Officer at ChanceLight Behavioral Health and Education
Maria Neira, Former Vice President, New York State United Teachers

Table of Contents

GRADE 4 • MODULE 6

Decimal Fractions

© 2015 Great Minds. eureka-math.org
G4-M6-TE-B5-1.3.1-01.2016

Grade 4 • Module 6

Decimal Fractions

OVERVIEW

This 20-day module gives students their first opportunity to explore decimal numbers via their relationship to decimal fractions, expressing a given quantity in both fraction and decimal forms. Utilizing the understanding of fractions developed throughout Module 5, students apply the same reasoning to decimal numbers, building a solid foundation for Grade 5 work with decimal operations. Previously referred to as whole numbers, all numbers written in the base-ten number system with place value units that are powers of 10 are hence forth referred to as decimal numbers, a set which now includes tenths and hundredths (e.g., 1, 15, 248, 0.3, 3.02, and 24.35).

In Topic A, students use their understanding of fractions to explore tenths. At the opening of the topic, they use metric measurement to see tenths in relation to different whole units: centimeters, meters, kilograms, and liters. Students explore, creating and identifying tenths of various wholes, as they draw lines of specified length, identify the weight of objects, and read the level of liquid measurements. Students connect these concrete experiences pictorially as tenths are represented on the number line and with tape diagrams as pictured to the right. Students express tenths as decimal fractions and are introduced to decimal notation. They write statements of equivalence in unit, fraction, and decimal forms (e.g., 3 tenths = $\frac{3}{10}$ = 0.3) (**4.NF.6**). Next, students return to the use of metric measurement to investigate decimal fractions greater than 1. Using a centimeter ruler, they draw lines that measure, for example, $2\frac{4}{10}$ or $6\frac{8}{10}$ centimeters. Using the area model, students see that numbers containing a whole number and fractional part (i.e., mixed numbers) can also be expressed using decimal notation, provided that the fractional part can be converted to a decimal number (**4.NF.6**). Students use place value disks to represent the value of each digit in a decimal number. Just as they wrote whole numbers in expanded form using multiplication, students write the value of a decimal number in expanded form using fractions and decimals; for example, 2 ones 4 tenths = $2\frac{4}{10} = (2 \times 1) + (4 \times \frac{1}{10})$ and 2.4 = (2 × 1) + (4 × 0.1). Additionally, students plot decimal numbers on the number line.

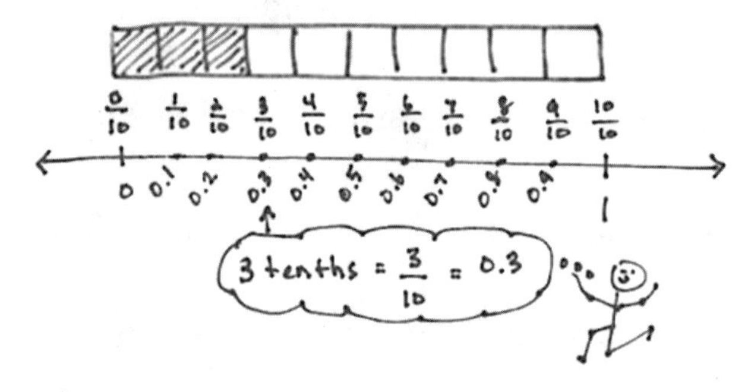

Students decompose tenths into 10 equal parts to create hundredths in Topic B. Through the decomposition of a meter, students identify 1 centimeter as 1 hundredth of a meter. As students count up by hundredths, they realize the equivalence of 10 hundredths and 1 tenth and go on to represent them as both decimal fractions and as decimal numbers (**4.NF.5**). Students use area models, tape diagrams, and place value disks on a place value chart to see and model the equivalence of numbers involving units of tenths and hundredths. They express the value of the number in both decimal and fraction expanded forms.

EUREKA MATH

© 2015 Great Minds. eureka-math.org
G4-M6-TE-B5-1.3.1-01.2016

$$31\tfrac{46}{100} = (3 \times 10) + (1 \times 1) + (4 \times \tfrac{1}{10}) + (6 \times \tfrac{1}{100})$$
$$31.46 = (3 \times 10) + (1 \times 1) + (4 \times 0.1) + (6 \times 0.01)$$

Symmetry with respect to the ones place

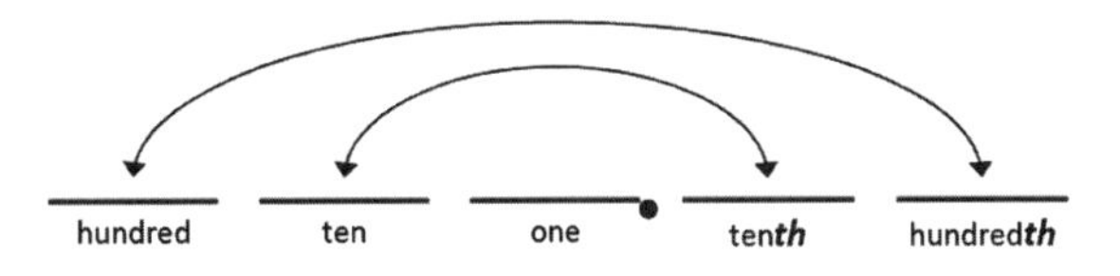

Close work with the place value chart helps students see that place value units are not symmetric about the decimal point— a common misconception that often leads students to mistakenly believe there is a *oneths* place. They explore the placement of decimal numbers to hundredths and recognize that the place value chart is symmetric about the ones column. This understanding helps students recognize that, even as we move to the units on the right side of the decimal on the place value chart, a column continues to represent a unit 10 times as large as that of the column to its right. This understanding builds on the place value work done in Module 1 and enables students to understand that 3.2, for example, might be modeled as 3 ones 2 tenths, 32 tenths, or 320 hundredths. Topic B concludes with students using their knowledge of fraction equivalence to work with decimal numbers expressed in unit form, fraction form, and decimal form (**4.NF.6**).

Mass of Rice Bags (kilograms)

Rice Bag	ones	.	tenths	hundredths
A	0	.	1	0
B	0	.	6	5
C	0	.	7	
D	0	.	4	6

0.7 kg, 0.65 kg, 0.46 kg, 0.1 kg

The focus of Topic C is comparison of decimal numbers (**4.NF.7**). To begin, students work with concrete representations of measurements. They see measurement of length on meter sticks, of mass using a scale, and of volume using graduated cylinders. In each case, students record the measurements on a place value chart and then compare them. They use their understanding of metric measurement and decimals to answer questions, such as, "Which is greater? Less? Which is longer? Shorter? Which is heavier? Lighter?" Comparing the decimals in the context of measurement supports students' justification of their comparisons and grounds their reasoning, while at the same time setting them up for work with decimal comparison at a more concrete level. Next, students use area models and number lines to compare decimal numbers and use the <, >, and = symbols to record their comparisons. All of their work with comparisons at the pictorial level helps to eradicate the common misconception that is often made when students assume a greater number of hundredths must be greater than a lesser number of tenths. For example, when comparing 7 tenths and 27 hundredths, students recognize that 7 tenths is greater than 27 hundredths because, as in any comparison, one must consider the *size of the units*. Students go on to arrange mixed groups of decimal fractions in unit, fraction, and decimal forms in order from greatest to least or least to greatest. They use their understanding of different ways of expressing equivalent values to arrange a set of decimal fractions as pictured below.

© 2015 Great Minds. eureka-math.org
G4-M6-TE-B5-1.3.1-01.2016

Topic D introduces the addition of decimals by way of finding equivalent decimal fractions and adding fractions. Students add tenths and hundredths, recognizing that they must convert the addends to the same units (**4.NF.5**). The sum is then converted back into a decimal (**4.NF.6**). They use their knowledge of like denominators and understanding of fraction equivalence to do so. Students use the same process to add and subtract mixed numbers involving decimal units. They then apply their new knowledge to solve word problems involving metric measurements.

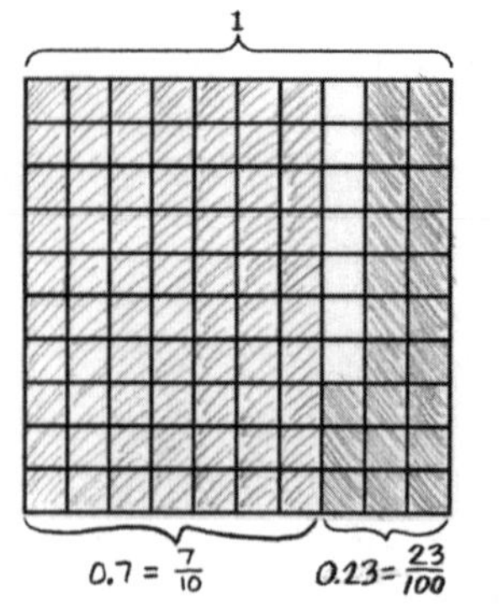

Students conclude their work with decimal fractions in Topic E by applying their knowledge to the real-world context of money. They recognize 1 penny as $\frac{1}{100}$ dollar, 1 dime as $\frac{1}{10}$ dollar, and 1 quarter as $\frac{25}{100}$ dollar. They apply their understanding of tenths and hundredths to write given amounts of money in both fraction and decimal forms. To do this, students decompose a given amount of money into dollars, quarters, dimes, and pennies and express the amount as a decimal fraction and decimal number. Students then add various numbers of coins and dollars using Grade 2 knowledge of the equivalence of 100 cents to 1 dollar. Addition and subtraction word problems are solved using unit form, adding dollars and cents. Multiplication and division word problems are solved using cents as the unit (**4.MD.2**). The final answer in each word problem is converted from cents into a decimal using a dollar symbol for the unit. For example, *Jack has 2 quarters and 7 dimes. Jim has 1 dollar, 3 quarters, and 6 pennies. How much money do they have together? Write your answer as a decimal.*

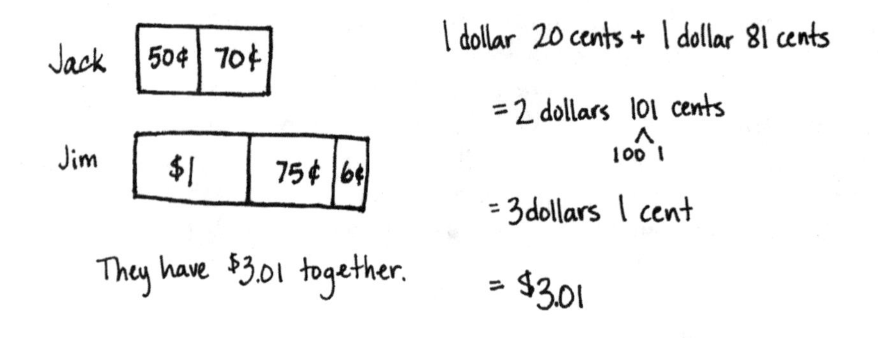

Notes on Pacing for Differentiation

In Module 6, students explore decimal numbers for the first time by means of the decimal numbers' relationship to decimal fractions. Module 6 builds directly from Module 5 and is foundational to students' Grade 5 work with decimal operations. Therefore, it is not recommended to omit any lessons from Module 6.

© 2015 Great Minds. eureka-math.org
G4-M6-TE-B5-1.3.1-01.2016

This diagram represents a suggested distribution of instructional minutes based on the emphasis of particular lesson components in different lessons throughout the module.

- Fluency Practice
- Concept Development
- Application Problems
- Student Debrief

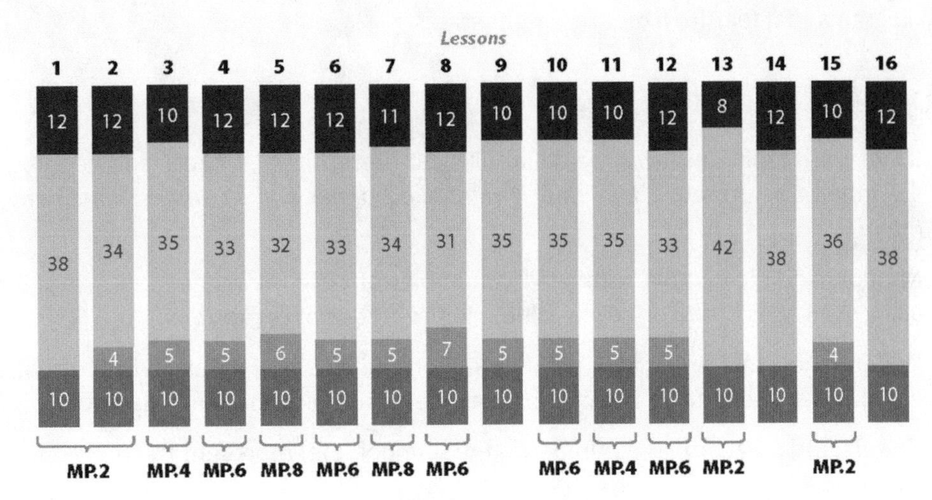

Focus Grade Level Standards

Understand decimal notation for fractions, and compare decimal fractions.

4.NF.5 Express a fraction with denominator 10 as an equivalent fraction with denominator 100, and use this technique to add two fractions with respective denominators 10 and 100. *For example, express 3/10 as 30/100, and add 3/10 + 4/100 = 34/100.* (Students who can generate equivalent fractions can develop strategies for adding fractions with unlike denominators in general. But addition and subtraction with unlike denominators in general is not a requirement at this grade.)

4.NF.6 Use decimal notation for fractions with denominators 10 or 100. *For example, rewrite 0.62 as 62/100; describe a length as 0.62 meters; locate 0.62 on a number line diagram.*

4.NF.7 Compare two decimals to hundredths by reasoning about their size. Recognize that comparisons are valid only when the two decimals refer to the same whole. Record the results of comparisons with the symbols >, =, or <, and justify the conclusions, e.g., by using a visual model.

© 2015 Great Minds. eureka-math.org
G4-M6-TE-B5-1.3.1-01.2016

Solve problems involving measurement and conversion of measurements from a larger unit to a smaller unit.[1]

4.MD.2 Use the four operations to solve word problems involving distances, intervals of time, liquid volumes, masses of objects, and money, including problems involving simple fractions or decimals, and problems that require expressing measurements given in a largerunit in terms of a smaller unit. Represent measurement quantities using diagrams such as number line diagrams that feature a measurement scale.

Foundational Standards

2. MD.8 Solve word problems involving dollar bills, quarters, dimes, nickels, and pennies, using $ and ¢ symbols appropriately. *Example: If you have 2 dimes and 3 pennies, how many cents do you have?*

3. NBT.3 Multiply one-digit whole numbers by multiples of 10 in the range 10–90 (e.g., 9 × 80, 5 × 60) using strategies based on place value and properties of operations.

3. NF.1 Understand a fraction $1/b$ as the quantity formed by 1 part when a whole is partitioned into b equal parts; understand a fraction a/b as the quantity formed by a parts of size $1/b$.

3. NF.2 Understand a fraction as a numberon the number line; represent fractions on a number line diagram.

a. Represent afraction a/b on a number line diagram by marking off a lengths $1/b$ from 0. Recognize that the resulting interval has size a/b and that its endpoint locates the number a/b on the number line.

3. NF.3 Explain equivalence of fractions in special cases, and compare fractions by reasoning about their size.

a. Recognize and generate simple equivalent fractions, (e.g., 1/2 = 2/4, 4/6 = 2/3). Explain why the fractions are equivalent, e.g., by using a visual fraction model.

b. Compare two fractions with the same numerator or the same denominator by reasoning about their size. Recognize that comparisons are valid only when the two fractions refer to the same whole. Record the results of comparisons with the symbols >, =, or <, and justify the conclusions, e.g., by using a visual fraction model.

3. MD.2 Measure and estimate liquid volumes and masses of objects using standard units of grams (g), kilograms (kg), and liters (l). (Excludes compound units such as cm^3 and finding the geometric volume of a container.) Add, subtract, multiply, or divide to solve one-step word problems involving masses or volumes that are given in the same units, e.g., by using drawings (such as a beaker with a measurement scale) to represent the problem. (Excludes multiplicative comparison problems [problems involving notions of "times as much"; see CCSS-M Glossary, Table 2]).

[1] 4.MD.1 is addressed in Modules 2 and 7; 4.MD.3 is addressed in Module 3.

© 2015 Great Minds. eureka-math.org
G4-M6-TE-B5-1.3.1-01.2016

Focus Standards for Mathematical Practice

MP.2 **Reason abstractly and quantitatively.** Throughout this module, students use area models, tape diagrams, place value disks, and number lines to represent decimal quantities. When determining the equivalence of a decimal fraction and a decimal number, students consider the units that are involved and attend to the meaning of the quantities of each. Further, students use metric measurement and money amounts to build an understanding of the decomposition of a whole into tenths and hundredths.

MP.4 **Model with mathematics.** Students represent decimals with various models throughout this module, including expanded form. Each of the models helps students to build understanding and to analyze the relationship and role of decimals within the number system. Students use a tape diagram to represent tenths and then to decompose one-tenth into hundredths. They use place value disks and a place value chart to extend their understanding of place value to include decimal fractions. Further, students use a place value chart along with the area model to compare decimals. A number line models decimal numbers to the hundredths.

MP.6 **Attend to precision.** Students attend to precision as they decompose a whole into tenths and tenths into hundredths. They also make statements such as 5 ones and 3 tenths equals 53 tenths. Focusing on the units of decimals, students examine equivalence, recognize that the place value chart is symmetric around 1, and compare decimal numbers. In comparing decimal numbers, students are required to consider the units involved. Students communicate their knowledge of decimals through discussion and then apply their learning to add decimals, recognizing the need to convert to like units when necessary.

MP.8 **Look for and express regularity in repeated reasoning.** As they progress through this module, students have multiple opportunities to explore the relationships between and among units of ones, tenths, and hundredths. Relationships between adjacent place values, for example, are the same on the right side of the decimal point as they are on the left side, and students investigate this fact working with tenths and hundredths. Further, adding tenths and hundredths requires finding like units just as it does with whole numbers, such as when adding centimeters and meters. Students come to understand equivalence, conversions, comparisons, and addition involving decimal fractions.

© 2015 Great Minds. eureka-math.org
G4-M6-TE-B5-1.3.1-01.2016

Overview of Module Topics and Lesson Objectives

Standards		Topics and Objectives		Days
4.NF.6 4.NBT.1 4.MD.1	A	**Exploration of Tenths**		3
		Lesson 1:	Use metric measurement to model the decomposition of one whole into tenths.	
		Lesson 2:	Use metric measurement and area models to represent tenths as fractions greater than 1 and decimal numbers.	
		Lesson 3:	Represent mixed numbers with units of tens, ones, and tenths with place value disks, on the number line, and in expanded form.	
4.NF.5 4.NF.6 4.NBT.1 4.NF.1 4.NF.7 4.MD.1	B	**Tenths and Hundredths**		5
		Lesson 4:	Use meters to model the decomposition of one whole into hundredths. Represent and count hundredths.	
		Lesson 5:	Model the equivalence of tenths and hundredths using the area model and place value disks.	
		Lesson 6:	Use the area model and number line to represent mixed numbers with units of ones, tenths, and hundredths in fraction and decimal forms.	
		Lesson 7:	Model mixed numbers with units of hundreds, tens, ones, tenths, and hundredths in expanded form and on the place value chart.	
		Lesson 8:	Use understanding of fraction equivalence to investigate decimal numbers on the place value chart expressed in different units.	
		Mid-Module Assessment: Topics A–B (assessment 1 day, return ½ day, remediation or further applications ½ day)		2
4.NF.7 4.MD.1 4.MD.2	C	**Decimal Comparison**		3
		Lesson 9:	Use the place value chart and metric measurement to compare decimals and answer comparison questions.	
		Lesson 10:	Use area models and the number line to compare decimal numbers, and record comparisons using <, >, and =.	
		Lesson 11:	Compare and order mixed numbers in various forms.	

© 2015 Great Minds. eureka-math.org
G4-M6-TE-B5-1.3.1-01.2016

Standards		Topics and Objectives		Days
4.NF.5 4.NF.6 4.NF.3c 4.MD.1	D	**Addition with Tenths and Hundredths**		3
		Lesson 12:	Apply understanding of fraction equivalence to add tenths and hundredths.	
		Lesson 13:	Add decimal numbers by converting to fraction form.	
		Lesson 14:	Solve word problems involving the addition of measurements in decimal form.	
4.MD.2 4.NF.5 4.NF.6	E	**Money Amounts as Decimal Numbers**		2
		Lesson 15:	Express money amounts given in various forms as decimal numbers.	
		Lesson 16:	Solve word problems involving money.	
		End-of-Module Assessment: Topics A–E (assessment 1 day, return ½ day, remediation or further applications ½ day)		2
Total Number of Instructional Days				**20**

Terminology

New or Recently Introduced Terms

- Decimal expanded form (e.g., $(2 \times 10) + (4 \times 1) + (5 \times 0.1) + (9 \times 0.01) = 24.59$)
- Decimal fraction (a fraction with a denominator of 10, 100, 1,000, etc.)
- Decimal number(a number written using place value units that are powers of 10)
- Decimal point (a period used to separate the whole number part from the fractional part of a decimal number)
- Fraction expanded form (e.g., $(2 \times 10) + (4 \times 1) + (5 \times \frac{1}{10}) + (9 \times \frac{1}{100}) = 24\frac{59}{100}$)
- Hundredth (a place value unit such that 100 hundredths equals 1 one)
- Tenth (a place value unit such that 10 tenths equals 1 one)

Familiar Terms and Symbols[2]

- Expanded form (e.g., $100 + 30 + 5 = 135$)
- Fraction (a numerical quantity that is not a whole number, e.g., $\frac{1}{3}$)

[2]These are terms and symbols students have seen previously.

© 2015 Great Minds. eureka-math.org
G4-M6-TE-B5-1.3.1-01.2016

Suggested Tools and Representations

- 1-liter container with milliliter marks
- Area Model
- Centimeter ruler
- Decimal place value disks (tenths and hundredths)
- Digital scale
- Meter stick
- Number line
- Place value chart with decimals to hundredths
- Tape diagram
- Whole number place value disks (hundreds, tens, and ones)

Scaffolds[3]

The scaffolds integrated into *A Story of Units®* give alternatives forhow students access information as well as express and demonstrate their learning. Strategically placed margin notes are provided within each lesson elaborating on the use of specific scaffolds at applicable times. They address many needs presented by English language learners, students with disabilities, students performing above grade level, and students performing below grade level. Many of the suggestions are organized by Universal Design for Learning (UDL) principles and are applicable to more than one population. To read more about the approach to differentiated instruction in *A Story of Units,* please refer to "How to Implement *A Story of Units*."

Assessment Summary

Type	Administered	Format	Standards Addressed
Mid-Module Assessment Task	After Topic B	Constructed response with rubric	4.NF.5 4.NF.6
End-of-Module Assessment Task	After Topic E	Constructed response with rubric	4.NF.5 4.NF.6 4.NF.7 4.MD.2

[3]Students with disabilities may require Braille, large print, audio, or special digital files. Please visit the website www.p12.nysed.gov/specialed/aim for specific information on how to obtain student materials that satisfy the National Instructional Materials Accessibility Standard (NIMAS) format.

© 2015 Great Minds. eureka-math.org
G4-M6-TE-B5-1.3.1-01.2016

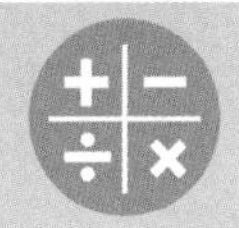

Topic A

Exploration of Tenths

4.NF.6, 4.NBT.1, 4.MD.1

Focus Standard:	4.NF.6	Use decimal notation for fractions with denominators 10 or 100. *For example, rewrite 0.62 as 62/100; describe a length as 0.62 meters; locate 0.62 on a number line diagram.*
Instructional Days:	3	
Coherence -Links from:	G3–M2	Place Value and Problem Solving with Units of Measure
	G3–M5	Fractions as Numbers on the Number Line
-Links to:	G5–M1	Place Value and Decimal Fractions

In Topic A, students use their understanding of fractions to explore tenths. In Lesson 1, students use metric measurement and see tenths in relation to one whole in the context of 1 kilogram, 1 meter, and 1 centimeter. Using bags of rice, each weighing $\frac{1}{10}$ kilogram, students see that the weight of 10 bags is equal to 1 kilogram. Through further exploration and observation of a digital scale, students learn that $\frac{1}{10}$ kilogram can also be expressed as 0.1 kilogram, that $\frac{2}{10}$ kilogram can be expressed as 0.2 kilogram, and that all expressions of tenths in fraction form (up to one whole) can be expressed in decimal form as well. Students then use their knowledge of pairs of 10 to determine how many more tenths are needed to bring a given number of tenths up to one whole. To bring together this metric measurement experience through a more abstract representation, tenths are represented on the number line and with tape diagrams as pictured below. Students express tenths as decimal fractions, are introduced to decimal notation, and write statements of equivalence in unit, fraction, and decimal forms (e.g., 3 tenths = $\frac{3}{10}$ = 0.3) (**4.NF.6**). Finally, meters and centimeters are decomposed into 10 equal parts in a manner similar to that in which 1 kilogram was decomposed.

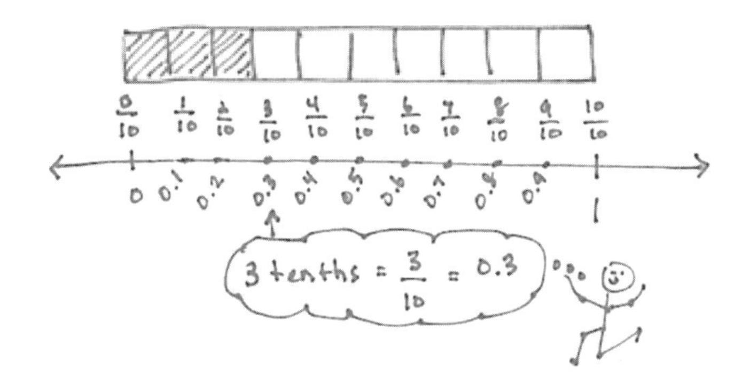

© 2015 Great Minds. eureka-math.org
G4-M6-TE-B5-1.3.1-01.2016

In Lesson 2, students return to the use of metric measurement, this time to investigate decimal fractions greater than 1. They use a centimeter ruler to draw lines that measure, for example, $2\frac{4}{10}$ or $6\frac{8}{10}$ centimeters, and recognize that those numbers can also be expressed in unit form as 24 tenths centimeters or 68 tenths centimeters. Students represent decimal numbers using the area model and see that numbers containing ones and fractions (i.e., mixed numbers) can also be expressed using decimal notation (e.g., 2.4 or 6.8); they also write more sophisticated statements of equivalence (e.g., $2\frac{4}{10} = 2 + \frac{4}{10}$ and $2.4 = 2 + 0.4$) (**4.NF.6**).

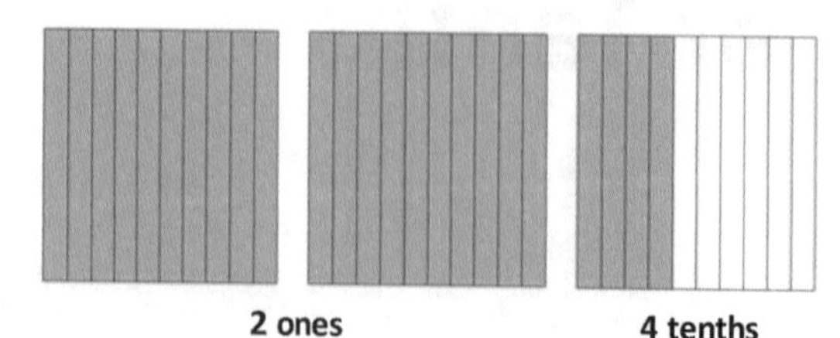

In Lesson 3, students work with place value disks and the number line to represent and identify decimal numbers with tenths as a unit. To explore the place value of each unit in a decimal number with tenths, students use place value disks to rename groups of 10 tenths as ones. Next, students learn to record the value of each digit of a mixed number in fraction expanded form, followed by decimal expanded form (e.g., 2 ones 4 tenths = $2\frac{4}{10} = (2 \times 1) + (4 \times \frac{1}{10})$ and $2.4 = (2 \times 1) + (4 \times 0.1)$). Finally, students model the value of decimal fractions within a mixed number by plotting decimal numbers on the number line.

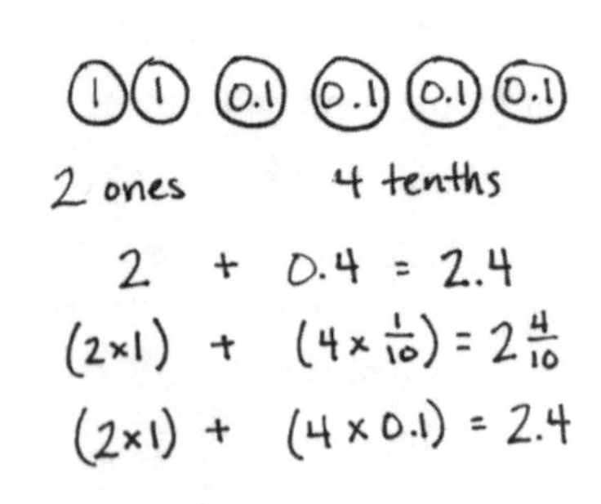

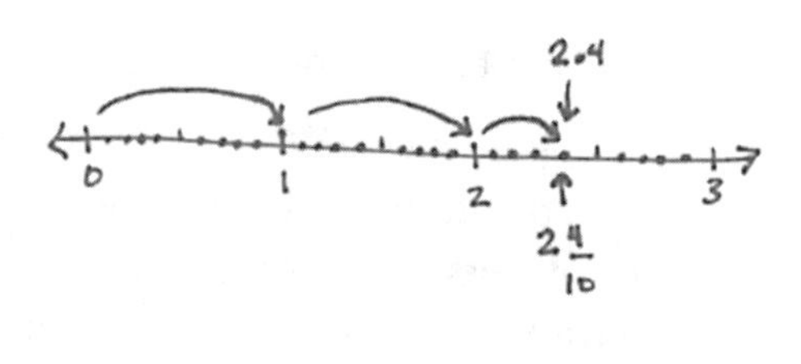

A Teaching Sequence Toward Mastery of Exploration of Tenths	
Objective 1:	**Use metric measurement to model the decomposition of one whole into tenths. (Lesson 1)**
Objective 2:	**Use metric measurement and area models to represent tenths as fractions greater than 1 and decimal numbers. (Lesson 2)**
Objective 3:	**Represent mixed numbers with units of tens, ones, and tenths with place value disks, on the number line, and in expanded form. (Lesson 3)**

© 2015 Great Minds. eureka-math.org
G4-M6-TE-B5-1.3.1-01.2016
EUREKA MATH

Lesson 1

Objective: Use metric measurement to model the decomposition of one whole into tenths.

Suggested Lesson Structure

■ Fluency Practice	(12 minutes)
■ Concept Development	(38 minutes)
■ Student Debrief	(10 minutes)
Total Time	**(60 minutes)**

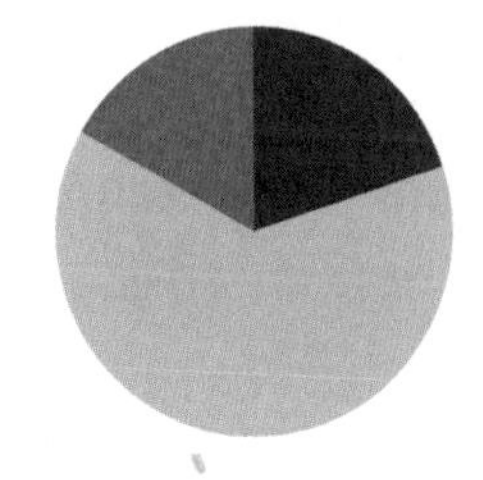

Fluency Practice (12 minutes)

- Divide by 10 **3.NBT.3** (4 minutes)
- Sprint: Divide by 10 **3.NBT.3** (8 minutes)

Divide by 10 (4 minutes)

Materials: (S) Personal white board

Note: This fluency activity prepares students for today's lesson.

T: (Project a tape diagram with a value of 20 partitioned into 10 units.) Say the whole.
S: 20.
T: How many units is 20 divided into?
S: 10.
T: Say the division sentence.
S: 20 ÷ 10 = 2.
T: (Write 2 inside each unit. Write 20 ÷ 10 = 2 beneath the diagram.)

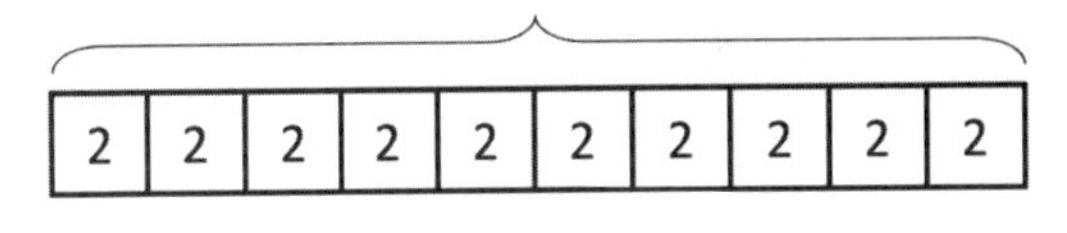

Continue with the following possible sequence: 200 ÷ 10, 240 ÷ 10, 400 ÷ 10, 430 ÷ 10, 850 ÷ 10, 8,500 ÷ 10, 8,570 ÷ 10, and 6,280 ÷ 10.

Sprint: Divide by 10 (8 minutes)

Materials: (S) Divide by 10 Sprint

Note: This Sprint prepares students for today's lesson.

© 2015 Great Minds. eureka-math.org
G4-M6-TE-B5-1.3.1-01.2016

Concept Development (38 minutes)

Materials: (T) 10 0.1-kilogram bags of rice, digital scale, 1-meter strip of paper, sticky notes, meter stick (S) Meter stick (per pair), blank meter strip of paper, centimeter ruler, markers or crayons, blank paper

Note: In preparing this lesson's materials, consider the following. If a digital scale is not available, a pan balance can be used with 100-gram weights labeled as 0.1 kg. Cash register tape can be used to make meter strip papers. During Activity 2, use sticky notes to label each of the 10 1-meter strips of paper with one number: 0.1 m, 0.2 m, 0.3 m, ..., 1.0 m.

Activity 1: Compose and decompose 1 kilogram, representing tenths in fraction form and decimal form.

MP.2

T: (Place 10 bags of rice on the scale.) Here are 10 equal bags of rice. Together, all of this rice weighs 1 kilogram.

T: Let's draw a tape diagram to show the total amount of rice. Draw the tape as long as you can on your blank paper. What is our total amount?

S: 1 kilogram.

T: Let's write 1 kg above the tape diagram to show that the whole tape represents 1 kilogram.

T: How can we represent the 10 equal bags on the tape diagram?

S: Make 10 equal parts.

T: Partition your tape diagram to show 10 equal parts. Each of these parts represents what fraction of the whole?

S: 1 tenth! (Divide the tape diagram into 10 equal parts.)

T: (Remove all bags from the scale. Hold 1 bag in front of the class.) What fractional part of 1 kilogram is 1 bag? Point to the part this 1 bag represents on your tape diagram.

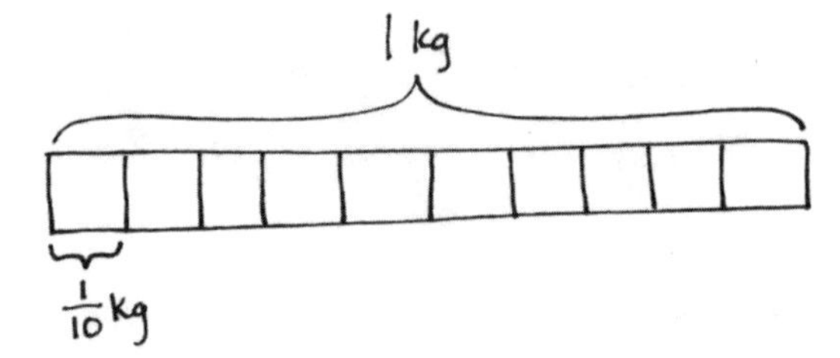

S: $\frac{1}{10}$. (Point to 1 part.)

T: Let's write the weight of this bag on your tape diagram. What is the weight of 1 bag?

S: $\frac{1}{10}$ kilogram.

T/S: (Write $\frac{1}{10}$ kg.)

T: (Place the second bag of rice in front of the class.) What is the weight of 2 bags?

S: $\frac{2}{10}$ kilogram.

Continue to count by tenths to compose 1 kilogram.

T: Let's make a number line the same length as the tape diagram, and mark the tenths to match the parts of the tape diagram. Label the endpoints 0 and 1.

T: Let's see what $\frac{1}{10}$ kilogram looks like on the scale. (Place 1 bag on the scale.) It says zero point one kilogram.

© 2015 Great Minds. eureka-math.org
G4-M6-TE-B5-1.3.1-01.2016
EUREKA MATH

T: (Write 0.1 on the number line.) This is a **decimal number**. We read this decimal as 1 **tenth**, just like the fraction $\frac{1}{10}$. The decimal form is written as zero point one. The dot in a decimal number is called a **decimal point**. (Write 1 tenth = $\frac{1}{10}$ = 0.1.) 1 tenth is written in unit form, as a **decimal fraction**, and as a decimal number. They are all equal.

T: Write 1 tenth in decimal form on your number line, just like I did.

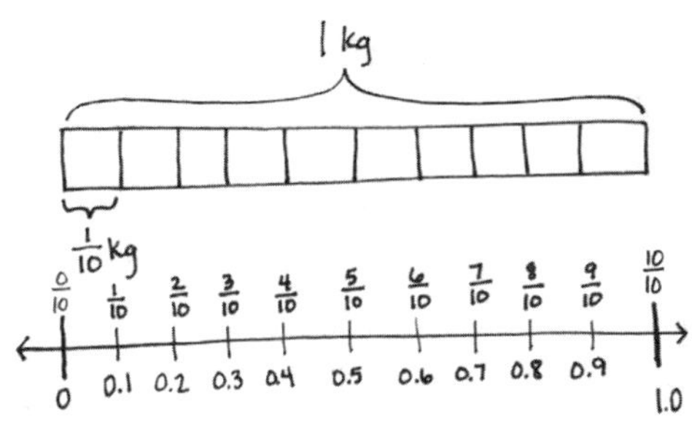

S: (Write 0.1 on the number line.)

T: Let's see how the number in decimal form changes as we add more bags or tenths of a kilogram.

T: We can express the weight of 1 bag two ways: zero point one kilogram, or 1 tenth kilogram. Tell me the weight of 2 bags using both ways. Start with the decimal point way.

S: Zero point two kilogram. 2 tenths kilogram.

T: (Invite a few students to the front of the room. Distribute two to three bags to each student.) As we add each bag, count and see how the scale shows the weight in decimal form, and record it on your number line.

S/T: Zero point two kilogram, 2 tenths kilogram, zero point three kilogram, 3 tenths kilogram, ..., zero point nine kilogram, 9 tenths kilogram, one point zero kilogram, 1 kilogram!

> **NOTES ON MULTIPLE MEANS OF ENGAGEMENT:**
>
> Students who are not invited to place weights on the scale may enjoy shading units or placing counters in the tape diagram for each bag placed on the scale.

T: Notice the scale uses decimal form for 10 tenths. 10 tenths is equal to how many ones and how many tenths?

S: 1 one and 0 tenths.

T: So, we record that as 1 point 0. Revise your number line.

T: (Take off 2 bags to show 0.8 kg.) How many tenths are on the scale now?

S: 8 tenths kilogram.

T: Record the weight of 8 bags in fraction form and decimal form. Use an equal sign.

S: (Write $\frac{8}{10}$ kg = 0.8 kg.)

T: I have 2 bags in my hand. Write the weight of this amount of rice in fraction form and decimal form. Use an equal sign.

S: (Write $\frac{2}{10}$ kg = 0.2 kg.)

T: When I put together $\frac{2}{10}$ kilogram and $\frac{8}{10}$ kilogram, I have...?

S: 1 kilogram!

T: (Write 0.2 kilogram + 0.8 kilogram = 1 kilogram.) What other pairs of tenths would make 1 kilogram when put together?

S: $\frac{3}{10}$ kilogram and $\frac{7}{10}$ kilogram. → $\frac{6}{10}$ kilogram and $\frac{4}{10}$ kilogram.

As students share out pairs, write the number sentences using decimal form.

© 2015 Great Minds. eureka-math.org
G4-M6-TE-B5-1.3.1-01.2016

Activity 2: Decompose 1 meter, representing tenths in fraction form and decimal form.

Give each pair of students a meter stick and two strips of paper that are each 1 meter long. Ask them to use their meter sticks to divide each paper strip into 10 equal parts. Have them then shade with markers or crayons to show different numbers of tenths. As they work, collect strips to make an ordered set on the board, starting with 1 meter to show 10 tenths, 9 tenths, etc. Generate and record the partner each strip needs to make 1 meter next to each strip (e.g., 0.9 meter + 0.1 meter = 1 meter). Have students then generate two or three equivalent number sentences showing the equality of fraction form and decimal form (e.g., $\frac{1}{10}$ meter = 0.1 meter).

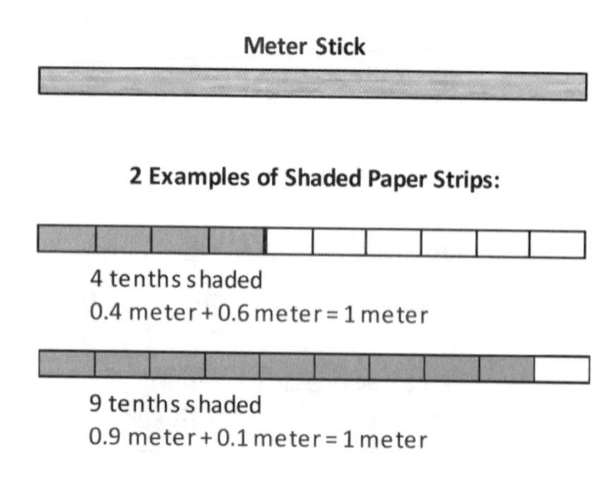

Activity 3: Decompose 1 centimeter, representing tenths in fraction form and decimal form.

T: Now that we have practiced decomposing a meter into tenths, let's use that same thinking to decompose a centimeter into tenths.

T: Take out your centimeter ruler, and draw a 1-centimeter line on the blank paper.

S: (Draw.)

T: Each centimeter has been partitioned into equal parts. How many equal parts are there from 0 to 1 centimeter?

S: 10 parts.

T: What fraction of a centimeter is one part?

S: 1 tenth.

T: How many units of 1 tenth equal 1 centimeter?

S: 10 tenths.

T: Label your line. 1 cm = $\frac{10}{10}$ cm.

T: Below your line, make a line that measures $\frac{9}{10}$ centimeter. Label your line in fraction form and decimal form.

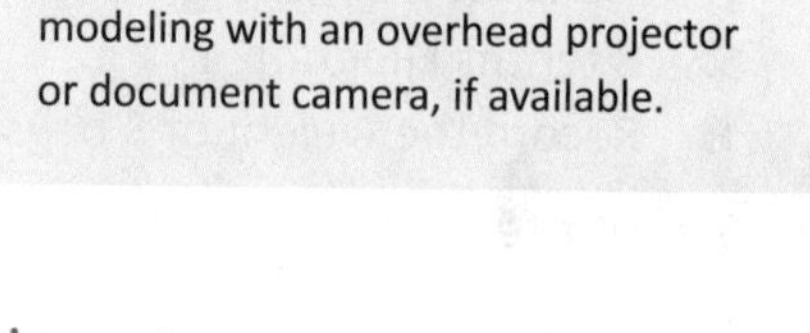

$\frac{9}{10}$ cm + $\frac{1}{10}$ cm = 1cm   0.9cm + 0.1cm = 1cm

$\frac{8}{10}$ cm + $\frac{2}{10}$ cm = 1cm   0.8cm + 0.2cm = 1cm

S: (Draw a line 0.9 cm in length. Write $\frac{9}{10}$ cm = 0.9 cm.)

T: How many more tenths of a centimeter do we need to have 1 centimeter?

S: We would need 0.1 cm more.

T: (Write $\frac{9}{10}$ cm + $\frac{1}{10}$ cm = 1 cm and 0.9 cm + 0.1 cm = 1 cm.)

NOTES ON MULTIPLE MEANS OF REPRESENTATION:

Students with low vision or other perceptual challenges may find drawing a 1-centimeter line and deciphering millimeters difficult. A centimeter stencil that students can easily trace may be beneficial. In addition to having students interact with a to-scale centimeter (such as a cube), it may help to project teacher modeling with an overhead projector or document camera, if available.

© 2015 Great Minds. eureka-math.org
G4-M6-TE-B5-1.3.1-01.2016

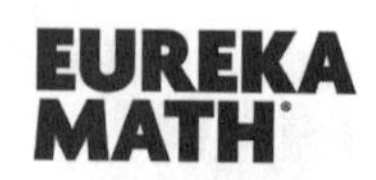

T: Now, draw a line below these lines that measures $\frac{8}{10}$ centimeter. Label this new line in fraction and decimal form. Write an addition sentence in both fraction and decimal form to show how many more tenths of a centimeter you need to get to 1 centimeter.

S: (Draw and label $\frac{8}{10}$ cm and 0.8 cm. Write $\frac{8}{10}$ cm + $\frac{2}{10}$ cm = 1 cm and 0.8 cm + 0.2 cm = 1 cm.)

T: Continue writing more pairs as you work, making a line that is $\frac{1}{10}$ centimeter shorter each time.

Select students to share so that the fraction form and decimal form of the number sentence are presented to the class.

Problem Set (10 minutes)

Students should do their personal best to complete the Problem Set within the allotted 10 minutes. Some problems do not specify a method for solving. This is an intentional reduction of scaffolding that invokes MP.5, Use Appropriate Tools Strategically. Students should solve these problems using the RDW approach used for Application Problems.

For some classes, it may be appropriate to modify the assignment by specifying which problems students should work on first. With this option, let the purposeful sequencing of the Problem Set guide the selections so that problems continue to be scaffolded. Balance word problems with other problem types to ensure a range of practice. Consider assigning incomplete problems for homework or at another time during the day.

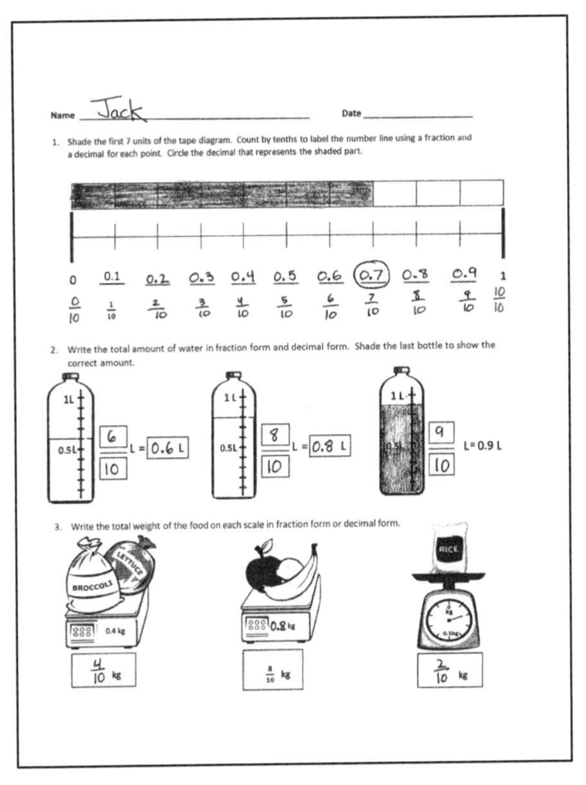
Name Jack Date

1. Shade the first 7 units of the tape diagram. Count by tenths to label the number line using a fraction and a decimal for each point. Circle the decimal that represents the shaded part.

0, 0.1, 0.2, 0.3, 0.4, 0.5, 0.6, (0.7), 0.8, 0.9, 1

$\frac{0}{10}$, $\frac{1}{10}$, $\frac{2}{10}$, $\frac{3}{10}$, $\frac{4}{10}$, $\frac{5}{10}$, $\frac{6}{10}$, $\frac{7}{10}$, $\frac{8}{10}$, $\frac{9}{10}$, $\frac{10}{10}$

2. Write the total amount of water in fraction form and decimal form. Shade the last bottle to show the correct amount.

$\frac{6}{10}$ L = 0.6 L $\frac{8}{10}$ L = 0.8 L $\frac{9}{10}$ L = 0.9 L

3. Write the total weight of the food on each scale in fraction form or decimal form.

$\frac{4}{10}$ kg $\frac{8}{10}$ kg $\frac{2}{10}$ kg

Student Debrief (10 minutes)

Lesson Objective: Use metric measurement to model the decomposition of one whole into tenths.

The Student Debrief is intended to invite reflection and active processing of the total lesson experience.

Invite students to review their solutions for the Problem Set. They should check work by comparing answers with a partner before going over answers as a class. Look for misconceptions or misunderstandings that can be addressed in the Debrief. Guide students in a conversation to debrief the Problem Set and process the lesson.

Any combination of the questions below may be used to lead the discussion.

- In Problem 2, 8 tenths liter was represented. How is that different from the 8 tenths kilogram in Problem 3? How is representing 8 tenths liter similar to representing 8 tenths kilogram?

© 2015 Great Minds. eureka-math.org
G4-M6-TE-B5-1.3.1-01.2016

- In Problem 2, we measured liters of water. What other type of material might we be measuring when we measure 6 tenths of a liter? Where have you seen or used liters in your everyday life?
- Look at Problem 5. How is getting to 1 centimeter similar to getting to 10, as you did in earlier grades? How did getting to 10 help you in the past? How do you think getting to 1 might help you now?
- What relationship does 1 **tenth** have to 1?
- How did your work with **decimal fractions** like $\frac{3}{10}$, $\frac{7}{10}$, or $\frac{9}{10}$ prepare you for this lesson?
- Today, we studied **decimal numbers**, and we wrote them in fraction form and decimal form. How are the two forms alike? How are they different?
- What purpose does a **decimal point** serve?
- During Fluency Practice, you divided numbers by 10. How did today's work of dividing one whole into parts relate to your fluency work? When you divide 20 by 10, what is your equal unit? When you divide 1 into 10 equal parts, what is your equal unit?

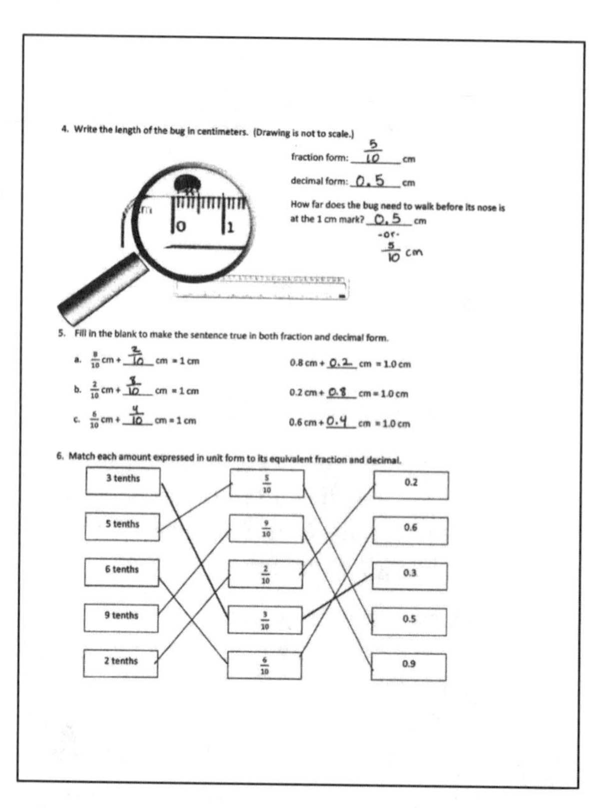

4. Write the length of the bug in centimeters. (Drawing is not to scale.)

fraction form: $\frac{5}{10}$ cm

decimal form: 0.5 cm

How far does the bug need to walk before its nose is at the 1 cm mark? 0.5 cm -or- $\frac{5}{10}$ cm

5. Fill in the blank to make the sentence true in both fraction and decimal form.

a. $\frac{8}{10}$ cm + $\frac{2}{10}$ cm = 1 cm 0.8 cm + 0.2 cm = 1.0 cm

b. $\frac{2}{10}$ cm + $\frac{8}{10}$ cm = 1 cm 0.2 cm + 0.8 cm = 1.0 cm

c. $\frac{6}{10}$ cm + $\frac{4}{10}$ cm = 1 cm 0.6 cm + 0.4 cm = 1.0 cm

6. Match each amount expressed in unit form to its equivalent fraction and decimal.

3 tenths	$\frac{5}{10}$	0.2
5 tenths	$\frac{9}{10}$	0.6
6 tenths	$\frac{2}{10}$	0.3
9 tenths	$\frac{3}{10}$	0.5
2 tenths	$\frac{6}{10}$	0.9

Exit Ticket (3 minutes)

After the Student Debrief, instruct students to complete the Exit Ticket. A review of their work will help with assessing students' understanding of the concepts that were presented in today's lesson and planning more effectively for future lessons. The questions may be read aloud to the students.

© 2015 Great Minds. eureka-math.org
G4-M6-TE-B5-1.3.1-01.2016

Number Correct: _______

A

Divide by 10

1.	20 ÷ 10 =	
2.	30 ÷ 10 =	
3.	40 ÷ 10 =	
4.	80 ÷ 10 =	
5.	50 ÷ 10 =	
6.	90 ÷ 10 =	
7.	70 ÷ 10 =	
8.	60 ÷ 10 =	
9.	10 ÷ 10 =	
10.	100 ÷ 10 =	
11.	20 ÷ 10 =	
12.	120 ÷ 10 =	
13.	50 ÷ 10 =	
14.	150 ÷ 10 =	
15.	80 ÷ 10 =	
16.	180 ÷ 10 =	
17.	280 ÷ 10 =	
18.	380 ÷ 10 =	
19.	680 ÷ 10 =	
20.	640 ÷ 10 =	
21.	870 ÷ 10 =	
22.	430 ÷ 10 =	

23.	50 ÷ 10 =	
24.	850 ÷ 10 =	
25.	1,850 ÷ 10 =	
26.	70 ÷ 10 =	
27.	270 ÷ 10 =	
28.	4,270 ÷ 10 =	
29.	90 ÷ 10 =	
30.	590 ÷ 10 =	
31.	7,590 ÷ 10 =	
32.	120 ÷ 10 =	
33.	1,200 ÷ 10 =	
34.	2,000 ÷ 10 =	
35.	240 ÷ 10 =	
36.	2,400 ÷ 10 =	
37.	4,000 ÷ 10 =	
38.	690 ÷ 10 =	
39.	6,900 ÷ 10 =	
40.	9,000 ÷ 10 =	
41.	940 ÷ 10 =	
42.	5,280 ÷ 10 =	
43.	6,700 ÷ 10 =	
44.	7,000 ÷ 10 =	

© 2015 Great Minds. eureka-math.org
G4-M6-TE-B5-1.3.1-01.2016

B

Divide by 10

Number Correct: ______

Improvement: ______

1.	10 ÷ 10 =	
2.	20 ÷ 10 =	
3.	30 ÷ 10 =	
4.	70 ÷ 10 =	
5.	40 ÷ 10 =	
6.	80 ÷ 10 =	
7.	60 ÷ 10 =	
8.	50 ÷ 10 =	
9.	90 ÷ 10 =	
10.	100 ÷ 10 =	
11.	30 ÷ 10 =	
12.	130 ÷ 10 =	
13.	60 ÷ 10 =	
14.	160 ÷ 10 =	
15.	90 ÷ 10 =	
16.	190 ÷ 10 =	
17.	290 ÷ 10 =	
18.	390 ÷ 10 =	
19.	690 ÷ 10 =	
20.	650 ÷ 10 =	
21.	860 ÷ 10 =	
22.	420 ÷ 10 =	

23.	40 ÷ 10 =	
24.	840 ÷ 10 =	
25.	1,840 ÷ 10 =	
26.	80 ÷ 10 =	
27.	280 ÷ 10 =	
28.	4,280 ÷ 10 =	
29.	60 ÷ 10 =	
30.	560 ÷ 10 =	
31.	7,560 ÷ 10 =	
32.	130 ÷ 10 =	
33.	1,300 ÷ 10 =	
34.	3,000 ÷ 10 =	
35.	250 ÷ 10 =	
36.	2,500 ÷ 10 =	
37.	5,000 ÷ 10 =	
38.	740 ÷ 10 =	
39.	7,400 ÷ 10 =	
40.	4,000 ÷ 10 =	
41.	910 ÷ 10 =	
42.	5,820 ÷ 10 =	
43.	7,600 ÷ 10 =	
44.	6,000 ÷ 10 =	

© 2015 Great Minds. eureka-math.org
G4-M6-TE-B5-1.3.1-01.2016

Name ______________________________ Date ______________

1. Shade the first 7 units of the tape diagram. Count by tenths to label the number line using a fraction and a decimal for each point. Circle the decimal that represents the shaded part.

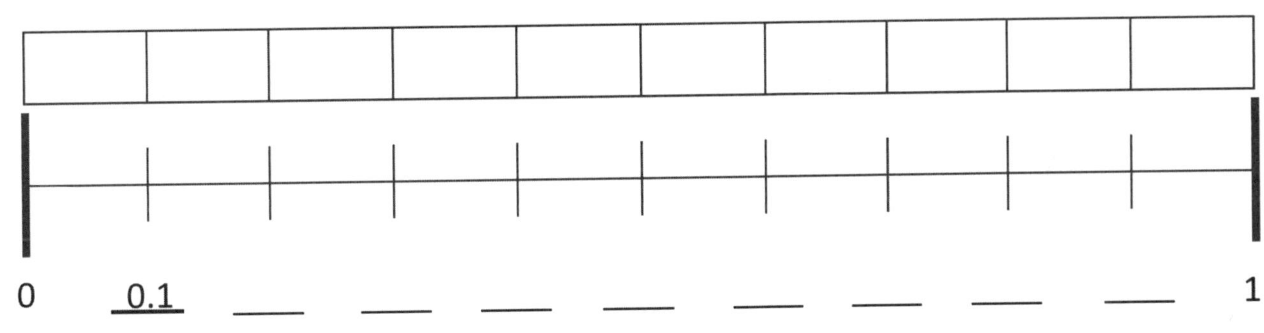

0   0.1 ___ ___ ___ ___ ___ ___ ___ ___ 1

$\frac{1}{10}$

2. Write the total amount of water in fraction form and decimal form. Shade the last bottle to show the correct amount.

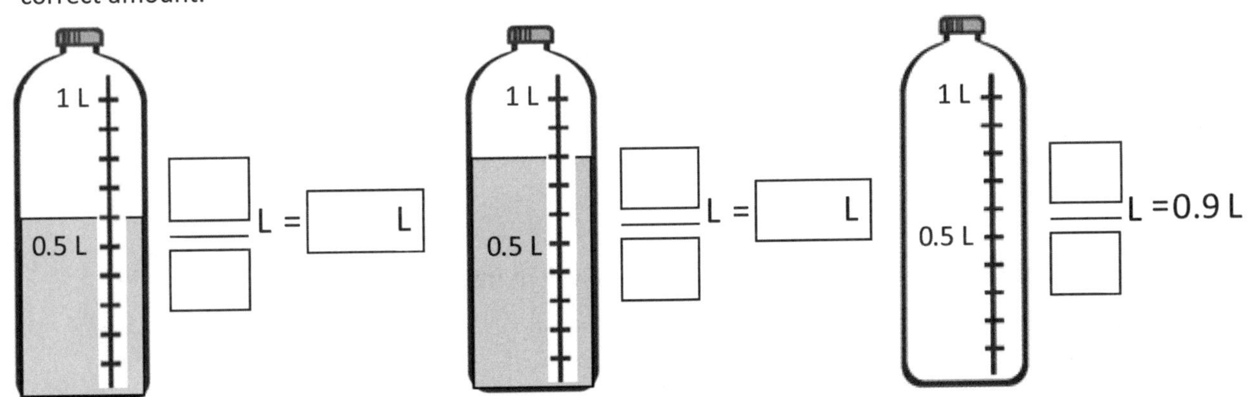

3. Write the total weight of the food on each scale in fraction form or decimal form.

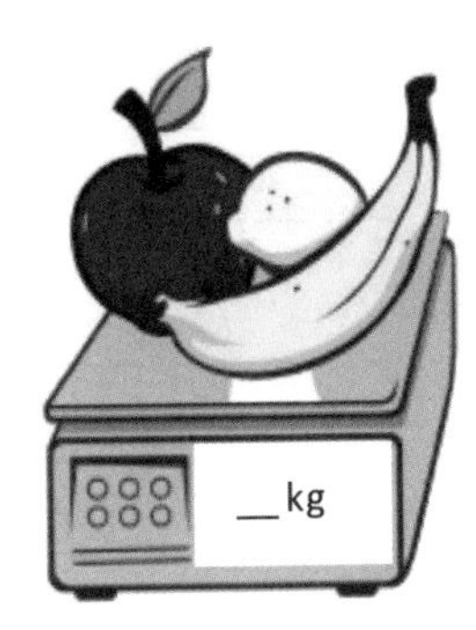

kg $\frac{8}{10}$ kg   kg

© 2015 Great Minds. eureka-math.org
G4-M6-TE-B5-1.3.1-01.2016

4. Write the length of the bug in centimeters. (The drawing is not to scale.)

Fraction form: __________ cm

Decimal form: __________ cm

How far does the bug need to walk before its nose is at the 1 cm mark? __________ cm

5. Fill in the blank to make the sentence true in both fraction form and decimal form.

a. $\frac{8}{10}$ cm + ______ cm = 1 cm 0.8 cm + ______ cm = 1.0 cm

b. $\frac{2}{10}$ cm + ______ cm = 1 cm 0.2 cm + ______ cm = 1.0 cm

c. $\frac{6}{10}$ cm + ______ cm = 1 cm 0.6 cm + ______ cm = 1.0 cm

6. Match each amount expressed in unit form to its equivalent fraction and decimal forms.

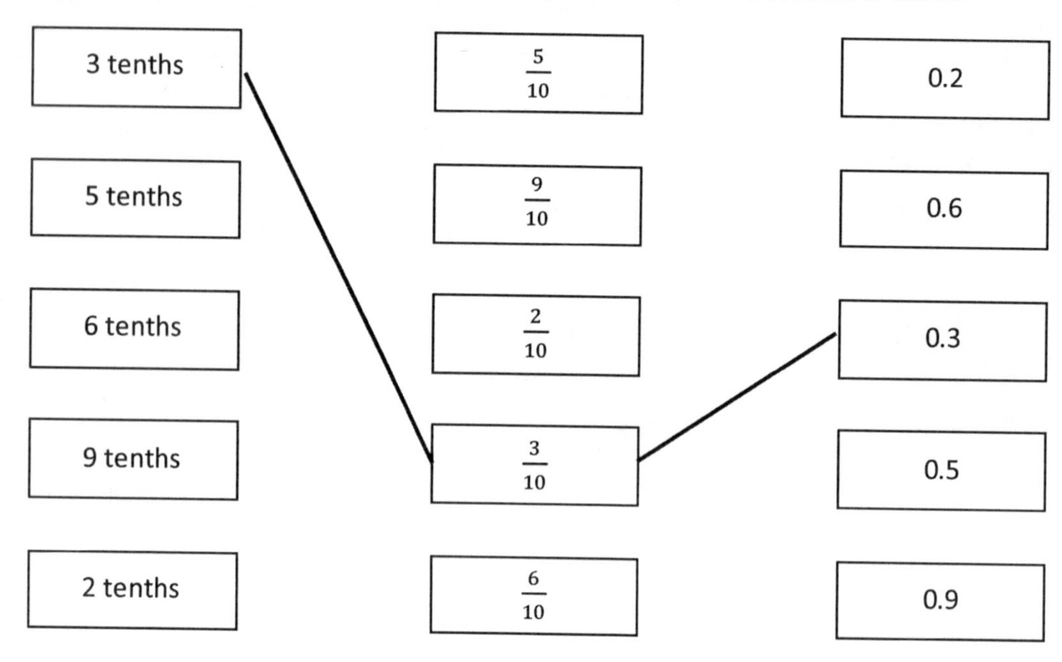

© 2015 Great Minds. eureka-math.org
G4-M6-TE-B5-1.3.1-01.2016
EUREKA MATH

Name ______________________________ Date ______________

1. Fill in the blank to make the sentence true in both fraction form and decimal form.

   a. $\frac{9}{10}$ cm + ______ cm = 1 cm 0.9 cm + ______ cm = 1.0 cm

   b. $\frac{4}{10}$ cm + ______ cm = 1 cm 0.4 cm + ______ cm = 1.0 cm

2. Match each amount expressed in unit form to its fraction form and decimal form.

3 tenths	$\frac{5}{10}$	0.8
8 tenths	$\frac{8}{10}$	0.3
5 tenths	$\frac{3}{10}$	0.5

© 2015 Great Minds. eureka-math.org
G4-M6-TE-B5-1.3.1-01.2016

Name ______________________________ Date ________________

Shade the first 4 units of the tape diagram. Count by tenths to label the number line using a fraction and a decimal for each point. Circle the decimal that represents the shaded part.

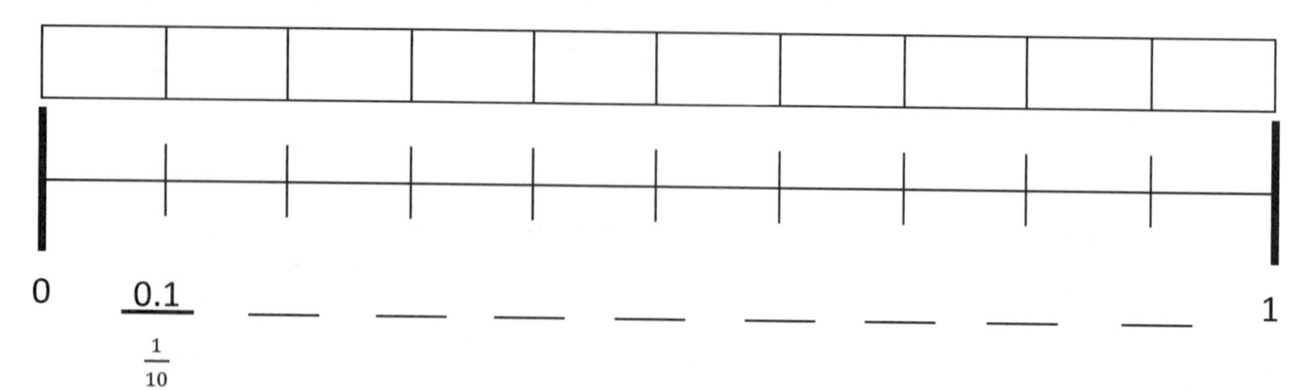

2. Write the total amount of water in fraction form and decimal form. Shade the last bottle to show the correct amount.

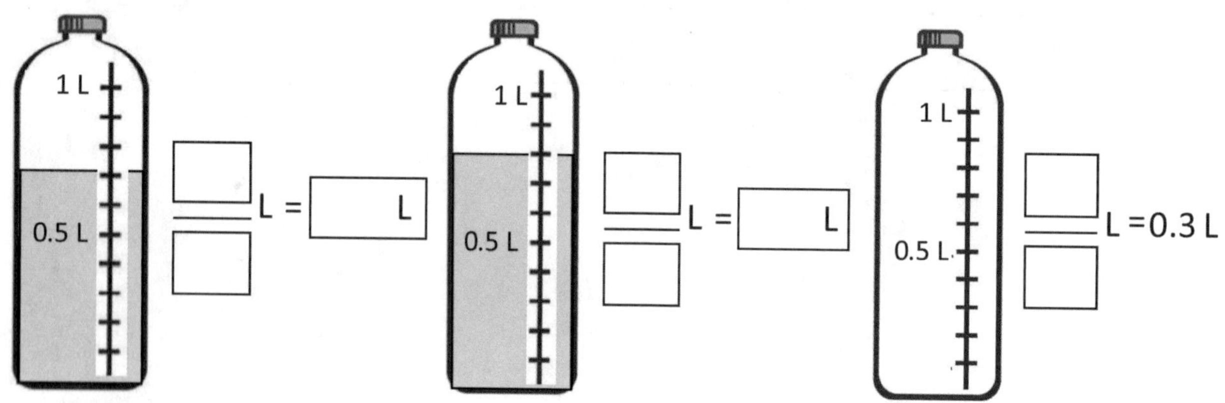

3. Write the total weight of the food on each scale in fraction form or decimal form.

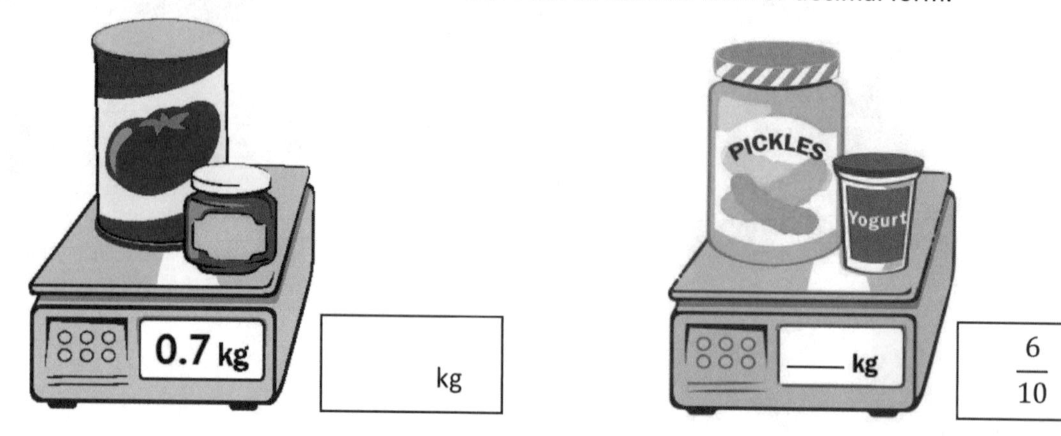

© 2015 Great Minds. eureka-math.org
G4-M6-TE-B5-1.3.1-01.2016

4. Write the length of the bug in centimeters. (The drawing is not to scale.)

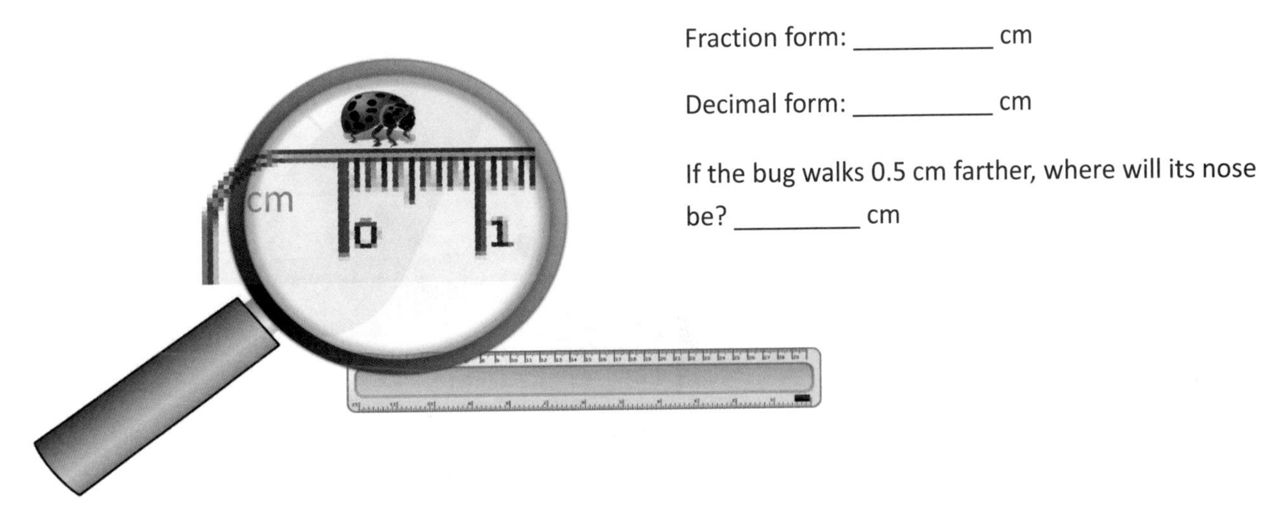

Fraction form: __________ cm

Decimal form: __________ cm

If the bug walks 0.5 cm farther, where will its nose be? _________ cm

5. Fill in the blank to make the sentence true in both fraction and decimal form.

a. $\frac{4}{10}$ cm + ______ cm = 1 cm   0.4 cm + ______ cm = 1.0 cm

b. $\frac{3}{10}$ cm + ______ cm = 1 cm   0.3 cm + ______ cm = 1.0 cm

c. $\frac{8}{10}$ cm + ______ cm = 1 cm   0.8 cm + ______ cm = 1.0 cm

6. Match each amount expressed in unit form to its equivalent fraction and decimal.

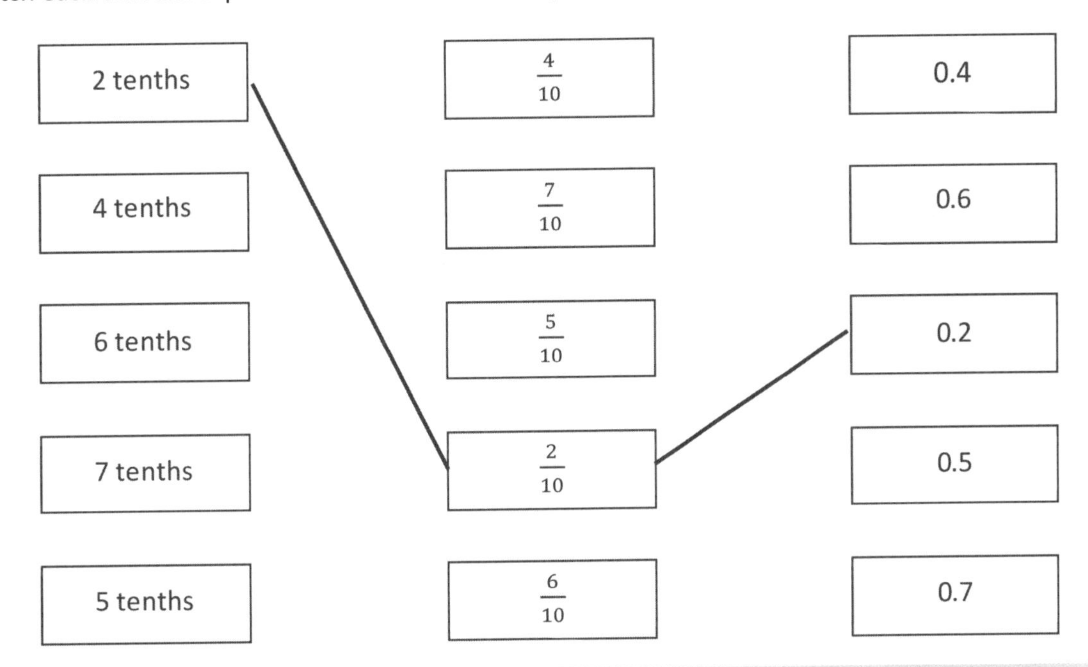

© 2015 Great Minds. eureka-math.org
G4-M6-TE-B5-1.3.1-01.2016

Lesson 2

Objective: Use metric measurement and area models to represent tenths as fractions greater than 1 and decimal numbers.

Suggested Lesson Structure

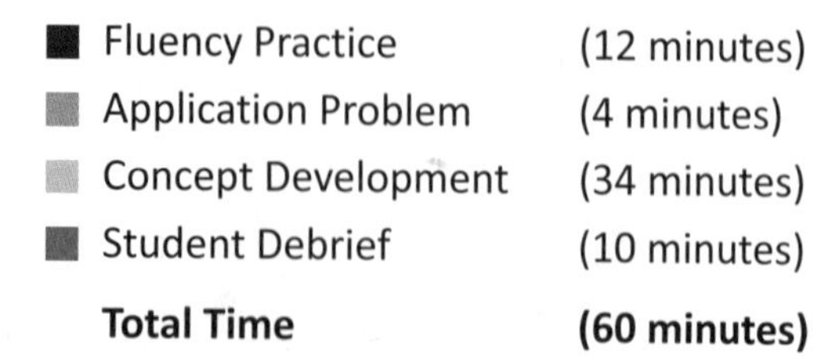

Fluency Practice	(12 minutes)
Application Problem	(4 minutes)
Concept Development	(34 minutes)
Student Debrief	(10 minutes)
Total Time	**(60 minutes)**

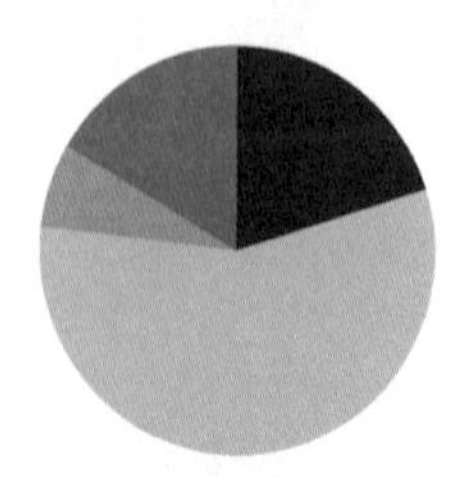

Fluency Practice (12 minutes)

- Divide by 10 **4.NF.6** (4 minutes)
- Write the Decimal or Fraction **4.NF.6** (3 minutes)
- Count by Tenths **4.NF.6** (5 minutes)

Divide by 10 (4 minutes)

Materials: (S) Personal white board

Note: This fluency activity reviews Lesson 1.

T: (Project a tape diagram with a value of 100 partitioned into 10 units.) Say the whole.
S: 100.
T: How many units is 100 divided into?
S: 10.
T: Say the division sentence.
S: 100 ÷ 10 = 10.
T: (Write 10 inside each unit. Write 100 ÷ 10 = 10 beneath the diagram.)
T: (Write 10 ÷ 10.) Draw a tape diagram showing 10 ÷ 10.
S: (Draw a tape diagram partitioned into 10 units. Write 10 at the top. Write 1 inside each unit. Beneath the tape diagram, write 10 ÷ 10 = 1.)

© 2015 Great Minds. eureka-math.org
G4-M6-TE-B5-1.3.1-01.2016

Write the Decimal or Fraction (3 minutes)

Materials: (S) Personal white board

Note: This fluency activity reviews Lesson 1.

T: (Write $\frac{1}{10}$.) Say the fraction.

S: 1 tenth.

T: (Write $\frac{1}{10}$ = ___.___.) Complete the number sentence.

S: (Write $\frac{1}{10}$ = 0.1.)

Continue with the following possible sequence: $\frac{2}{10}$, $\frac{7}{10}$, and $\frac{9}{10}$.

T: (Write 0.3 = —.) Complete the number sentence.

S: (Write 0.3 = $\frac{3}{10}$.)

Continue with the following possible sequence: 0.4, 0.8, and 0.6.

T: (Write $\frac{10}{10}$.) Say the fraction.

S: 10 tenths.

T: Complete the number sentence, writing 10 tenths as a whole number.

S: (Write $\frac{10}{10}$ = 1.)

Count by Tenths (5 minutes)

Note: This fluency activity reviews Lesson 1.

T: Count by ones to 10, starting at zero.

S: 0, 1, 2, 3, 4, 5, 6, 7, 8, 9, 10.

T: Count by tenths to 10 tenths, starting at zero tenths.

S: $\frac{0}{10}, \frac{1}{10}, \frac{2}{10}, \frac{3}{10}, \frac{4}{10}, \frac{5}{10}, \frac{6}{10}, \frac{7}{10}, \frac{8}{10}, \frac{9}{10}, \frac{10}{10}$.

T: 1 one is the same as how many tenths?

S: 10 tenths.

T: Let's count to 10 tenths again. This time, when you come to 1, say one.

S: $\frac{0}{10}, \frac{1}{10}, \frac{2}{10}, \frac{3}{10}, \frac{4}{10}, \frac{5}{10}, \frac{6}{10}, \frac{7}{10}, \frac{8}{10}, \frac{9}{10}$, 1.

T: Count by tenths again. This time, stop when I raise my hand.

S: $\frac{0}{10}, \frac{1}{10}, \frac{2}{10}, \frac{3}{10}$.

T: (Raise hand.) Say 3 tenths using digits. For example, 1 tenth would be said as zero point one.

S: Zero point three.

© 2015 Great Minds. eureka-math.org
G4-M6-TE-B5-1.3.1-01.2016

T: Continue counting using fraction form.

S: $\frac{4}{10}, \frac{5}{10}, \frac{6}{10}, \frac{7}{10}$.

T: (Raise hand.) Say 7 tenths using digits.

S: Zero point seven.

T: Continue counting in fraction form.

S: $\frac{8}{10}, \frac{9}{10}, 1$.

Use the same process to count down to zero tenths.

T: Count by twos to 10 starting at zero.

S: 0, 2, 4, 6, 8, 10.

T: Count by 2 tenths to 10 tenths, starting at zero.

S: $\frac{0}{10}, \frac{2}{10}, \frac{4}{10}, \frac{6}{10}, \frac{8}{10}, \frac{10}{10}$.

T: Count by 2 tenths again. This time, when you come to the whole number, say it.

S: $\frac{0}{10}, \frac{2}{10}, \frac{4}{10}, \frac{6}{10}, \frac{8}{10}, 1$.

T: Count backward by 2 tenths, starting at 1.

S: $1, \frac{8}{10}, \frac{6}{10}, \frac{4}{10}, \frac{2}{10}, \frac{0}{10}$.

Application Problem (4 minutes)

Yesterday, Ben's bamboo plant grew 0.5 centimeter. Today it grew another $\frac{8}{10}$ centimeter. How many centimeters did Ben's bamboo plant grow in 2 days?

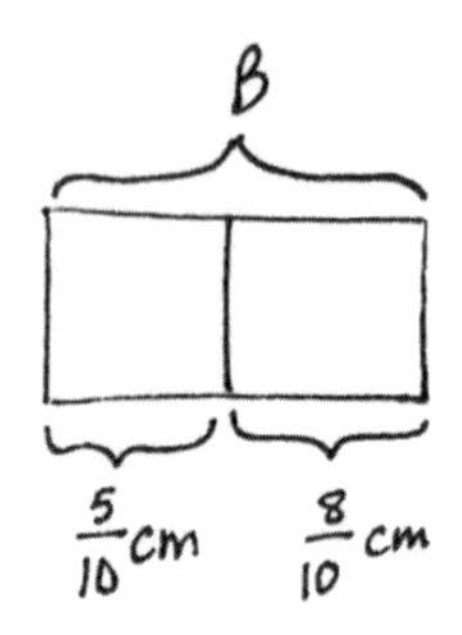

$0.5 = \frac{5}{10}$

$\frac{5}{10} + \frac{8}{10} = \frac{13}{10} = 1\frac{3}{10}$

$B = 1\frac{3}{10}$ cm

Ben's bamboo plant grew $1\frac{3}{10}$ centimeters in 2 days.

Note: This Application Problem builds from Module 5, in which students added fractions with like units. To do so, students use what they learned in Lesson 1 to convert a decimal number to fraction form to add.

EUREKA MATH
© 2015 Great Minds. eureka-math.org
G4-M6-TE-B5-1.3.1-01.2016

Concept Development (34 minutes)

Materials: (T) Centimeter ruler, tenths area model (Template), document camera (S) Centimeter ruler, pencil, blank paper, tenths area model (Template), personal white board

Problem 1: Draw line segments of given lengths, and express each segment as a mixed number and a decimal.

T: (Place a centimeter ruler under the document camera. If a document camera is unavailable, circulate to check students' work.) Using your pencil and ruler, draw a line that measures 2 centimeters. (Write 2 cm on the board.)

S: (Draw a line with the length of 2 centimeters.)

T: Extend the line 6 tenths centimeter.

S: (Extend the 2 centimeters line by 6 tenths centimeter.)

T: How many centimeters did you draw initially?

S: 2 centimeters.

T: (Label 2 cm below the line, as pictured to the right.)

T: How many tenths of a centimeter did you draw after drawing 2 centimeters?

S: 6 tenths centimeter.

T: (Label $\frac{6}{10}$ centimeter. Complete the expression 2 cm + $\frac{6}{10}$ cm below the line, as pictured to the right.)

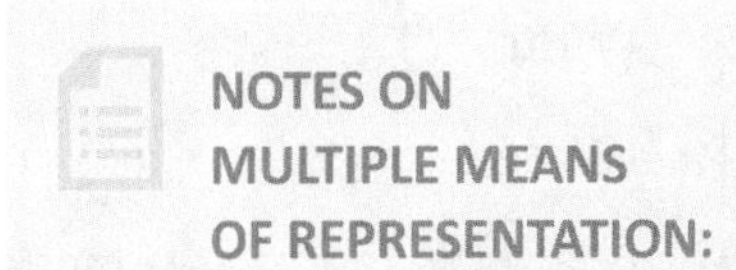

> **NOTES ON MULTIPLE MEANS OF REPRESENTATION:**
>
> Some learners may benefit from using a large print or tactile ruler that has raised lines for every centimeter. Consider adhering dried glue or rubber bands to student rulers to help learners with low vision gauge the centimeter and millimeter measures. Another possibility is providing hand-held magnifying lenses.

T: Record a number sentence showing the total length of your line as a mixed number.

S: (Write 2 cm + $\frac{6}{10}$ cm = $2\frac{6}{10}$ cm.)

T: Let's rewrite this expression in decimal form. (Write 2 cm + 0.6 cm = 2.6 cm.) Rewrite your fraction addition in decimal form, and explain to your partner the relationship between the two number sentences and the line you drew. (Allow students time to work.)

T: $2\frac{6}{10}$ cm is written in decimal form like this: 2.6 cm. We read this as 2 and 6 tenths centimeters.

Repeat the process as necessary with $3\frac{5}{10}$ cm and $4\frac{8}{10}$ cm. Next, call out lengths verbally (e.g., 1 and 5 tenths centimeters). Students quickly draw the line and write the corresponding length in mixed number and decimal form. Suggested sequence: 1.5 cm, 5.4 cm, 3.9 cm, 9.6 cm, and 8.1 cm.

Problem 2: Use the area model to represent tenths as fractions greater than 1 and as decimal numbers.

T: (Cover up the ruler to show only 1 cm.) How many tenths are in 1?

S: 10 tenths.

© 2015 Great Minds. eureka-math.org
G4-M6-TE-B5-1.3.1-01.2016

MP.2

T: (Reveal another centimeter, showing 2 cm.) How many tenths are in 2?
S: 20 tenths.
T: (Reveal 2.6 cm.) How many tenths are in 2 and 6 tenths?
S: 26 tenths.
T: Express 26 tenths in fraction form.
S: (Write $\frac{26}{10}$.)
T: (Write $\frac{20}{10}$ cm + $\frac{6}{10}$ cm = $\frac{26}{10}$ cm.)
T: (Place the tenths area model template in a personal white board as students do the same, turn the board horizontally, and project it with a document camera.) How many rectangles are on your template?
S: 5 rectangles.
T: Each rectangle represents 1 one. How many ones do we have?
S: 5 ones.
T: Each rectangle has been partitioned equally. How many tenths are there in all?
S: 50 tenths.
T: (Write $2\frac{6}{10}$.)
T: How many ones are in this number?
S: 2 ones.
T: (Begin showing the number bond, taking out 2.) Shade in 2 ones.
S: (Shade in 2 rectangles.)
T: How many tenths do we still need to shade in?
S: 6 tenths.
T: (Complete the number bond by writing $\frac{6}{10}$.) Shade in 6 tenths more.

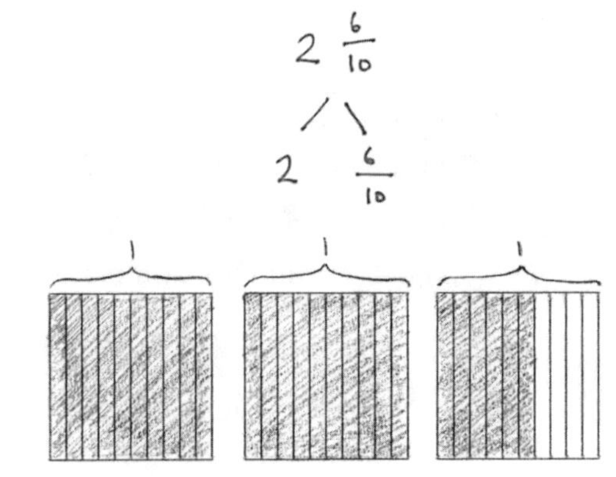

T: (As students are shading their template, write $2\frac{6}{10} = 2 + \frac{6}{10}$.)
T: With your partner, rewrite $2 + \frac{6}{10}$, using decimal form to add the tenths.

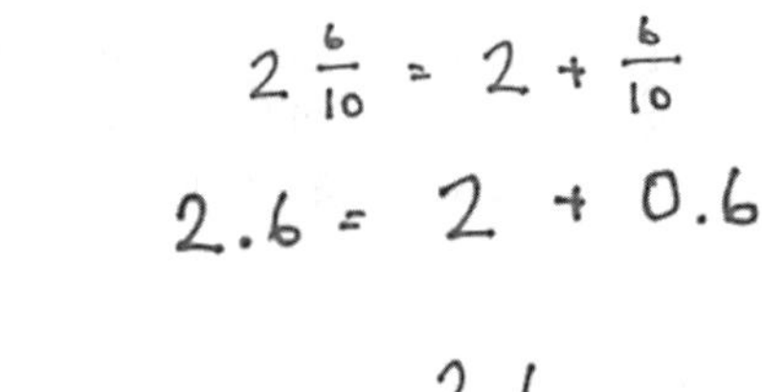

S: (Write 2 + 0.6.)
T: 2 + 0.6 can be written as ...?
S: 2 point 6.
T: (Write 2.6 = 2 + 0.6.) With your partner, draw a number bond, this time using decimal form.

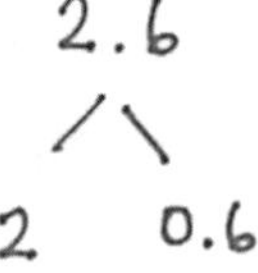

Students erase their templates. Continue the process with $2\frac{7}{10}$, $2\frac{2}{10}$, $3\frac{2}{10}$, $\frac{31}{10}$, $\frac{48}{10}$, and $\frac{26}{10}$. When appropriate, conclude each experience by asking how many more are needed to get to the next whole number, as demonstrated as follows:

© 2015 Great Minds. eureka-math.org
G4-M6-TE-B5-1.3.1-01.2016

T: You just shaded $3\frac{2}{10}$ and wrote this mixed number as 3 + 0.2 = 3.2. Look at your area model. How many tenths do you need to get to 4 ones?

S: 8 tenths.

T: How do you know?

S: I looked at the area model and saw that 8 tenths more have to be shaded in to complete one whole. → 2 tenths plus 8 tenths equals 10 tenths, and that makes one whole.

T: Express 8 tenths as a fraction and decimal.

With the final two or three examples, extend the question by asking how many more tenths are needed to get to 5.

Problem Set (10 minutes)

Students should do their personal best to complete the Problem Set within the allotted 10 minutes. For some classes, it may be appropriate to modify the assignment by specifying which problems they work on first. Some problems do not specify a method for solving. Students should solve these problems using the RDW approach used for Application Problems.

Student Debrief (10 minutes)

Lesson Objective: Use metric measurement and area models to represent tenths as fractions greater than 1 and decimal numbers.

The Student Debrief is intended to invite reflection and active processing of the total lesson experience.

Invite students to review their solutions for the Problem Set. They should check work by comparing answers with a partner before going over answers as a class. Look for misconceptions or misunderstandings that can be addressed in the Debrief. Guide students in a conversation to debrief the Problem Set and process the lesson.

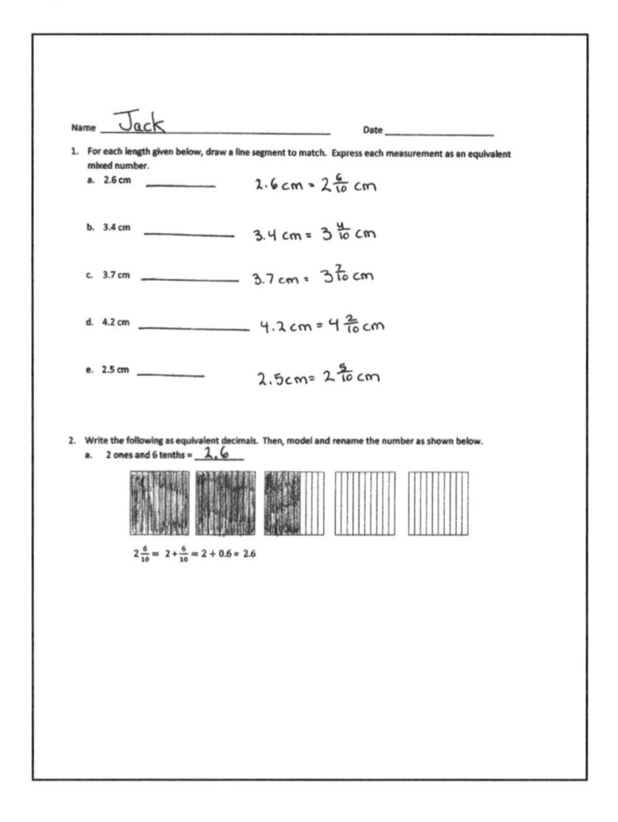
Name Jack Date

1. For each length given below, draw a line segment to match. Express each measurement as an equivalent mixed number.
   a. 2.6 cm $2.6\text{ cm} = 2\frac{6}{10}\text{ cm}$
   b. 3.4 cm $3.4\text{ cm} = 3\frac{4}{10}\text{ cm}$
   c. 3.7 cm $3.7\text{ cm} = 3\frac{7}{10}\text{ cm}$
   d. 4.2 cm $4.2\text{ cm} = 4\frac{2}{10}\text{ cm}$
   e. 2.5 cm $2.5\text{ cm} = 2\frac{5}{10}\text{ cm}$

2. Write the following as equivalent decimals. Then, model and rename the number as shown below.
   a. 2 ones and 6 tenths = 2.6

$2\frac{6}{10} = 2 + \frac{6}{10} = 2 + 0.6 = 2.6$

Any combination of the questions below may be used to lead the discussion.

- Look at Problems 1(a) and 2(a). What do you notice? How could you apply what you did in Problem 2(a) to Problem 1(a)? Are there other similarities within Problems 1 and 2?
- Look at Problem 2(e). How did you know how much of the rectangles to shade in? What is the most efficient way to determine how many rectangles you would need to shade in?

© 2015 Great Minds. eureka-math.org
G4-M6-TE-B5-1.3.1-01.2016

- Look at Problem 2(e) with your partner. Explain to each other how you decided how much more is needed to get to 5.
- How did the Application Problem connect to today's lesson with decimal fractions?

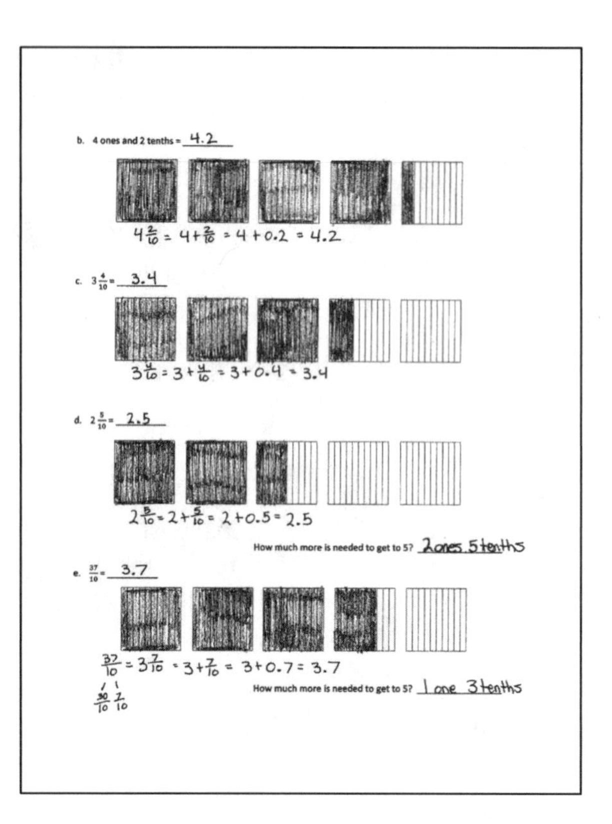

Exit Ticket (3 minutes)

After the Student Debrief, instruct students to complete the Exit Ticket. A review of their work will help with assessing the students' understanding of the concepts that were presented in today's lesson and planning more effectively for future lessons. The questions may be read aloud to the students.

EUREKA MATH
© 2015 Great Minds. eureka-math.org
G4-M6-TE-B5-1.3.1-01.2016

Name ______________________________ Date ________________

1. For each length given below, draw a line segment to match. Express each measurement as an equivalent mixed number.

   a. 2.6 cm

   b. 3.4 cm

   c. 3.7 cm

   d. 4.2 cm

   e. 2.5 cm

2. Write the following as equivalent decimals. Then, model and rename the number as shown below.

   a. 2 ones and 6 tenths = __________

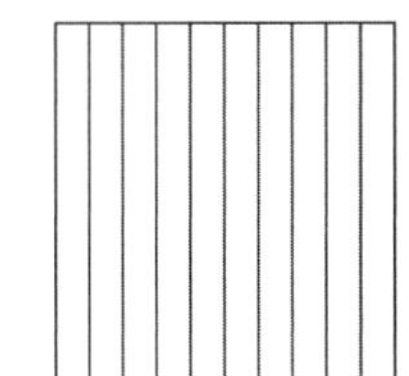
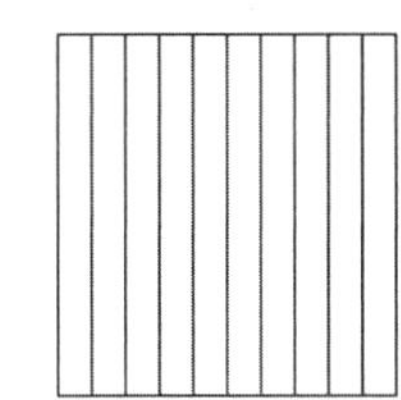
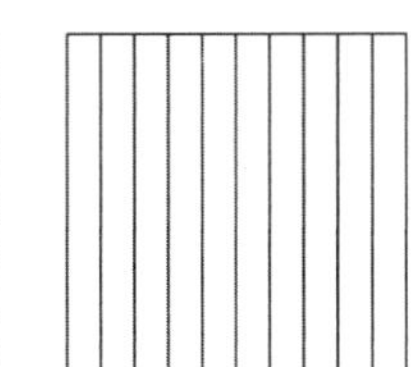
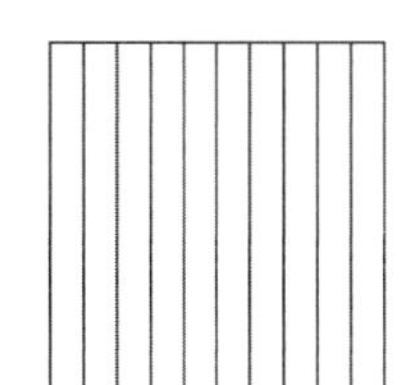
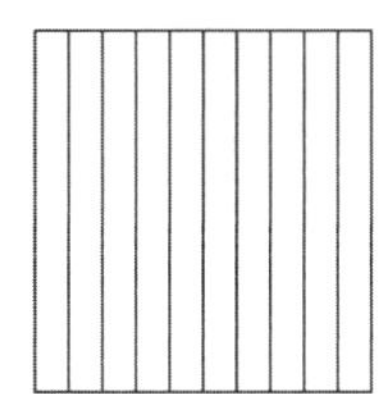

$2\frac{6}{10} = 2 + \frac{6}{10} = 2 + 0.6 = 2.6$

© 2015 Great Minds. eureka-math.org
G4-M6-TE-B5-1.3.1-01.2016

b. 4 ones and 2 tenths = __________

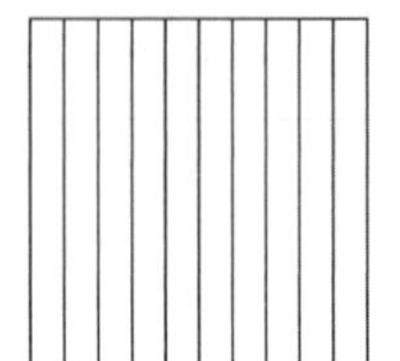 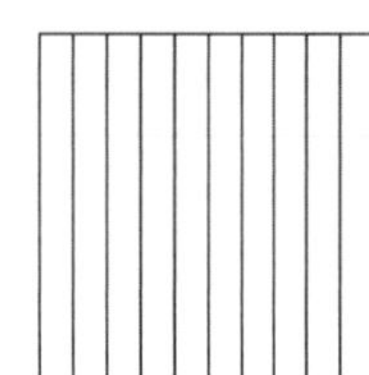 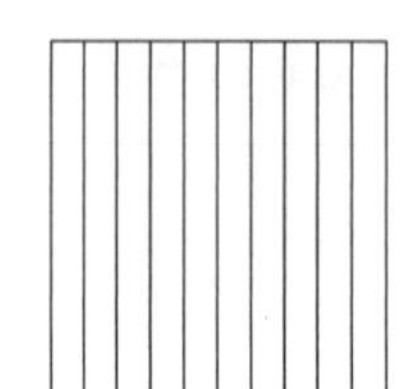 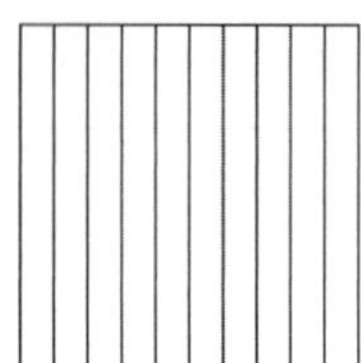 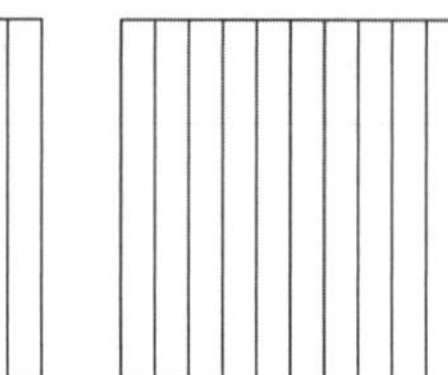

c. $3\frac{4}{10}$ = __________

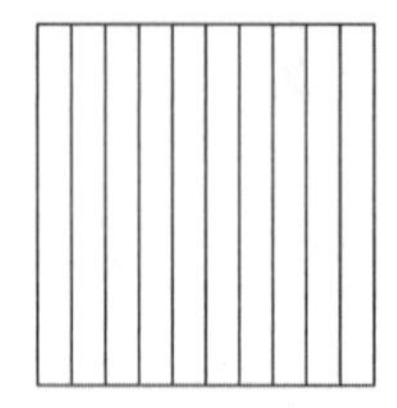 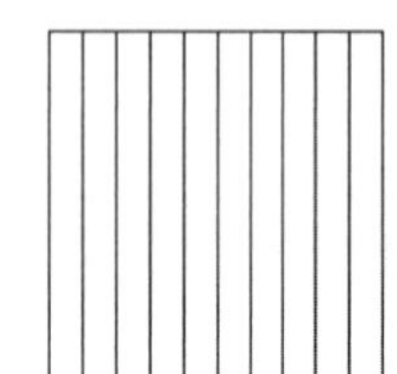 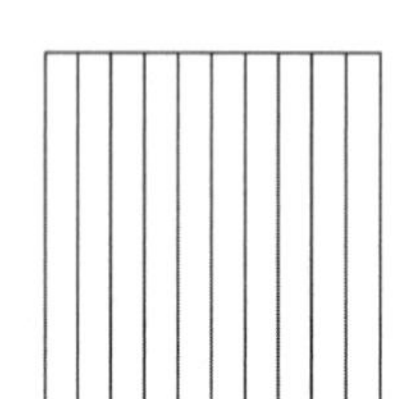 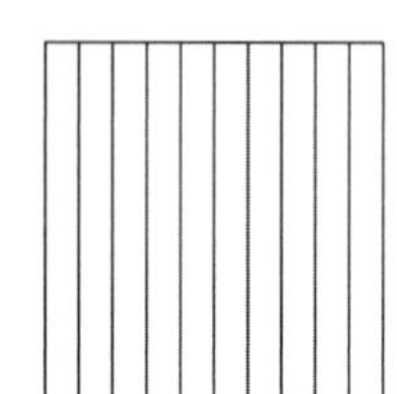 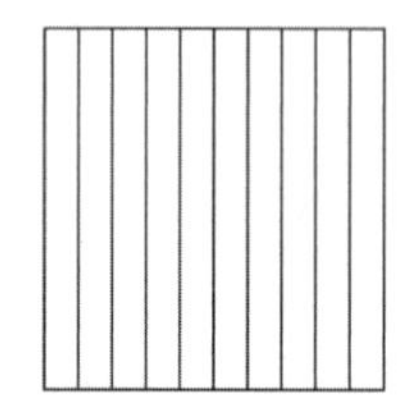

d. $2\frac{5}{10}$ = __________

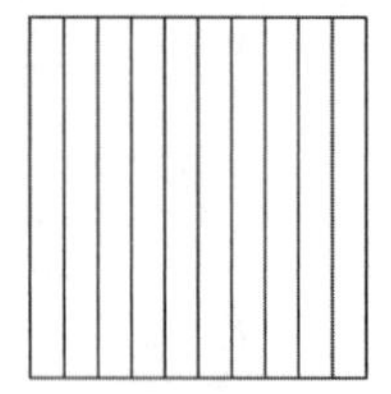 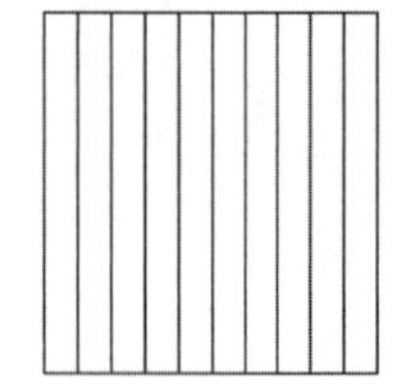 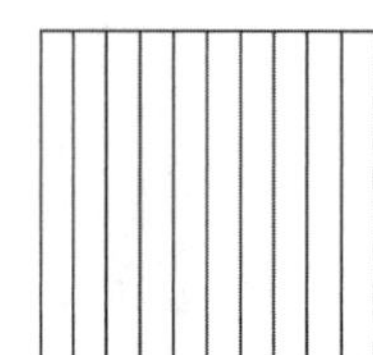 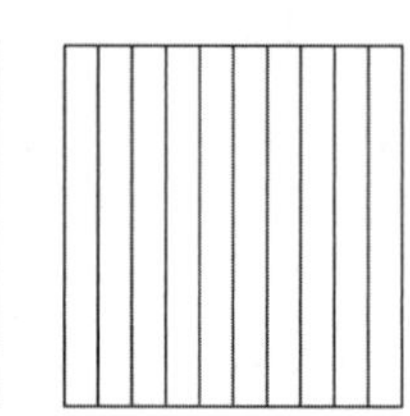 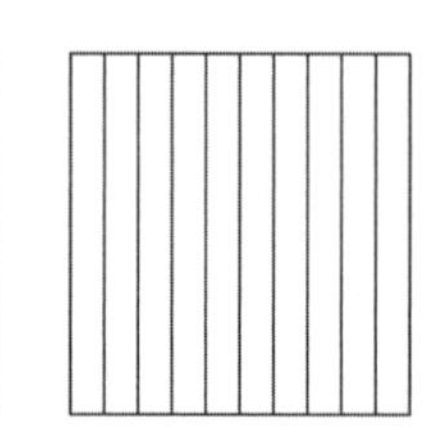

How much more is needed to get to 5? ______________

e. $\frac{37}{10}$ = __________

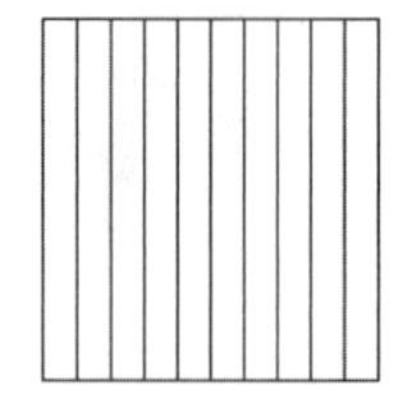 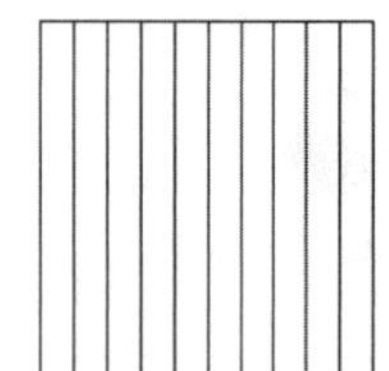 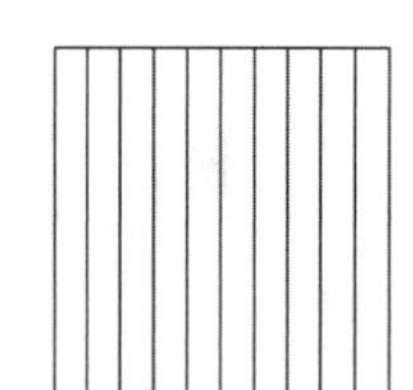 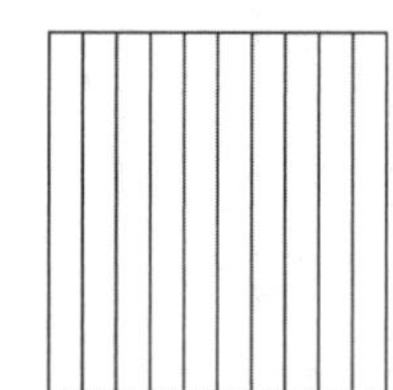 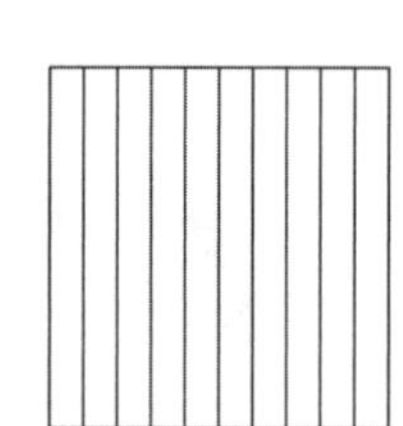

How much more is needed to get to 5? ______________

© 2015 Great Minds. eureka-math.org
G4-M6-TE-B5-1.3.1-01.2016

Name ______________________________ Date ______________

1. For the length given below, draw a line segment to match. Express the measurement as an equivalent mixed number.

   4.8 cm

2. Write the following in decimal form and as a mixed number. Shade the area model to match.

   a. 3 ones and 7 tenths = __________ = __________

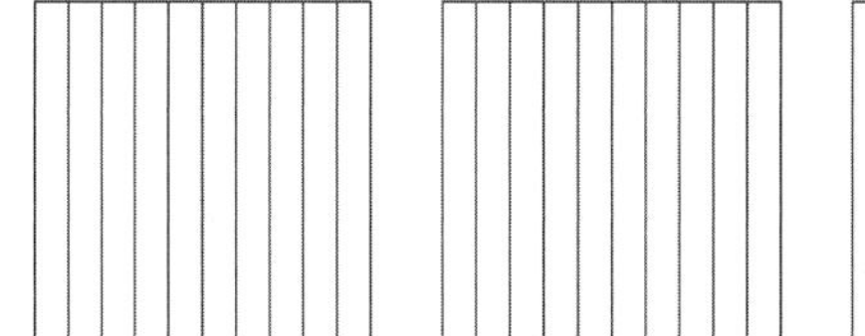
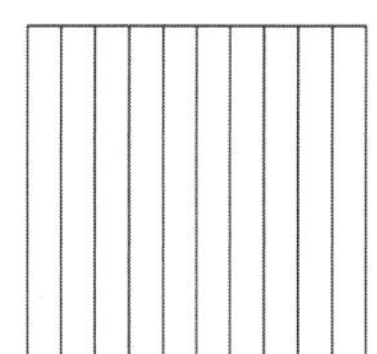
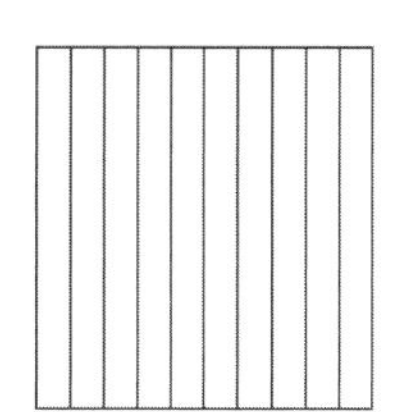
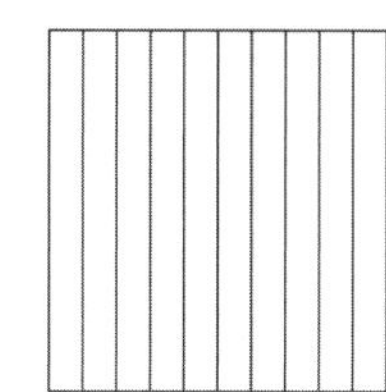

   b. $\frac{24}{10}$ = __________ = __________

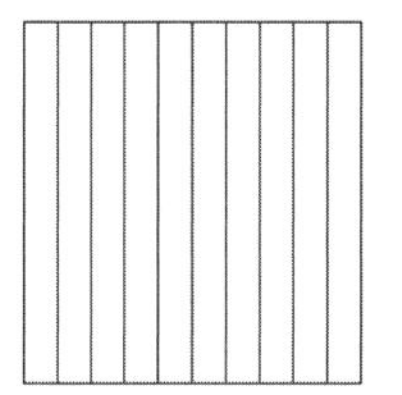
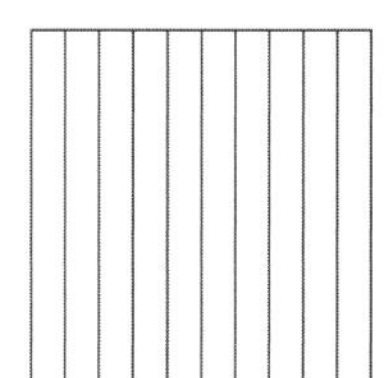
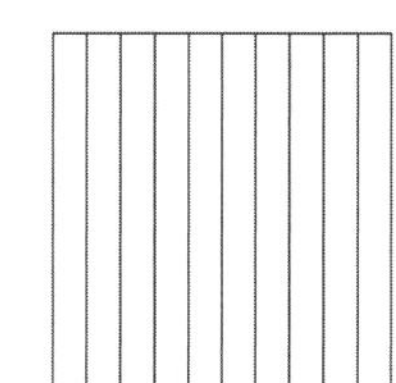
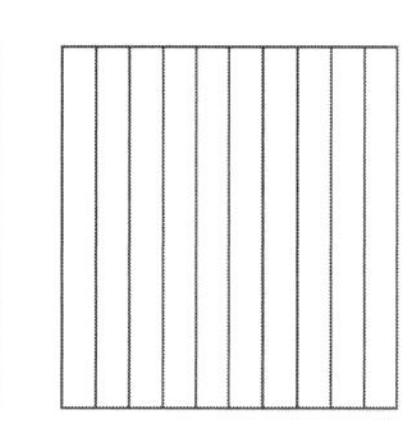
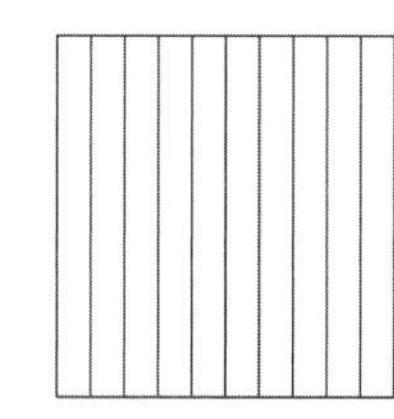

How much more is needed to get to 5? ______________

© 2015 Great Minds. eureka-math.org
G4-M6-TE-B5-1.3.1-01.2016

Name ______________________________ Date ______________

1. For each length given below, draw a line segment to match. Express each measurement as an equivalent mixed number.

   a. 2.6 cm

   b. 3.5 cm

   c. 1.7 cm

   d. 4.3 cm

   e. 2.2 cm

2. Write the following in decimal form. Then, model and rename the number as shown below.

   a. 2 ones and 4 tenths = ________

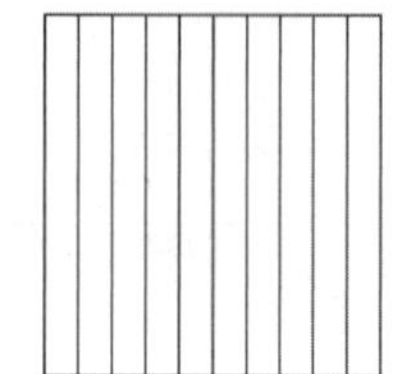
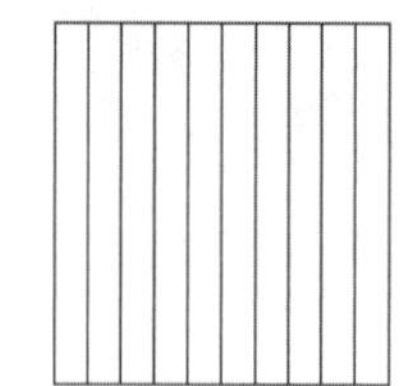
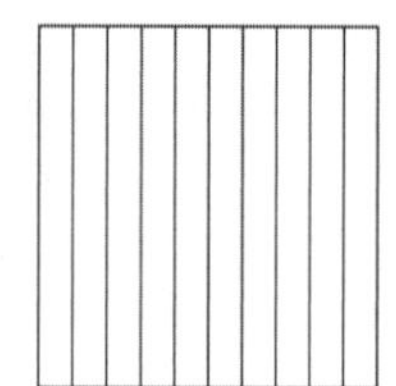

$2\frac{4}{10} = 2 + \frac{4}{10} = 2 + 0.4 = 2.4$

EUREKA MATH

© 2015 Great Minds. eureka-math.org
G4-M6-TE-B5-1.3.1-01.2016

b. 3 ones and 8 tenths = __________

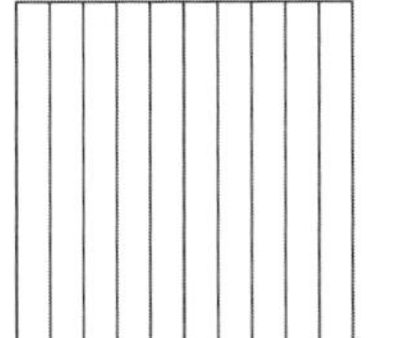 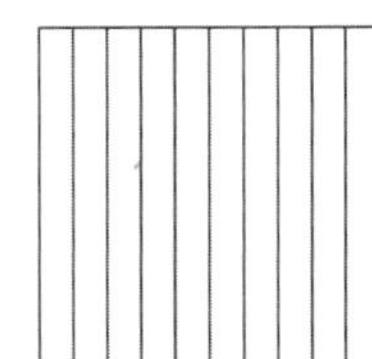 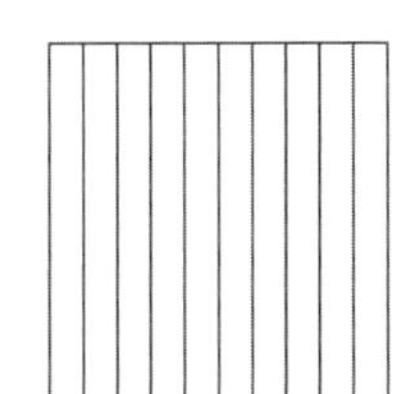 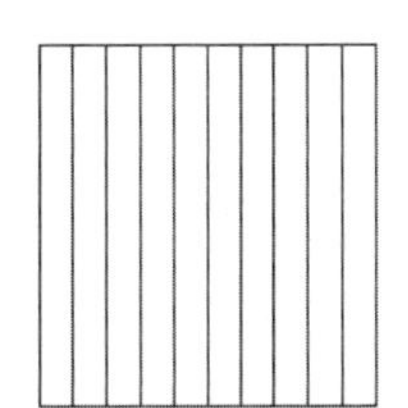 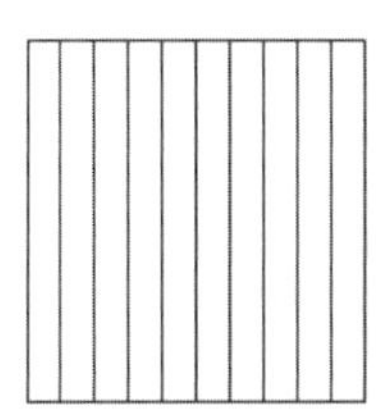

c. $4\frac{1}{10}$ = __________

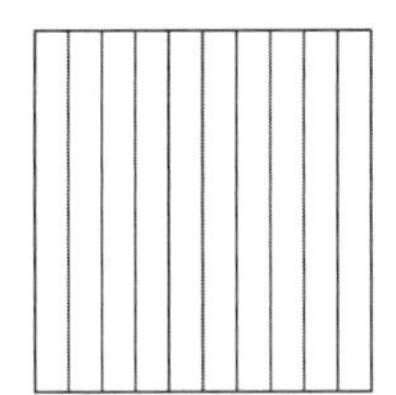 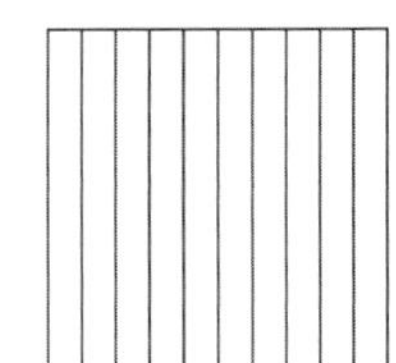 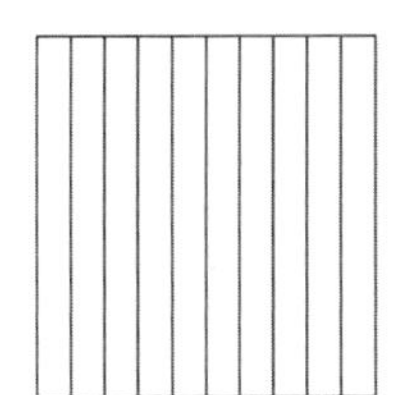 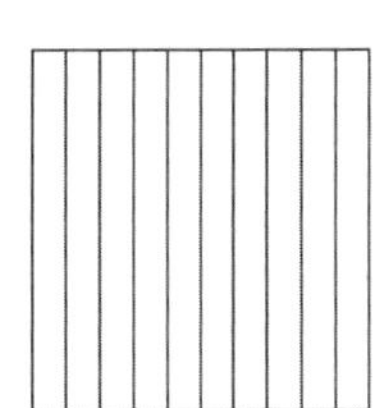 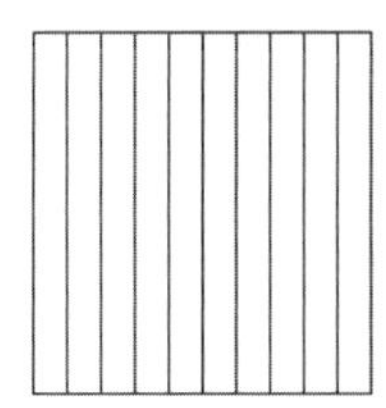

d. $1\frac{4}{10}$ = __________

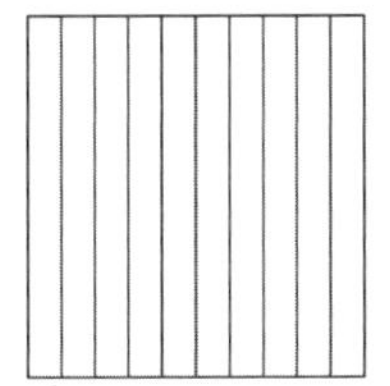 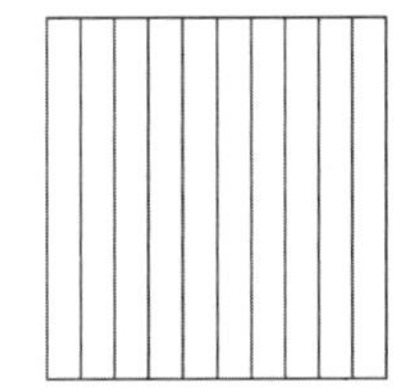 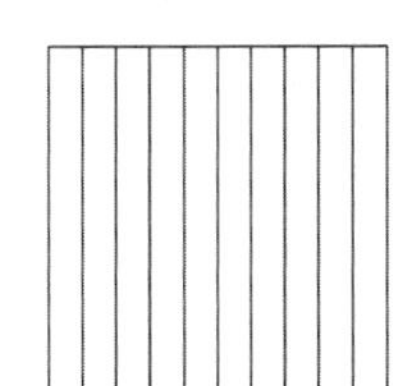 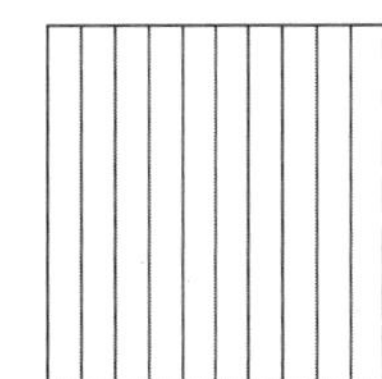 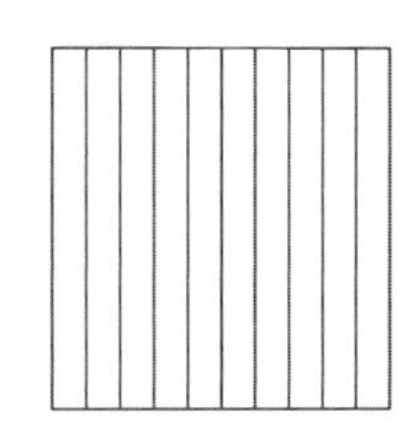

How much more is needed to get to 5? ________________

e. $\frac{33}{10}$ = __________

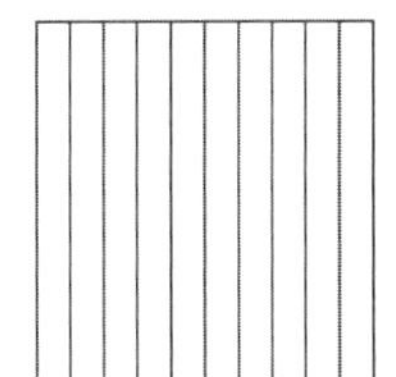 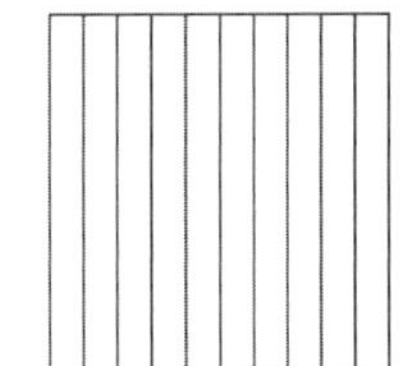 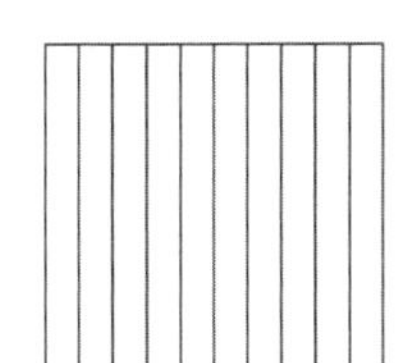 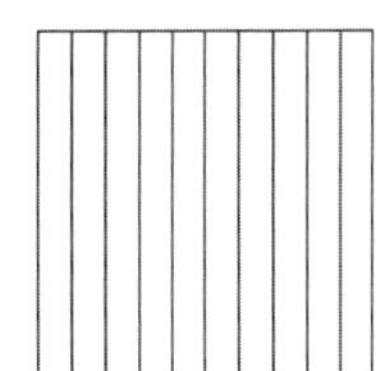 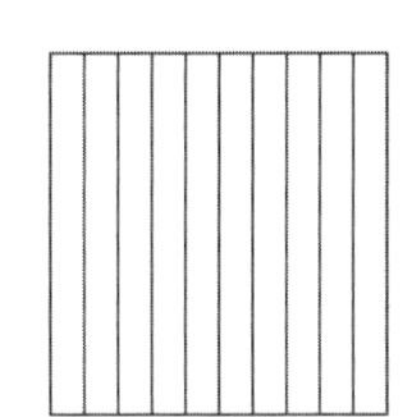

How much more is needed to get to 5? ________________

© 2015 Great Minds. eureka-math.org
G4-M6-TE-B5-1.3.1-01.2016

tenths area model

© 2015 Great Minds. eureka-math.org
G4-M6-TE-B5-1.3.1-01.2016

Lesson 3

Objective: Represent mixed numbers with units of tens, ones, and tenths with place value disks, on the number line, and in expanded form.

Suggested Lesson Structure

■ Fluency Practice	(10 minutes)
■ Application Problem	(5 minutes)
■ Concept Development	(35 minutes)
■ Student Debrief	(10 minutes)
Total Time	**(60 minutes)**

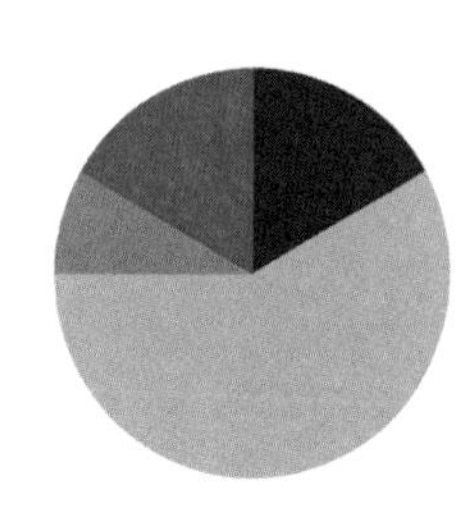

Fluency Practice (10 minutes)

- Write the Decimal or Fraction **4.NF.6** (5 minutes)
- Count by Tenths **4.NF.6** (5 minutes)

Write the Decimal or Fraction (5 minutes)

Materials: (S) Personal white board

Note: This fluency activity reviews Lessons 1–2.

T: (Write $\frac{1}{10}$.) Say the fraction.

S: 1 tenth.

T: (Write $\frac{1}{10}$ = __.__.) Write 1 tenth as a decimal to complete the number sentence.

S: (Write $\frac{1}{10}$ = 0.1.)

Continue with the following possible sequence: $\frac{2}{10}$, $\frac{7}{10}$, and $\frac{9}{10}$.

T: (Write 0.3 = —.) Write zero point three as a fraction to complete the number sentence.

S: (Write 0.3 = $\frac{3}{10}$.)

Continue with the following possible sequence: 0.4, 0.8, and 0.6.

T: (Write $\frac{10}{10}$.) 10 tenths equals what whole number?

S: 1.

© 2015 Great Minds. eureka-math.org
G4-M6-TE-B5-1.3.1-01.2016

T: (Write $\frac{10}{10}$ = 1. Beneath it, write $\frac{30}{10}$.) How many ones is 30 tenths?

S: 3 ones.

T: (Write $\frac{50}{10}$.) How many ones is 50 tenths?

S: 5 ones.

T: (Write $\frac{13}{10}$.) Write 13 tenths as a mixed number.

S: (Write $\frac{13}{10} = 1\frac{3}{10}$.)

T: (Write $\frac{13}{10} = 1\frac{3}{10}$ = ___.___.) Write $1\frac{3}{10}$ in decimal form.

S: (Write $\frac{13}{10} = 1\frac{3}{10} = 1.3$.)

Continue with the following possible sequence: $\frac{17}{10}$, $\frac{37}{10}$, $\frac{34}{10}$, and $\frac{49}{10}$.

T: (Write 2.1.) Write two point one as a mixed number.

S: (Write $2.1 = 2\frac{1}{10}$.)

Continue with the following possible sequence: 3.1, 5.1, 5.9, and 1.7.

Count by Tenths (5 minutes)

Materials: (T) Personal white board

Note: This fluency activity reviews Lessons 1–2.

T: Count by fives to 50, starting at zero.

$\frac{0}{10}$	$\frac{5}{10}$	$\frac{10}{10}$	$\frac{15}{10}$	$\frac{20}{10}$	$\frac{25}{10}$	$\frac{30}{10}$	$\frac{35}{10}$	$\frac{40}{10}$	$\frac{45}{10}$	$\frac{50}{10}$
0		1		2		3		4		5

S: 0, 5, 10, 15, 20, 25, 30, 35, 40, 45, 50.

T: Count by 5 tenths to 50 tenths, starting at 0 tenths. (Write as students count.)

S: $\frac{0}{10}, \frac{5}{10}, \frac{10}{10}, \frac{15}{10}, \frac{20}{10}, \frac{25}{10}, \frac{30}{10}, \frac{35}{10}, \frac{40}{10}, \frac{45}{10}, \frac{50}{10}$.

T: 1 is the same as how many tenths?

S: 10 tenths.

T: (Beneath $\frac{10}{10}$, write 1.)

Continue the process, identifying the number of tenths in 2, 3, 4, and 5.

T: Let's count by 5 tenths again. This time, when you come to a whole number, say the whole number. Try not to look at the board.

S: $\frac{0}{10}, \frac{5}{10}, 1, \frac{15}{10}, 2, \frac{25}{10}, 3, \frac{35}{10}, 4, \frac{45}{10}, 5$.

© 2015 Great Minds. eureka-math.org
G4-M6-TE-B5-1.3.1-01.2016

T: Count backward by 5 tenths, starting at 5.

S: 5, $\frac{45}{10}$, 4, $\frac{35}{10}$, 3, $\frac{25}{10}$, 2, $\frac{15}{10}$, 1, $\frac{5}{10}$, $\frac{0}{10}$.

T: Count by 5 tenths again. This time, stop when I raise my hand.

S: $\frac{0}{10}$, $\frac{5}{10}$, 1, $\frac{15}{10}$.

T: (Raise hand.) Say 15 tenths using digits.

S: One point five.

Continue the process counting up to 5 and down from 5, asking students to say the improper fractions using digits.

Application Problem (5 minutes)

Ed bought 4 pieces of salmon weighing a total of 2 kilograms. One piece weighed $\frac{4}{10}$ kg, and two of the pieces weighed $\frac{5}{10}$ kg each. What was the weight of the fourth piece of salmon?

2 kg

$\frac{4}{10}$ kg	$\frac{5}{10}$ kg	$\frac{5}{10}$ kg	w

The 4th piece of salmon weighed $\frac{6}{10}$ kg.

Solution A

$\frac{4}{10} + \frac{5}{10} + \frac{5}{10} = 1\frac{4}{10}$

$2 - 1\frac{4}{10} = \frac{6}{10}$ (2 = $1\frac{10}{10}$)

$w = \frac{6}{10}$ kg

Solution B

$\frac{5}{10}$ kg $+ \frac{5}{10}$ kg $= 1$ kg

$1\frac{4}{10}$ kg $\xrightarrow{+\frac{6}{10}\text{ kg}}$ 2 kg

$w = \frac{6}{10}$ kg

Note: This Application Problem anticipates decimal fraction addition and reinforces the concept of how many more to make one.

Concept Development (35 minutes)

Materials: (T/S) Whole number place value disks (tens and ones), decimal place value disks (tenths), personal white board, tenths on a number line (Template)

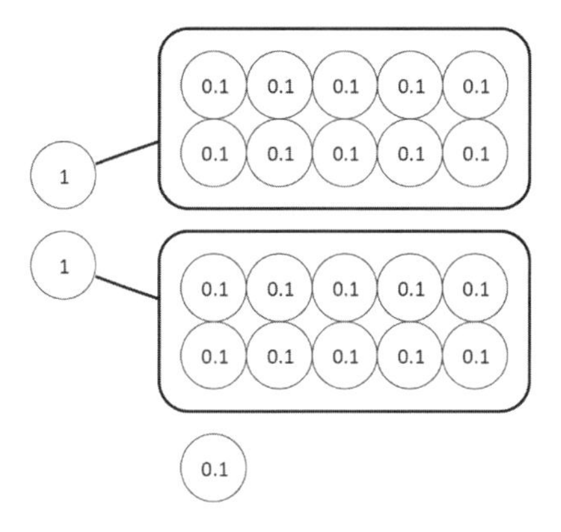

Problem 1: Make groups of 10 tenths to rename as ones. Write the number in decimal form.

T: With a partner, use place value disks to show 21 units of 1 tenth in five-group formation.

S: (Lay out 21 disks, all tenths, in five-group formation, as shown.)

© 2015 Great Minds. eureka-math.org
G4-M6-TE-B5-1.3.1-01.2016

T: Talk with your partner. Is there any way we can use *fewer* disks to show this same value?

S: We can bundle 10 tenths to make one. → There are 2 groups of 10 tenths, so we can show 21 tenths as 2 ones 1 tenth. → In the five-groups, I can see 2 groups of 10 disks. 10 tenths is 1 whole. We have 1 (circling group with finger), 2 (circling group with finger) groups that make 2 ones, and then 1 tenth (touching final 0.1 disk).

T: Let's group 10 tenths together and trade them for...?

S: 1 one.

T: How many times can we do this?

S: 1 more time. → 2 times.

T: What disks do we have now?

S: 2 ones and 1 tenth.

T: Express this number in decimal form.

S: (Write 2.1.)

T: How many more tenths would we have needed to have 3 ones?

S: 9 tenths more. → 0.9.

Repeat the process using disks to model 17 tenths. Then, continue the process having the students draw disks for 24 tenths. Have students circle the disks being bundled.

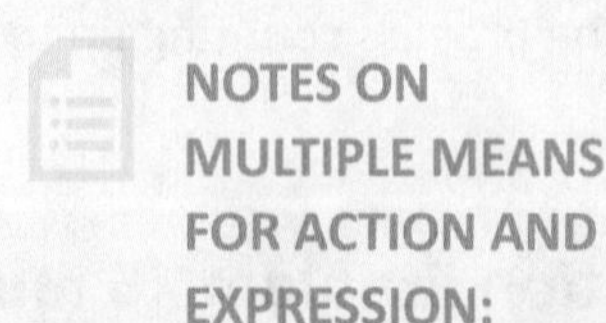

NOTES ON MULTIPLE MEANS FOR ACTION AND EXPRESSION:

Be sure to enunciate /*th*/ at the end of *tenths* to help English language learners distinguish *tenths* and *tens*. Try to speak more slowly, pause more frequently, or couple language with a tape diagram. Check for student understanding and correct pronunciation of fraction names.

Problem 2: Represent mixed numbers with units of tens, ones, and tenths in expanded form.

T: Hold up a place value disk with a value of 1 ten. We say the value of this disk is...?

S: 1 ten. → Ten.

T: (Draw or show 4 tens disks.) The total value of 4 of these is...?

S: 4 tens. → Forty.

T: 4 tens written as a multiplication expression is?

S: 4 × 1 ten. → 4 × 10.

T: (Write the expression below the disks, as pictured to the right.) 4 × 10 is...?

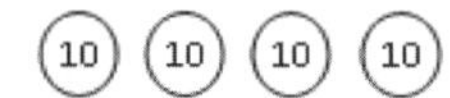

$4 \times 10 = 40$

S: 40.

T: (Complete the number sentence. Draw or show 2 ones disks.) The total value of these 2 disks is...?

S: 2 ones. → Two.

T: 2 ones written as a multiplication expression is...?

S: 2 × 1.

T: (Write the expression below the disks, as pictured to the right.) (4 × 10) + (2 × 1) is...?

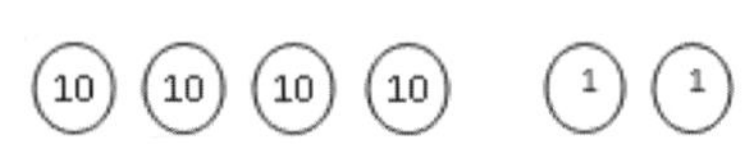

$(4 \times 10) + (2 \times 1) = 42$

S: 42.

EUREKA MATH

© 2015 Great Minds. eureka-math.org
G4-M6-TE-B5-1.3.1-01.2016

T: (Complete the number sentence. Draw or show a tenth disk.) This place value disk says zero point one on it. We say the value of this disk is...?

S: 1 tenth.

T: (Draw or show 6 one-tenth disks in five-group formation.) The total value of 6 of these disks is ...?

10 10 10 10 1 1 0.1 0.1 0.1 0.1 0.1 0.1

$$(4 \times 10) + (2 \times 1) + \left(6 \times \frac{1}{10}\right) = 42\frac{6}{10}$$

$$(4 \times 10) + (2 \times 1) + (6 \times 0.1) = 42.6$$

S: 6 tenths.

T: 6 tenths written as a multiplication expression is...?

S: $6 \times \frac{1}{10}$.

MP.4

T: (Write the expression below the disks, as pictured above.) Discuss the total value of the number represented by the disks with your partner.

S: Do what is in the parentheses first, and then find the sum. $40 + 2 + \frac{6}{10}$ is $42\frac{6}{10}$. → 4 tens, 2 ones, 6 tenths. → It is like expanded form.

T: We have written $42\frac{6}{10}$ in expanded form, writing each term as a multiplication expression. Just like with whole numbers, the expanded form allows us to see the place value unit for each digit.

T: (Point to $(4 \times 10) + (2 \times 1) + (6 \times \frac{1}{10}) = 42\frac{6}{10}$.) Talk with your partner. How could you write this using **decimal expanded form** instead of **fraction expanded form**? Explain how you know.

S: (Work with partners, and write $(4 \times 10) + (2 \times 1) + (6 \times 0.1) = 42.6$.) I know that 1 tenth can be written as zero point one, and 42 and 6 tenths can be written as forty-two point six. → We looked at our disks. We had 4 tens, 2 ones, and 6 disks that had 0.1 on them. → We knew it was 42 + 0.6, so that helped us rewrite $42\frac{6}{10}$ as 42.6.

Continue the process of showing a mixed number with place value disks, and then writing the expanded fraction form and expanded decimal form for the following numbers: 24 ones 6 tenths, 13 ones 8 tenths, and 68 ones 3 tenths. Challenge students to think how much each number needs to get to the next *one.*

Problem 3: Use the number line to model mixed numbers with units of ones and tenths.

T: (Distribute the Lesson 3 Template, tenths on a number line, and insert it into personal white boards.) Label the larger intervals from 0 to 5.

T: The segment between each whole number is divided up into how many equal parts?

S: 10 equal parts.

T: Plot a point on the number line to represent 4 and 1 tenth.

T: In the chart below your number line, let's plot the same number on a shorter number line partitioned into tenths. What will the endpoints of this shorter number line be?

S: 4 and 5.

© 2015 Great Minds. eureka-math.org
G4-M6-TE-B5-1.3.1-01.2016

T: (Fill out the chart to show 4.1 plotted on a number line between 4 and 5, in decimal form, as a mixed number, and in expanded form.)

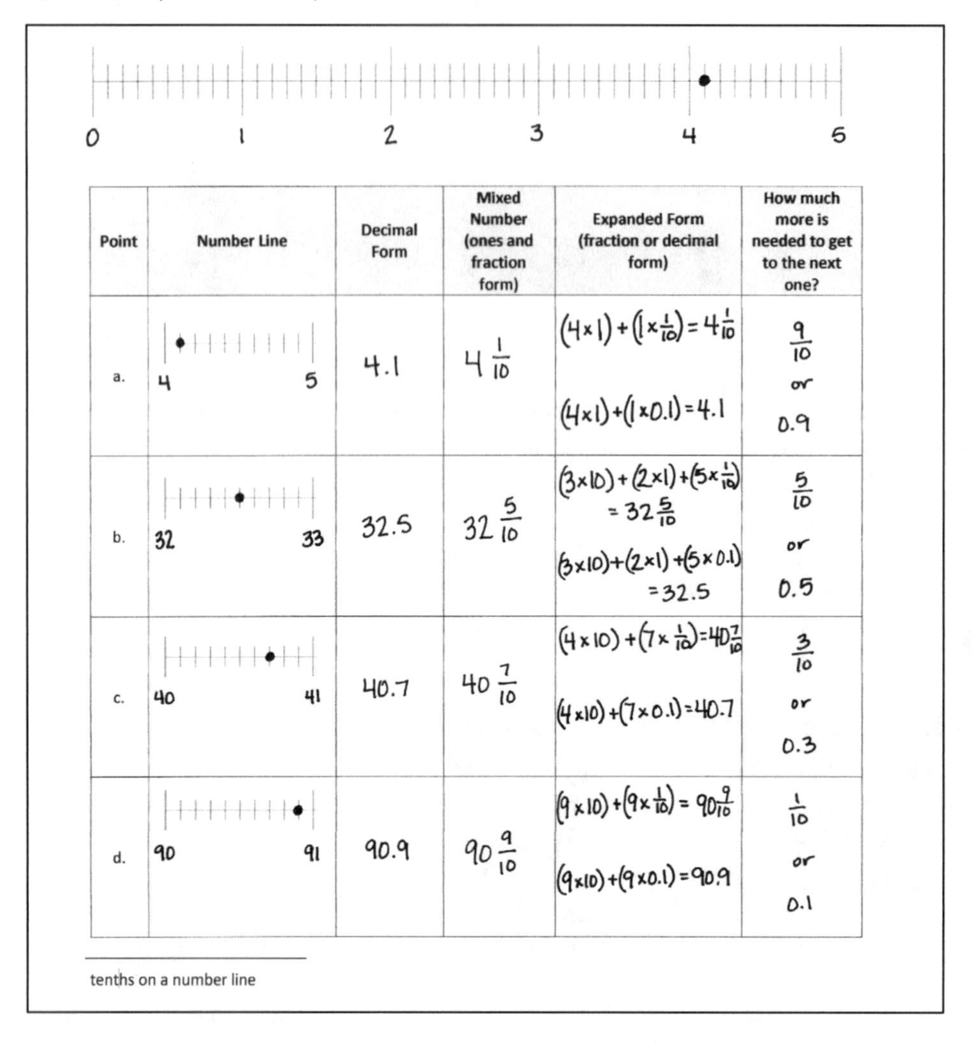

Point	Number Line	Decimal Form	Mixed Number (ones and fraction form)	Expanded Form (fraction or decimal form)	How much more is needed to get to the next one?
a.	4 5	4.1	$4\frac{1}{10}$	$(4 \times 1) + (1 \times \frac{1}{10}) = 4\frac{1}{10}$ $(4 \times 1) + (1 \times 0.1) = 4.1$	$\frac{9}{10}$ or 0.9
b.	32 33	32.5	$32\frac{5}{10}$	$(3 \times 10) + (2 \times 1) + (5 \times \frac{1}{10}) = 32\frac{5}{10}$ $(3 \times 10) + (2 \times 1) + (5 \times 0.1) = 32.5$	$\frac{5}{10}$ or 0.5
c.	40 41	40.7	$40\frac{7}{10}$	$(4 \times 10) + (7 \times \frac{1}{10}) = 40\frac{7}{10}$ $(4 \times 10) + (7 \times 0.1) = 40.7$	$\frac{3}{10}$ or 0.3
d.	90 91	90.9	$90\frac{9}{10}$	$(9 \times 10) + (9 \times \frac{1}{10}) = 90\frac{9}{10}$ $(9 \times 10) + (9 \times 0.1) = 90.9$	$\frac{1}{10}$ or 0.1

tenths on a number line

S: (Write 4 ones and 1 tenth, 4.1, $4\frac{1}{10}$, $(4 \times 1) + (1 \times 0.1) = 4.1$. → $(4 \times 1) + (1 \times \frac{1}{10}) = 4\frac{1}{10}$.)

T: How many more tenths are needed to get to 5? Explain to your partner how you know, and complete the final column of the chart.

S: 9 tenths. → $\frac{9}{10}$. → 0.9. → I know because it takes 10 tenths to make a one. If we have 1 tenth, we need 9 more tenths to make 1.

Repeat the process by naming the following points for students to plot. Then, have them complete and share their charts. The longer number line with 5 whole number intervals can either be relabeled to show a broader range of numbers than those included in the chart or omitted for parts (b)–(d) below.

b. 3 tens 2 ones and 5 tenths
c. 4 tens 7 tenths
d. 9 tens 9 tenths

© 2015 Great Minds. eureka-math.org
G4-M6-TE-B5-1.3.1-01.2016

Problem Set (10 minutes)

Students should do their personal best to complete the Problem Set within the allotted 10 minutes. For some classes, it may be appropriate to modify the assignment by specifying which problems they work on first. Some problems do not specify a method for solving. Students should solve these problems using the RDW approach used for Application Problems.

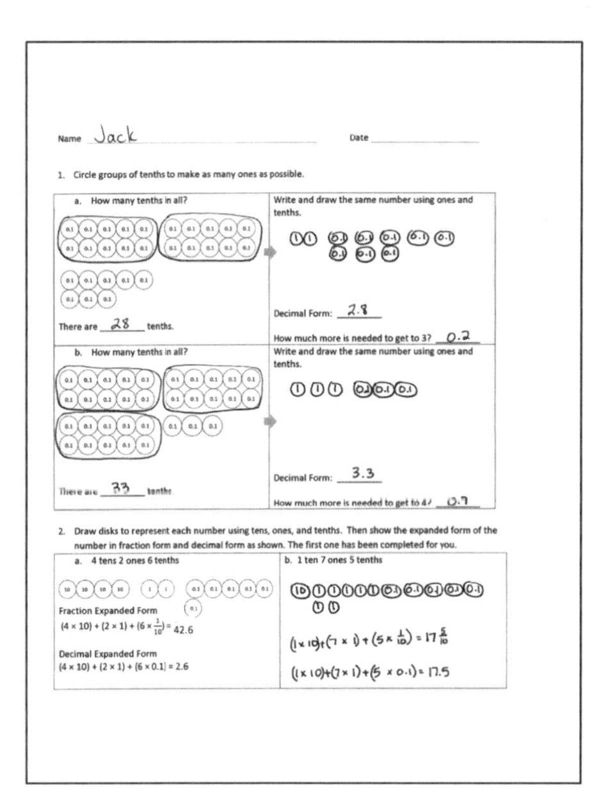

Name Jack Date

1. Circle groups of tenths to make as many ones as possible.

a. How many tenths in all?	Write and draw the same number using ones and tenths.
There are 28 tenths.	Decimal Form: 2.8 How much more is needed to get to 3? 0.2

b. How many tenths in all?	Write and draw the same number using ones and tenths.
There are 33 tenths.	Decimal Form: 3.3 How much more is needed to get to 4? 0.7

2. Draw disks to represent each number using tens, ones, and tenths. Then show the expanded form of the number in fraction form and decimal form as shown. The first one has been completed for you.

a. 4 tens 2 ones 6 tenths	b. 1 ten 7 ones 5 tenths
Fraction Expanded Form $(4 \times 10) + (2 \times 1) + (6 \times \frac{1}{10}) = 42.6$ Decimal Expanded Form $(4 \times 10) + (2 \times 1) + (6 \times 0.1) = 2.6$	$(1 \times 10) + (7 \times 1) + (5 \times \frac{1}{10}) = 17\frac{5}{10}$ $(1 \times 10) + (7 \times 1) + (5 \times 0.1) = 17.5$

Student Debrief (10 minutes)

Lesson Objective: Represent mixed numbers with units of tens, ones, and tenths with place value disks, on the number line, and in expanded form.

The Student Debrief is intended to invite reflection and active processing of the total lesson experience.

Invite students to review their solutions for the Problem Set. They should check work by comparing answers with a partner before going over answers as a class. Look for misconceptions or misunderstandings that can be addressed in the Debrief. Guide students in a conversation to debrief the Problem Set and process the lesson.

Any combination of the questions below may be used to lead the discussion.

- Look at Problem 3(b). Today, we showed mixed numbers in **decimal expanded form** and **fraction expanded form**. How could you represent this number with place value disks? With an area model? Draw a line that is 17.5 cm in length.
- Look at Problem 3(a). How would you represent this number using only tenths? With your partner, use the number line or centimeter ruler to prove that 39 tenths is the same as 3 ones and 9 tenths.
- Look at Problems 2(d) and 3(c). How are these two problems alike?
- In Problems 2(c), 2(d), and 3(e) we have the same number of tens as tenths. Explain to your partner the difference in value between the tens place and the tenths place. Notice that the ones are sandwiched between the tens and tenths.

c. 2 tens 3 ones 2 tenths	d. 7 tens 4 ones 7 tenths
$(2 \times 10) + (3 \times 1) + (2 \times 0.1) = 23.2$ $(2 \times 10) + (3 \times 1) + (2 \times \frac{1}{10}) = 23\frac{2}{10}$	$(7 \times 10) + (4 \times 1) + (7 \times 0.1) = 74.7$ $(7 \times 10) + (4 \times 1) + (7 \times \frac{1}{10}) = 74\frac{7}{10}$

3. Complete the chart.

	Number Line	Decimal Form	Mixed Number (ones and fraction form)	Expanded Form (fraction or decimal form)	How much to get to the next one?
a.	3 — 4	3.9	$3\frac{9}{10}$	$(3 \times 1) + (9 \times \frac{1}{10})$	0.1
b.	17 — 18	17.5	$17\frac{5}{10}$	$(1 \times 10) + (7 \times 1) + (5 \times 0.1)$	0.5
c.	74 — 75	74.7	$74\frac{7}{10}$	$(7 \times 10) + (4 \times 1) + (7 \times \frac{1}{10})$	0.3
d.	22 — 23	22.2	$22\frac{2}{10}$	$(2 \times 10) + (2 \times 1) + (2 \times 0.1)$	0.8
e.	80 — 81	80.8	$80\frac{8}{10}$	$(8 \times 10) + (8 \times 0.1)$	0.2

© 2015 Great Minds. eureka-math.org
G4-M6-TE-B5-1.3.1-01.2016

- How did you locate points on the number line?

Exit Ticket (3 minutes)

After the Student Debrief, instruct students to complete the Exit Ticket. A review of their work will help with assessing students' understanding of the concepts that were presented in today's lesson and planning more effectively for future lessons. The questions may be read aloud to the students.

© 2015 Great Minds. eureka-math.org
G4-M6-TE-B5-1.3.1-01.2016

Name ______________________________ Date ______________

1. Circle groups of tenths to make as many ones as possible.

a. How many tenths in all?

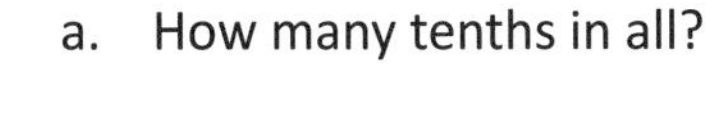

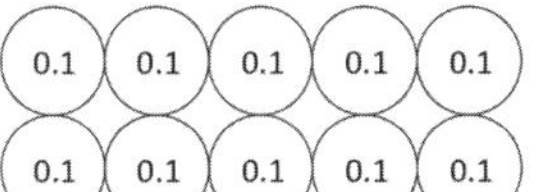

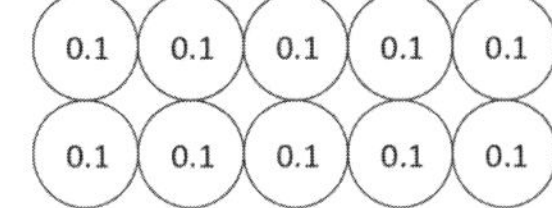

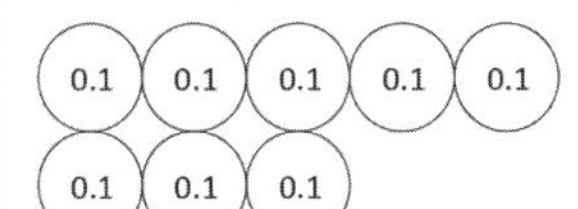

There are _________ tenths.

Write and draw the same number using ones and tenths.

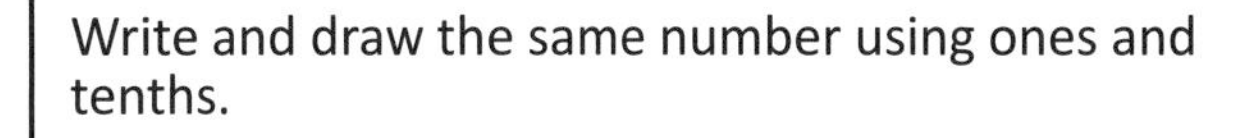

Decimal Form: __________

How much more is needed to get to 3? _________

b. How many tenths in all?

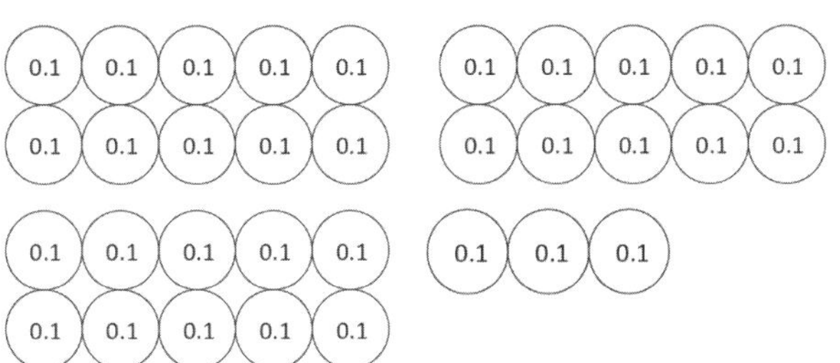

There are _________ tenths.

Write and draw the same number using ones and tenths.

Decimal Form: _________

How much more is needed to get to 4? _________

2. Draw disks to represent each number using tens, ones, and tenths. Then, show the expanded form of the number in fraction form and decimal form as shown. The first one has been completed for you.

a. 4 tens 2 ones 6 tenths

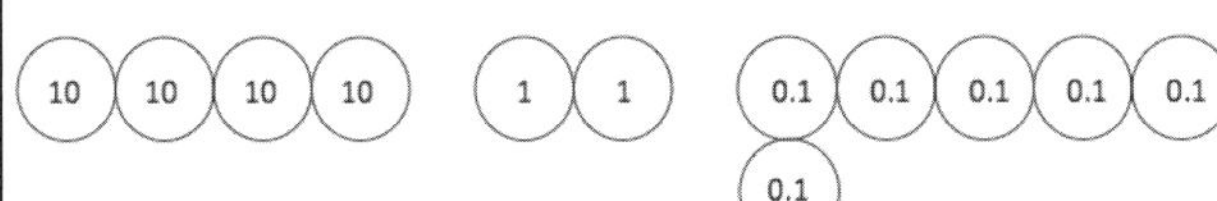

Fraction Expanded Form

$(4 \times 10) + (2 \times 1) + (6 \times \frac{1}{10}) = 42\frac{6}{10}$

Decimal Expanded Form

$(4 \times 10) + (2 \times 1) + (6 \times 0.1) = 42.6$

b. 1 ten 7 ones 5 tenths

© 2015 Great Minds. eureka-math.org
G4-M6-TE-B5-1.3.1-01.2016

c. 2 tens 3 ones 2 tenths	d. 7 tens 4 ones 7 tenths

3. Complete the chart.

Point	Number Line	Decimal Form	Mixed Number (ones and fraction form)	Expanded Form (fraction or decimal form)	How much to get to the next one?
a.			$3\frac{9}{10}$		0.1
b.	17 18				
c.				$(7 \times 10) + (4 \times 1) + (7 \times \frac{1}{10})$	
d.			$22\frac{2}{10}$		
e.				$(8 \times 10) + (8 \times 0.1)$	

EUREKA MATH

© 2015 Great Minds. eureka-math.org
G4-M6-TE-B5-1.3.1-01.2016

Name ______________________________ Date ____________

1. Circle groups of tenths to make as many ones as possible.

How many tenths in all?	Write and draw the same number using ones and tenths.
0.1 0.1 0.1 0.1 0.1 0.1 0.1 0.1 0.1 0.1 0.1 0.1 0.1 0.1 0.1 0.1 0.1 0.1 There are ________ tenths.	Decimal Form: ________ How much more is needed to get to 2? ________

2. Complete the chart.

Point	Number Line	Decimal Form	Mixed Number (ones and fraction form)	Expanded Form (fraction or decimal form)	How much to get to the next one?
a.			$12\frac{9}{10}$		
b.		70.7			

© 2015 Great Minds. eureka-math.org
G4-M6-TE-B5-1.3.1-01.2016

Name ______________________________ Date ________________

1. Circle groups of tenths to make as many ones as possible.

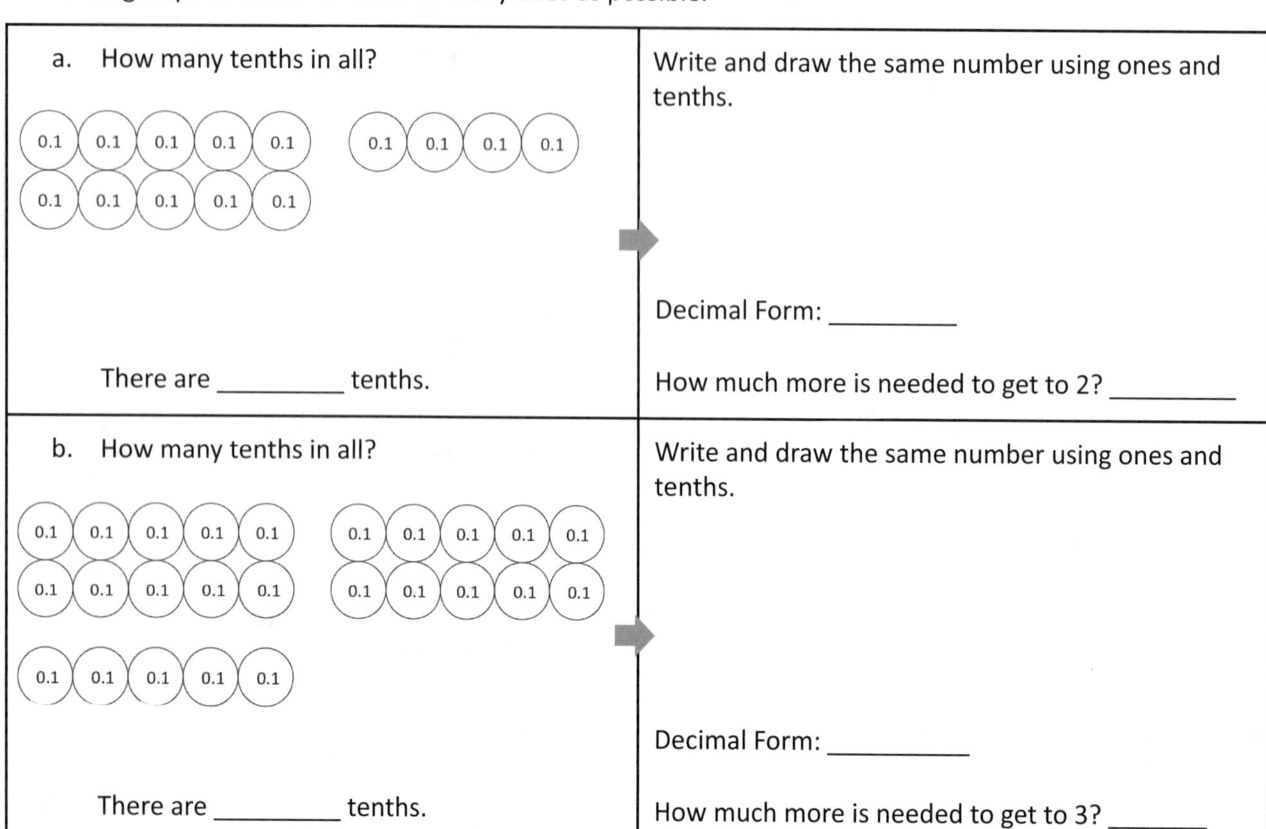

a. How many tenths in all? 0.1 0.1 0.1 0.1 0.1 0.1 0.1 0.1 0.1 0.1 0.1 0.1 0.1 0.1 There are _______ tenths.	Write and draw the same number using ones and tenths. Decimal Form: _______ How much more is needed to get to 2? _______
b. How many tenths in all? 0.1 0.1 0.1 0.1 0.1 0.1 0.1 0.1 0.1 0.1 0.1 0.1 0.1 0.1 0.1 0.1 0.1 0.1 0.1 0.1 0.1 0.1 0.1 0.1 0.1 There are _______ tenths.	Write and draw the same number using ones and tenths. Decimal Form: _______ How much more is needed to get to 3? _______

2. Draw disks to represent each number using tens, ones, and tenths. Then, show the expanded form of the number in fraction form and decimal form as shown. The first one has been completed for you.

a. 3 tens 4 ones 3 tenths

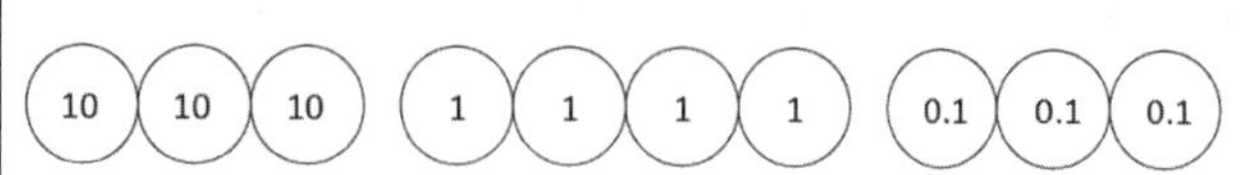

Fraction Expanded Form

$(3 \times 10) + (4 \times 1) + (3 \times \frac{1}{10} =)\ 34\frac{3}{10}$

Decimal Expanded Form

$(3 \times 10) + (4 \times 1) + (3 \times 0.1) = 34.3$

b. 5 tens 3 ones 7 tenths

© 2015 Great Minds. eureka-math.org
G4-M6-TE-B5-1.3.1-01.2016

c. 3 tens 2 ones 3 tenths	d. 8 tens 4 ones 8 tenths

3. Complete the chart.

Point	Number Line	Decimal Form	Mixed Number (ones and fraction form)	Expanded Form (fraction or decimal form)	How much to get to the next one?
a.			$4\frac{6}{10}$		
b.	24 25				0.5
c.				$(6 \times 10) + (3 \times 1) + (6 \times \frac{1}{10})$	
d.			$71\frac{3}{10}$		
e.				$(9 \times 10) + (9 \times 0.1)$	

© 2015 Great Minds. eureka-math.org
G4-M6-TE-B5-1.3.1-01.2016

Point	Number Line	Decimal Form	Mixed Number (ones and fraction form)	Expanded Form (fraction or decimal form)	How much more is needed to get to the next one?
a.					
b.					
c.					
d.					

tenths on a number line

© 2015 Great Minds. eureka-math.org
G4-M6-TE-B5-1.3.1-01.2016

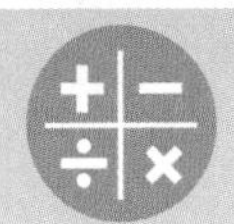

Topic B
Tenths and Hundredths

4.NF.5, 4.NF.6, 4.NBT.1, 4.NF.1, 4.NF.7, 4.MD.1

Focus Standards:	4.NF.5	Express a fraction with denominator 10 as an equivalent fraction with denominator 100, and use this technique to add two fractions with respective denominators 10 and 100. *For example, express 3/10 as 30/100, and add 3/10 + 4/100 = 34/100.* (Students who can generate equivalent fractions can develop strategies for adding fractions with unlike denominators in general. But addition and subtraction with unlike denominators in general is not a requirement at this grade.)
	4.NF.6	Use decimal notation for fractions with denominators 10 or 100. *For example, rewrite 0.62 as 62/100; describe a length as 0.62 meters; locate 0.62 on a number line diagram.*
Instructional Days:	5	
Coherence -Links from:	G3–M2	Place Value and Problem Solving with Units of Measure
	G3–M5	Fractions as Numbers on the Number Line
-Links to:	G5–M1	Place Value and Decimal Fractions

In Topic B, students decompose tenths into 10 equal parts to create hundredths. In Lesson 4, they once again use metric measurement as a basis for exploration. Using a meter stick, they locate 1 tenth meter and then locate 1 hundredth meter. They identify 1 centimeter as $\frac{1}{100}$ meter and count $\frac{1}{100}, \frac{2}{100}, \frac{3}{100}$, up to $\frac{10}{100}$, and, at the concrete level, realize the equivalence of $\frac{10}{100}$ meter and $\frac{1}{10}$ meter. They represent $\frac{1}{100}$ meter as 0.01 meter, counting up to $\frac{25}{100}$ or 0.25, both in fraction and decimal form. They then model the meter with a tape diagram and partition it into tenths, as they did in Lesson 1. Students locate 25 centimeters and see that it is equal to 25 hundredths by counting up, $\frac{10}{100}, \frac{20}{100}, \frac{21}{100}, \frac{22}{100}, \frac{23}{100}, \frac{24}{100}, \frac{25}{100}$. They represent this as $\frac{20}{100} + \frac{5}{100} = \frac{25}{100}$ and, using decimal notation, write 0.25. A number bond shows the decomposition of 0.25 into the fractional parts of $\frac{2}{10}$ and $\frac{5}{100}$.

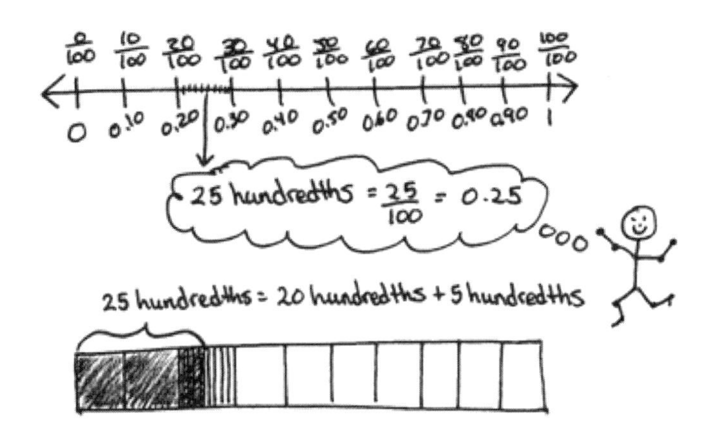

© 2015 Great Minds. eureka-math.org
G3-M7-TE-B7-1.3.1-01.2016

In Lesson 5, students relate hundredths to the area model (pictured below), to a tape diagram, and to place value disks. They see and represent the equivalence of tenths and hundredths pictorially and numerically.

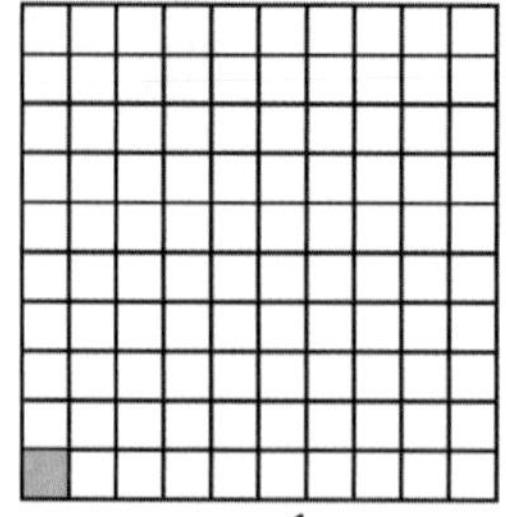

1 hundredth $= \frac{1}{100} = 0.01$

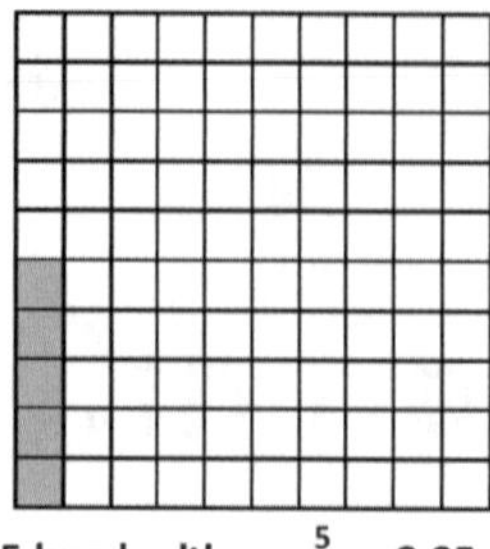

5 hundredths $= \frac{5}{100} = 0.05$

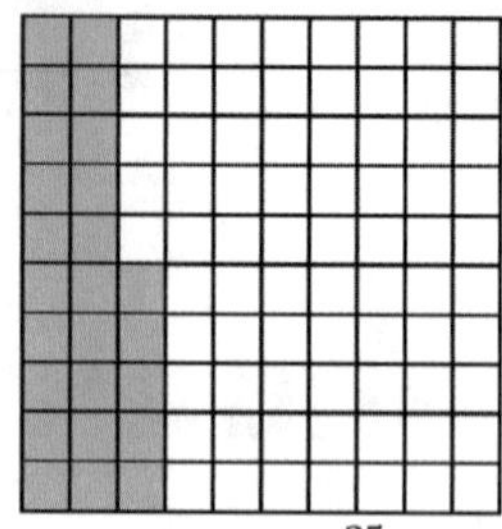

25 hundredths $= \frac{25}{100} = 0.25$

Students count up from $\frac{1}{100}$ with place value disks just as they did with centimeters in Lesson 4. This time, the 10 hundredths are traded for 1 tenth, and the equivalence is expressed as $\frac{1}{10} = \frac{10}{100} = 0.1 = 0.10$ (**4.NF.5**, **4.NF.6**). The equivalence of tenths and hundredths is also realized through multiplication and division (e.g., $\frac{1}{10} = \frac{1 \times 10}{10 \times 10} = \frac{10}{100}$ and $\frac{10}{100} = \frac{10 \div 10}{100 \div 10} = \frac{1}{10}$), establishing that 1 tenth is 10 times as much as 1 hundredth. They see, too, that 16 hundredths is 1 tenth and 6 hundredths, and that 25 hundredths is 2 tenths and 5 hundredths.

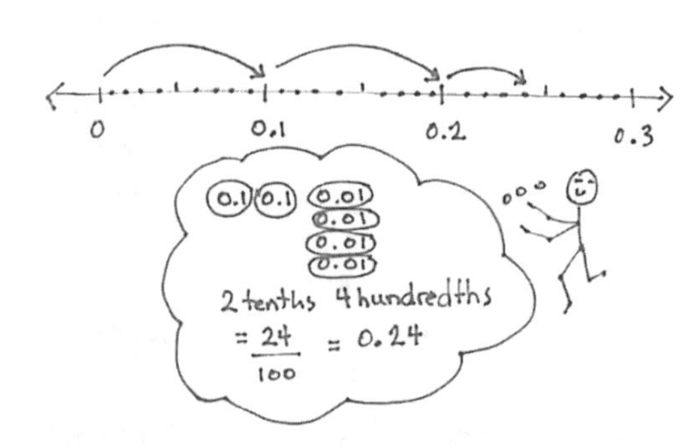

In Lesson 6, students draw representations of three-digit decimal numbers (with ones, tenths, and hundredths) with the area model.

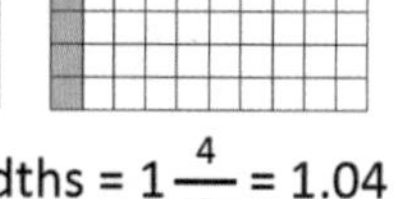

1 one 4 hundredths $= 1\frac{4}{100} = 1.04$

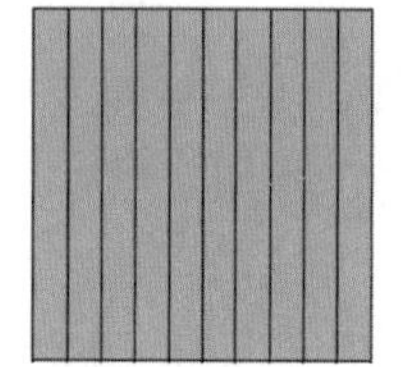
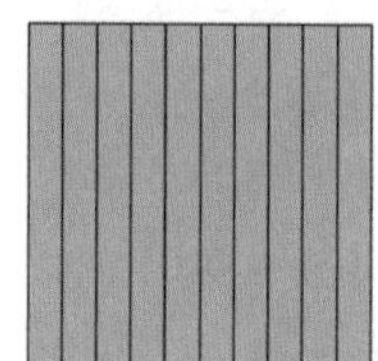
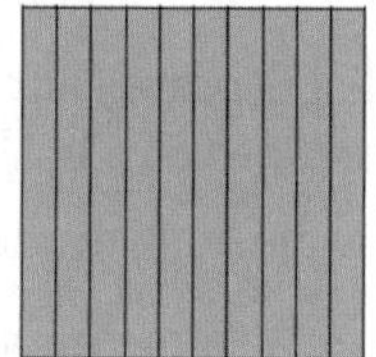
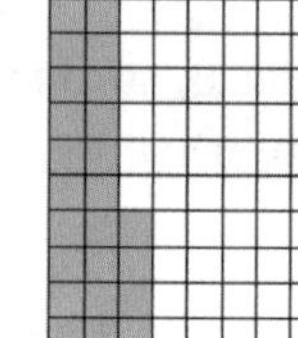

3 ones 24 hundredths $= 3\frac{24}{100} = 3.24$

Students also further extend their use of the number line to show the ones, tenths, and hundredths as lengths. Lesson 6 concludes with students coming to understand that tenths and hundredths each hold a special place within a decimal number, establishing that 3.80 and 3.08 are different and distinguishable values.

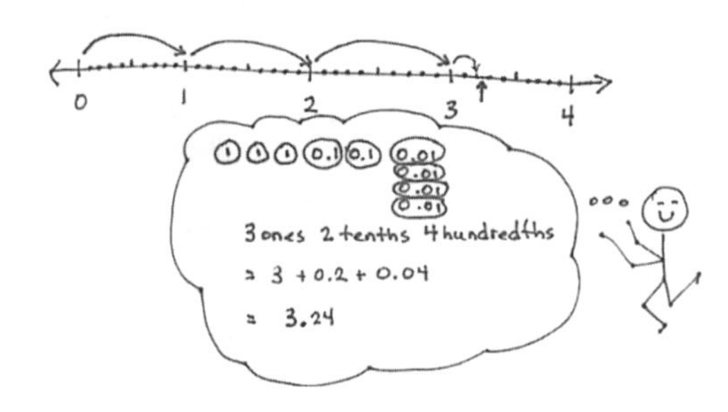

EUREKA MATH

© 2015 Great Minds. eureka-math.org
G4-M6-TE-B5-1.3.1-01.2016

In Lesson 7, decimal numbers to hundredths are modeled with disks and written on the place value chart, where each digit's value is analyzed. The value of the total number is represented in both fraction and decimal expanded form as pictured below.

Hundreds	Tens	Ones	•	Tenths	Hundredths
3	7	8		7	3
3 hundreds	7 tens	8 ones		7 tenths	3 hundredths

$$(3 \times 100) + (7 \times 10) + (8 \times 1) + \left(7 \times \frac{1}{10}\right) + \left(3 \times \frac{1}{100}\right) = 378\frac{73}{100}$$

$$(3 \times 100) + (7 \times 10) + (8 \times 1) + (7 \times 0.1) + (3 \times 0.01) = 378.73$$

In the Debrief, students discuss the symmetry of the place value chart around 1, seeing the ones place as the "mirror" for tens and tenths and hundreds and hundredths, thereby avoiding the misconception of the *oneths* place or the decimal point itself as the point of symmetry. This understanding helps students recognize that, even as we move to the decimal side of the place value chart, a column continues to represent a unit 10 times as large as that of the column to its right.

In Lesson 8, students use what they know about fractions to represent decimal numbers in terms of different units. For example, 3.2 might be modeled as 3 ones 2 tenths, 32 tenths, or 320 hundredths. Students show these renamings in unit form, fraction form, and decimal form.

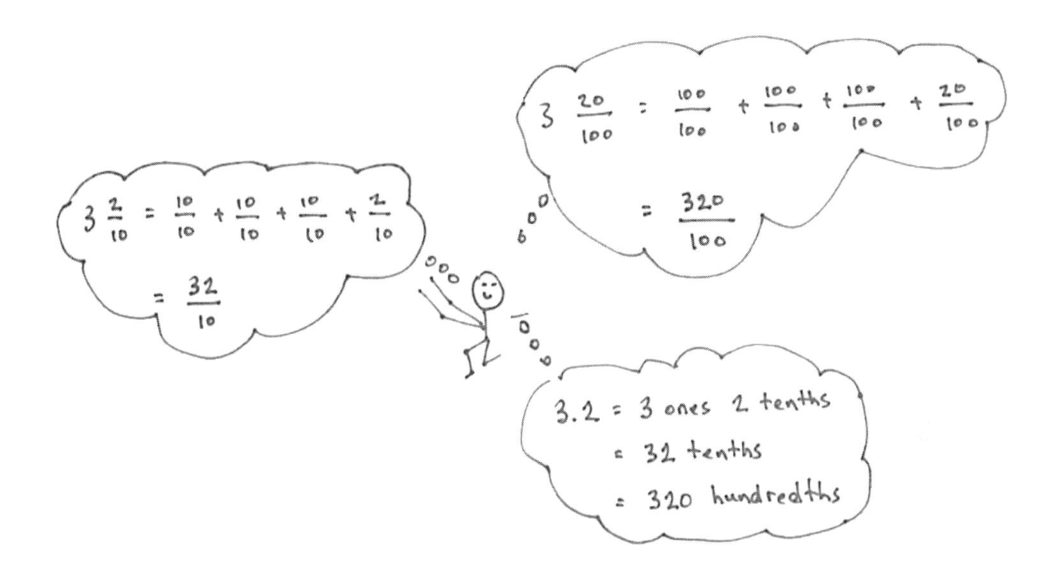

© 2015 Great Minds. eureka-math.org
G4-M6-TE-B5-1.3.1-01.2016

A Teaching Sequence Toward Mastery of Tenths and Hundredths	
Objective 1:	**Use meters to model the decomposition of one whole into hundredths. Represent and count hundredths.** **(Lesson 4)**
Objective 2:	**Model the equivalence of tenths and hundredths using the area model and place value disks.** **(Lesson 5)**
Objective 3:	**Use the area model and number line to represent mixed numbers with units of ones, tenths, and hundredths in fraction and decimal forms.** **(Lesson 6)**
Objective 4:	**Model mixed numbers with units of hundreds, tens, ones, tenths, and hundredths in expanded form and on the place value chart.** **(Lesson 7)**
Objective 5:	**Use understanding of fraction equivalence to investigate decimal numbers on the place value chart expressed in different units.** **(Lesson 8)**

© 2015 Great Minds. eureka-math.org
G4-M6-TE-B5-1.3.1-01.2016

Lesson 4

Objective: Use meters to model the decomposition of one whole into hundredths. Represent and count hundredths.

Suggested Lesson Structure

- Fluency Practice (12 minutes)
- Application Problem (5 minutes)
- Concept Development (33 minutes)
- Student Debrief (10 minutes)

Total Time (60 minutes)

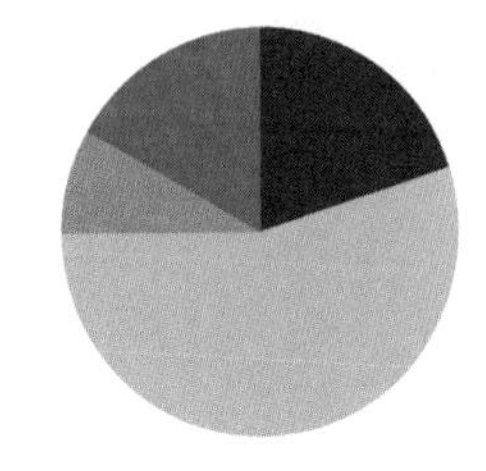

Fluency Practice (12 minutes)

- Sprint: Write Fractions and Decimals **4.NF.6** (9 minutes)
- Count by Tenths **4.NF.6** (3 minutes)

Sprint: Write Fractions and Decimals (9 minutes)

Materials: (S) Write Fractions and Decimals Sprint

Note: This Sprint reviews Lessons 1–3.

Count by Tenths (3 minutes)

Materials: (S) Personal white board

Note: This fluency activity reviews Lessons 1–2.

T: Count by twos to 20, starting at zero. (Write as students count.)

$\frac{0}{10}$	$\frac{2}{10}$	$\frac{4}{10}$	$\frac{6}{10}$	$\frac{8}{10}$	$\frac{10}{10}$	$\frac{12}{10}$	$\frac{14}{10}$	$\frac{16}{10}$	$\frac{18}{10}$	$\frac{20}{10}$
0					1					2

S: 0, 2, 4, 6, 8, 10, 12, 14, 16, 18, 20.

T: Count by 2 tenths to 20 tenths, starting at 0 tenths. (Write as students count.)

S: $\frac{0}{10}, \frac{2}{10}, \frac{4}{10}, \frac{6}{10}, \frac{8}{10}, \frac{10}{10}, \frac{12}{10}, \frac{14}{10}, \frac{16}{10}, \frac{18}{10}, \frac{20}{10}$.

© 2015 Great Minds. eureka-math.org
G4-M6-TE-B5-1.3.1-01.2016

T: 1 is the same as how many tenths?

S: 10 tenths.

T: (Beneath $\frac{10}{10}$, write 1.)

Continue the process for 2.

T: Let's count by 2 tenths again. This time, when you come to a whole number, say the whole number. Try not to look at the board.

S: $0, \frac{2}{10}, \frac{4}{10}, \frac{6}{10}, \frac{8}{10}, 1, \frac{12}{10}, \frac{14}{10}, \frac{16}{10}, \frac{18}{10}, 2.$

T: Count backward by 2 tenths, starting at 2.

S: $2, \frac{18}{10}, \frac{16}{10}, \frac{14}{10}, \frac{12}{10}, 1, \frac{8}{10}, \frac{6}{10}, \frac{4}{10}, \frac{2}{10}, \frac{0}{10}.$

Application Problem (5 minutes)

Ali is knitting a scarf that will be 2 meters long. So far, she has knitted $1\frac{2}{10}$ meters.

a. How many more meters does Ali need to knit to complete the scarf? Write the answer as a fraction and as a decimal.

b. How many more centimeters does Ali need to knit to complete the scarf?

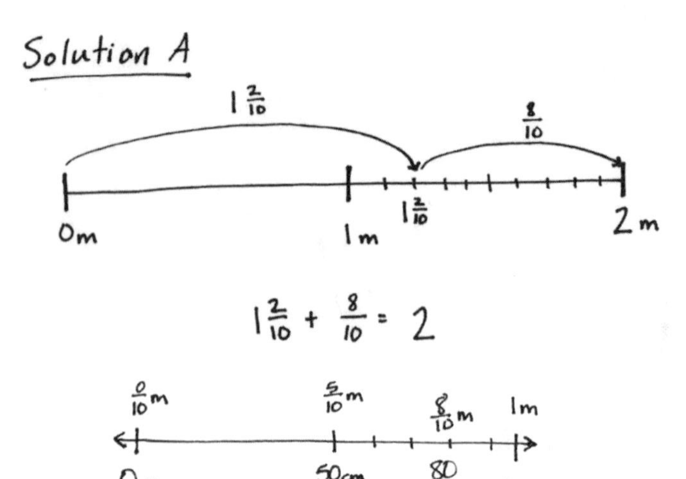

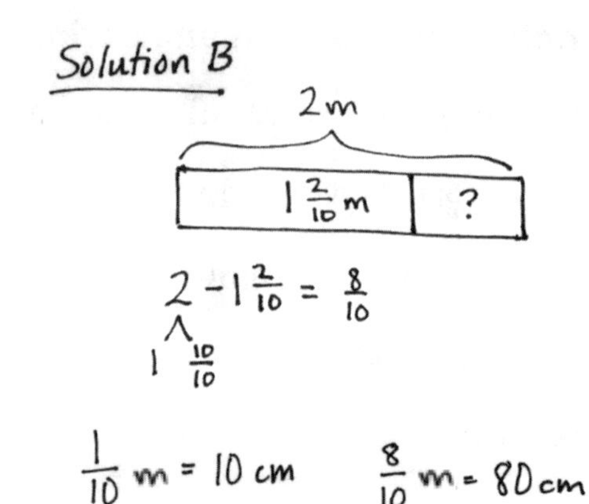

a) Ali needs to knit $\frac{8}{10}$ meters or 0.8 meters more.

b) Ali needs to knit 80 more centimeters.

Note: This Application Problem reviews mixed decimal fractions and *counting on* to make 1 more. Revisit the problem in the Debrief to answer in hundredths meters.

© 2015 Great Minds. eureka-math.org
G4-M6-TE-B5-1.3.1-01.2016

Concept Development (33 minutes)

Materials: (T) Meter stick, 1-meter strip of paper partitioned into 10 equal parts by folds or dotted lines
(S) Personal white board, tape diagram in tenths (Template), pencil

Problem 1: Recognize 1 centimeter as $\frac{1}{100}$ of a meter, which can be written as $\frac{1}{100}$ m and as 0.01 m.

T: This is a meter stick. What is its length?

S: 1 meter.

T: How many centimeters are in a meter?

S: 100 centimeters.

T: (Write on the board 1 m = 100 cm.)

T: (Show centimeters on the meter stick.) A meter is made of 100 centimeters. What fraction of a meter is 1 centimeter?

S: $\frac{1}{100}$ meter.

T: (Write $\frac{1}{100}$ m = 1 cm.) In decimal form, $\frac{1}{100}$ meter can be written as zero point zero one meter. (Write 0.01 m.)

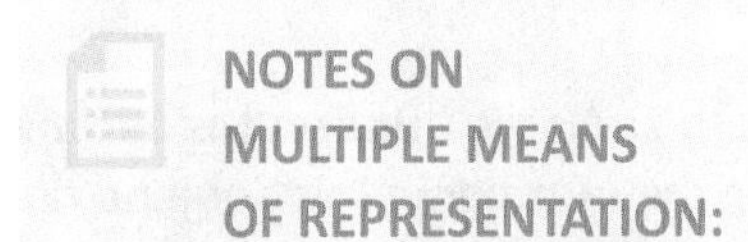

NOTES ON MULTIPLE MEANS OF REPRESENTATION:

Be sure to enunciate *th* at the end of *hundredths* to help English language learners distinguish *hundredths* and *hundreds*. If possible, speak more slowly, pause more frequently, or couple the language with a place value chart. Check for student understanding and correct pronunciation of fraction names.

T: 1 **hundredth** is written as zero point zero one. How do you think we represent $\frac{3}{100}$ meter in decimal form? Talk with your partner, and write your thoughts on your personal white board.

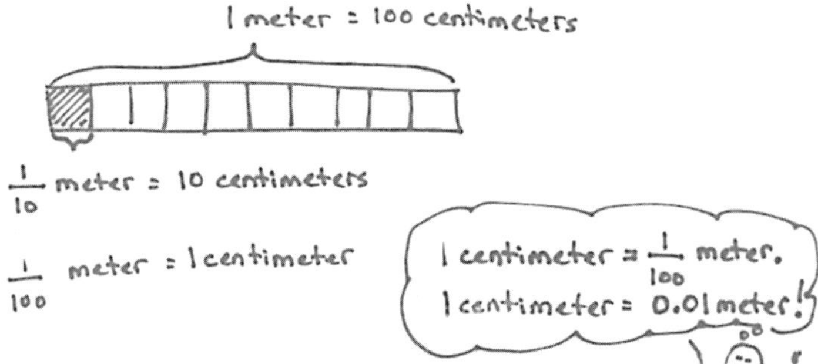

S: 0.03 meter.

T: Yes. $\frac{3}{100}$ meter can be shown as a fraction or in decimal form. (Write $\frac{3}{100}$ m = 0.03 m.)

T: (Show the meter strip of paper.) This 1-meter paper strip is partitioned into 10 equal parts. Let's shade $\frac{1}{10}$ meter. How many centimeters equal $\frac{1}{10}$ meter?

S: 10 centimeters.

T: How many hundredths of a meter equal $\frac{1}{10}$ meter?

S: $\frac{10}{100}$ meter.

T: (Write $\frac{1}{10}$ m = $\frac{10}{100}$ m.) We can write this number as a fraction. We can also write it in decimal form. (Write 0.1 m = 0.10 m.) This (pointing to the latter) is how you express $\frac{10}{100}$ meter as a decimal.

© 2015 Great Minds. eureka-math.org
G4-M6-TE-B5-1.3.1-01.2016

T: Let's decompose $\frac{1}{10}$ meter into 10 smaller units to prove that this number sentence, 0.1 m = 0.10 m, is true. (Partition the tenth into 10 parts.) Is each of these new smaller units $\frac{1}{100}$ meter and 1 centimeter in length?

S: Yes.

T: Explain to your partner why.

Repeat the process by shading the next tenth of the meter. Partition it into hundredths, and have students reason about the truth of the following number sentence: $\frac{2}{10}$ m = $\frac{20}{100}$ m = 0.2 m = 0.20 m.

Problem 2: Name hundredths as tenths and some hundredths, stating the number in fraction and decimal form.

NOTES ON MULTIPLE MEANS FOR ACTION AND EXPRESSION:

Some learners may find partitioning hundredths on the meter strip challenging. Alternatively, have students model with an area model (e.g., a 10 by 10 square partitioned into 100 unit squares). Or, enlarge the template (and ta pe diagrams on the Problem Set) to ease the task for students working below grade level and others. It may be helpful to use color to help students read hundredths on the Problem Set.

MP.6

T: (Show the meter strip of paper with 2 tenths shaded.) How many tenths of this meter strip of paper are shaded?

S: $\frac{2}{10}$ meter.

T: Use the tape diagram in tenths template to represent this amount. Lightly shade 2 tenths using a pencil.

T: (Write $\frac{2}{10}$ m + $\frac{5}{100}$ m on the board.) Let's shade in $\frac{5}{100}$ meter more. What will you have to do first in order to shade $\frac{5}{100}$ meter?

S: Partition the next tenth of a meter into 10 equal parts.

S: (Partition the next tenth meter into 10 equal parts, and shade $\frac{5}{100}$ meter.)

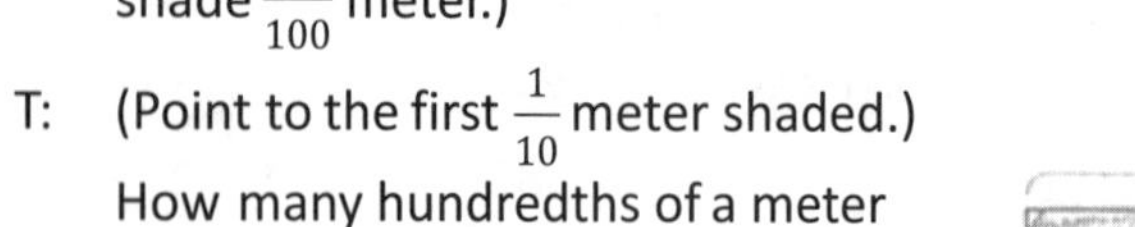

T: (Point to the first $\frac{1}{10}$ meter shaded.) How many hundredths of a meter are shaded here?

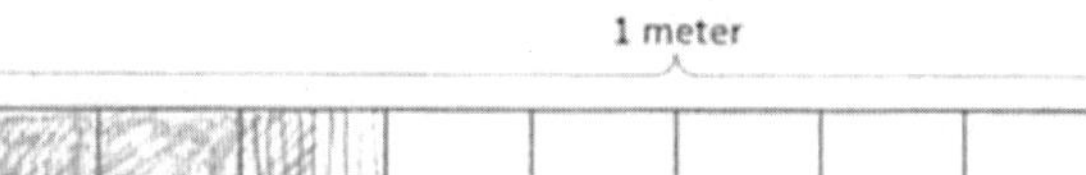

S: $\frac{10}{100}$ meter.

T: (Point to the second $\frac{1}{10}$ meter shaded.) How many hundredths of a meter are shaded here?

S: $\frac{10}{100}$ meter.

T: How many hundredths of a meter are shaded altogether? Explain your thinking.

S: $\frac{25}{100}$ meter. → I see $\frac{10}{100}$ meter in each of the first two parts that were shaded. That is $\frac{20}{100}$ meter. Then, we shaded $\frac{5}{100}$ meter more. $\frac{20}{100}$ m + $\frac{5}{100}$ m = $\frac{25}{100}$ m .

T: (Write 0.25.) 25 hundredths can be written as a decimal in this way.

© 2015 Great Minds. eureka-math.org
G4-M6-TE-B5-1.3.1-01.2016

MP.6

T: (Make a number bond as shown to the right.) So, 25 hundredths is made of 2 tenths and...?

S: 5 hundredths.

T: (Write $\frac{2}{10} + \frac{5}{100} = \frac{25}{100}$.) Explain to your partner why this is true.

S: 2 tenths is the same as 20 hundredths, so it is the same as $\frac{20}{100} + \frac{5}{100}$. → 2 tenths is the same as $\frac{1}{10} + \frac{1}{10}$, and each tenth is $\frac{10}{100}$. So, $\frac{10}{100} + \frac{10}{100} + \frac{5}{100} = \frac{25}{100}$.

0.25

$\frac{2}{10}$ $\frac{5}{100}$

Have students continue by writing the total as a decimal and in a number bond to represent the tenths and hundredths fractions that compose the following decimals:

- 28 hundredths
- 31 hundredths
- 41 hundredths
- 79 hundredths

Problem Set (10 minutes)

Students should do their personal best to complete the Problem Set within the allotted 10 minutes. For some classes, it may be appropriate to modify the assignment by specifying which problems they work on first. Some problems do not specify a method for solving. Students should solve these problems using the RDW approach used for Application Problems.

Student Debrief (10 minutes)

Lesson Objective: Use meters to model the decomposition of one whole into hundredths. Represent and count hundredths.

The Student Debrief is intended to invitereflection and active processing of the total lesson experience.

Invite students to review their solutions for the Problem Set. They should check work by comparing answers with a partner before going over answers as a class. Look for misconceptions or misunderstandings that can be addressed in the Debrief. Guide students in a conversation to debrief the Problem Set and process the lesson.

Any combination of the questions below may be used to lead the discussion.

- In Problem 2(b), you showed that $\frac{1}{10}$ m = $\frac{10}{100}$ m. Write each number in decimal form. What do you notice?

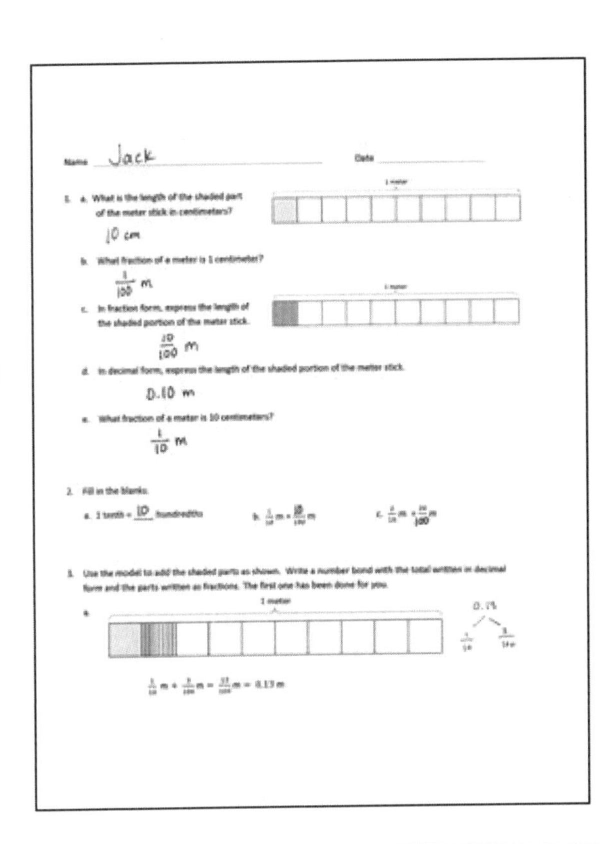

Name Jack Date

1. a. What is the length of the shaded part of the meter stick in centimeters?

10 cm

b. What fraction of a meter is 1 centimeter?

$\frac{1}{100}$ m

c. In fraction form, express the length of the shaded portion of the meter stick.

$\frac{10}{100}$ m

d. In decimal form, express the length of the shaded portion of the meter stick.

0.10 m

e. What fraction of a meter is 10 centimeters?

$\frac{1}{10}$ m

2. Fill in the blanks.

a. 1 tenth = 10 hundredths

3. Use the model to add the shaded parts as shown. Write a number bond with the total written in decimal form and the parts written as fractions. The first one has been done for you.

© 2015 Great Minds. eureka-math.org
G4-M6-TE-B5-1.3.1-01.2016

- Look at Problem 4(a). You shaded $\frac{8}{10}$ meter on a tape diagram. Can this be named in any other way? Use a diagram to explain your thinking, and show that number in decimal form.
- Share your number bond for Problem 3(b). How could you write this number bond showing both parts as hundredths? Why is it easier to show as much of the tape diagram as tenths as you can?
- Look at Problem 3(c). Why did we partition the fourth tenth into hundredths but left the first three tenths without partitioning?
- In Problem 5, how did you know how many tenths you could take out of the hundredths to make each number bond? Use a specific example to explain your reasoning.
- How do *hundredths* enable us to measure and communicate more precisely than tenths?
- Explain how hundredths are different from tenths.
- Refer to your solution for the Application Problem, and rename your answer using hundredths.

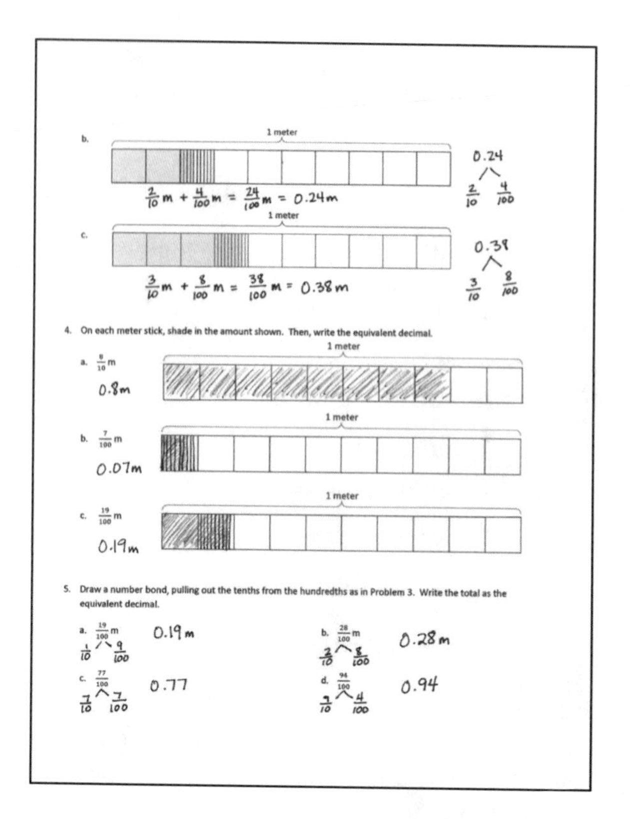

b. 1 meter

$\frac{2}{10}$ m + $\frac{4}{100}$ m = $\frac{24}{100}$ m = 0.24m

0.24: $\frac{2}{10}$ and $\frac{4}{100}$

c. 1 meter

$\frac{3}{10}$ m + $\frac{8}{100}$ m = $\frac{38}{100}$ m = 0.38m

0.38: $\frac{3}{10}$ and $\frac{8}{100}$

4. On each meter stick, shade in the amount shown. Then, write the equivalent decimal.

a. $\frac{8}{10}$ m — 1 meter — 0.8m

b. $\frac{7}{100}$ m — 1 meter — 0.07m

c. $\frac{19}{100}$ m — 1 meter — 0.19m

5. Draw a number bond, pulling out the tenths from the hundredths as in Problem 3. Write the total as the equivalent decimal.

a. $\frac{19}{100}$ m: $\frac{1}{10}$ and $\frac{9}{100}$ — 0.19m

b. $\frac{28}{100}$ m: $\frac{2}{10}$ and $\frac{8}{100}$ — 0.28m

c. $\frac{77}{100}$: $\frac{7}{10}$ and $\frac{7}{100}$ — 0.77

d. $\frac{94}{100}$: $\frac{9}{10}$ and $\frac{4}{100}$ — 0.94

Exit Ticket (3 minutes)

After the Student Debrief, instruct students to complete the Exit Ticket. A review of their work will help with assessing students' understanding of the concepts that were presented in today's lesson and planning more effectively for future lessons. The questions may be read aloud to the students.

© 2015 Great Minds. eureka-math.org
G4-M6-TE-B5-1.3.1-01.2016

EUREKA MATH

Number Correct: ________

A

Write Fractions and Decimals

1.	$\frac{2}{10}$ =	.
2.	$\frac{3}{10}$ =	.
3.	$\frac{4}{10}$ =	.
4.	$\frac{8}{10}$ =	.
5.	$\frac{6}{10}$ =	.
6.	0.1 =	$\frac{}{10}$
7.	0.2 =	$\frac{}{10}$
8.	0.3 =	$\frac{}{10}$
9.	0.7 =	$\frac{}{10}$
10.	0.5 =	$\frac{}{10}$
11.	$\frac{5}{10}$ =	.
12.	0.8 =	$\frac{}{10}$
13.	$\frac{7}{10}$ =	.
14.	0.4 =	$\frac{}{10}$
15.	$\frac{9}{10}$ =	.
16.	$\frac{10}{10}$ =	.
17.	$\frac{11}{10}$ =	.
18.	$\frac{12}{10}$ =	.
19.	$\frac{15}{10}$ =	.
20.	$\frac{25}{10}$ =	.
21.	$\frac{45}{10}$ =	.
22.	$\frac{38}{10}$ =	.

23.	1 =	$\frac{}{10}$
24.	2 =	$\frac{}{10}$
25.	5 =	$\frac{}{10}$
26.	4 =	$\frac{}{10}$
27.	4.1 =	$\frac{}{10}$
28.	4.2 =	$\frac{}{10}$
29.	4.6 =	$\frac{}{10}$
30.	2.6 =	$\frac{}{10}$
31.	3.6 =	$\frac{}{10}$
32.	3.4 =	$\frac{}{10}$
33.	2.3 =	$\frac{}{10}$
34.	$4\frac{3}{10}$ =	.
35.	$\frac{20}{10}$ =	.
36.	1.8 =	$\frac{}{10}$
37.	$3\frac{4}{10}$ =	.
38.	$\frac{50}{10}$ =	.
39.	4.7 =	$\frac{}{10}$
40.	$2\frac{8}{10}$ =	.
41.	$\frac{30}{10}$ =	.
42.	3.2 =	$\frac{}{10}$
43.	$\frac{20}{10}$ =	.
44.	2.1 =	$\frac{}{10}$

© 2015 Great Minds. eureka-math.org
G4-M6-TE-B5-1.3.1-01.2016

B

Number Correct: _______

Improvement: _______

Write Fractions and Decimals

1.	$\frac{1}{10}$ =	.
2.	$\frac{2}{10}$ =	.
3.	$\frac{3}{10}$ =	.
4.	$\frac{7}{10}$ =	.
5.	$\frac{5}{10}$ =	.
6.	0.2 =	$\frac{}{10}$
7.	0.3 =	$\frac{}{10}$
8.	0.4 =	$\frac{}{10}$
9.	0.8 =	$\frac{}{10}$
10.	0.6 =	$\frac{}{10}$
11.	$\frac{4}{10}$ =	.
12.	0.9 =	$\frac{}{10}$
13.	$\frac{6}{10}$ =	.
14.	0.5 =	$\frac{}{10}$
15.	$\frac{9}{10}$ =	.
16.	$\frac{10}{10}$ =	.
17.	$\frac{11}{10}$ =	.
18.	$\frac{12}{10}$ =	.
19.	$\frac{17}{10}$ =	.
20.	$\frac{27}{10}$ =	.
21.	$\frac{47}{10}$ =	.
22.	$\frac{34}{10}$ =	.

23.	1 =	$\frac{}{10}$
24.	2 =	$\frac{}{10}$
25.	4 =	$\frac{}{10}$
26.	3 =	$\frac{}{10}$
27.	3.1 =	$\frac{}{10}$
28.	3.2 =	$\frac{}{10}$
29.	3.6 =	$\frac{}{10}$
30.	1.6 =	$\frac{}{10}$
31.	2.6 =	$\frac{}{10}$
32.	4.2 =	$\frac{}{10}$
33.	2.5 =	$\frac{}{10}$
34.	$3\frac{4}{10}$ =	.
35.	$\frac{50}{10}$ =	.
36.	1.7 =	$\frac{}{10}$
37.	$4\frac{3}{10}$ =	.
38.	$\frac{20}{10}$ =	.
39.	4.6 =	$\frac{}{10}$
40.	$2\frac{4}{10}$ =	.
41.	$\frac{40}{10}$ =	.
42.	2.3 =	$\frac{}{10}$
43.	$\frac{30}{10}$ =	.
44.	4.1 =	$\frac{}{10}$

© 2015 Great Minds. eureka-math.org
G4-M6-TE-B5-1.3.1-01.2016

Name ______________________________ Date ______________

1. a. What is the length of the shaded part of the meter stick in centimeters?

1 meter

b. What fraction of a meter is 1 centimeter?

1 meter

c. In fraction form, express the length of the shaded portion of the meter stick.

d. In decimal form, express the length of the shaded portion of the meter stick.

e. What fraction of a meter is 10 centimeters?

2. Fill in the blanks.

a. 1 tenth = _____ hundredths

b. $\frac{1}{10}$ m = $\frac{}{100}$ m

c. $\frac{2}{10}$ m = $\frac{20}{}$ m

3. Use the model to add the shaded parts as shown. Write a number bond with the total written in decimal form and the parts written as fractions. The first one has been done for you.

a.

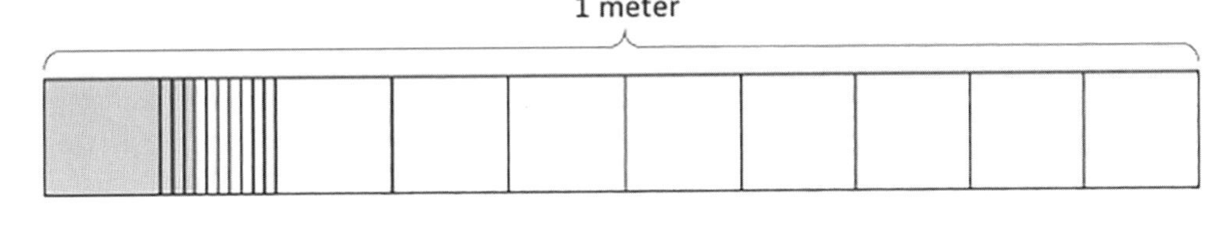

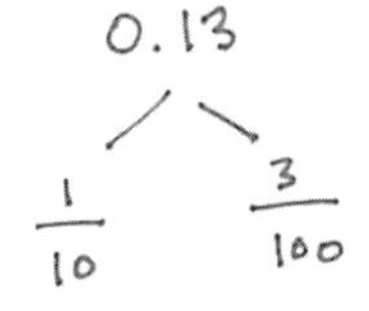

$\frac{1}{10}$ m + $\frac{3}{100}$ m = $\frac{13}{100}$ m = 0.13 m

© 2015 Great Minds. eureka-math.org
G4-M6-TE-B5-1.3.1-01.2016

b.

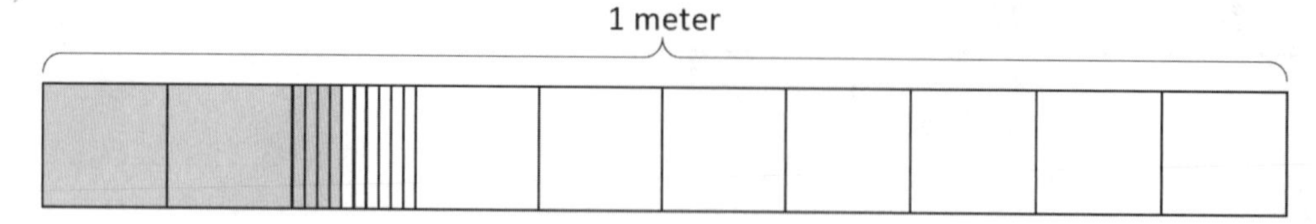

c.

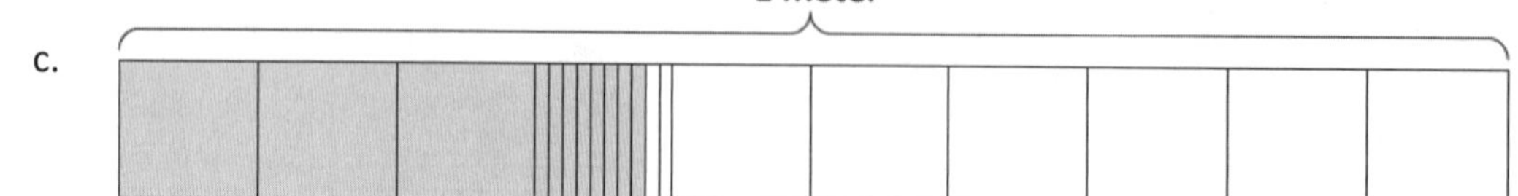

4. On each meter stick, shade in the amount shown. Then, write the equivalent decimal.

a. $\frac{8}{10}$ m

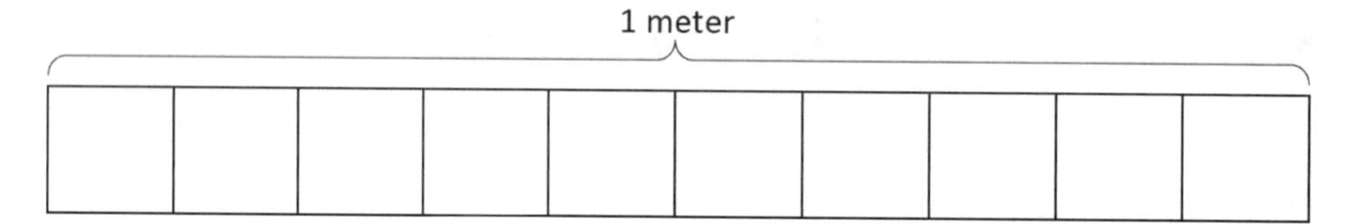

b. $\frac{7}{100}$ m

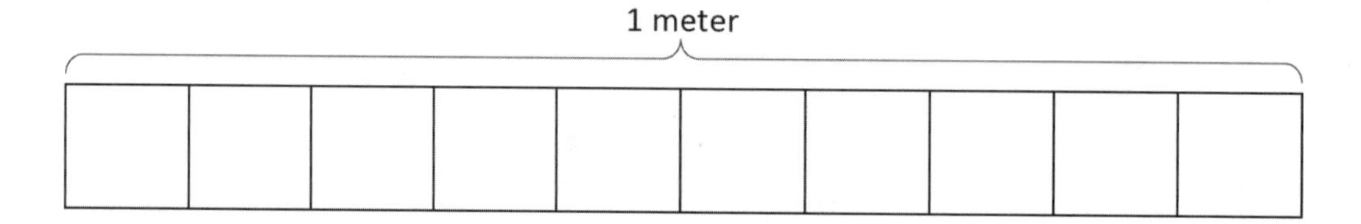

c. $\frac{19}{100}$ m

1 meter

5. Draw a number bond, pulling out the tenths from the hundredths as in Problem 3. Write the total as the equivalent decimal.

a. $\frac{19}{100}$ m

b. $\frac{28}{100}$ m

c. $\frac{77}{100}$

d. $\frac{94}{100}$

© 2015 Great Minds. eureka-math.org
G4-M6-TE-B5-1.3.1-01.2016

Name ______________________________ Date ______________

1. Shade in the amount shown. Then, write the equivalent decimal.

$\frac{6}{10}$ m

1 meter

2. Draw a number bond, pulling out the tenths from the hundredths. Write the total as the equivalent decimal.

a. $\frac{62}{100}$ m

b. $\frac{27}{100}$

© 2015 Great Minds. eureka-math.org
G4-M6-TE-B5-1.3.1-01.2016

Name ______________________________ Date ________________

1. a. What is the length of the shaded part of the meter stick in centimeters?

1 meter

b. What fraction of a meter is 3 centimeters?

c. In fraction form, express the length of the shaded portion of the meter stick.

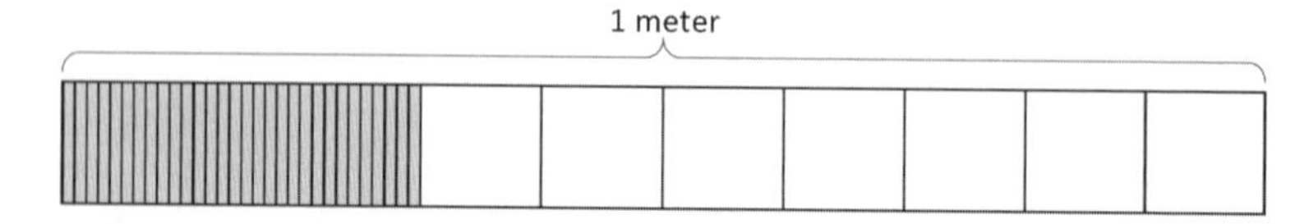

d. In decimal form, express the length of the shaded portion of the meter stick.

e. What fraction of a meter is 30 centimeters?

2. Fill in the blanks.

a. 5 tenths = _____ hundredths

b. $\frac{5}{10}\text{ m} = \frac{\_\_\_}{100}\text{ m}$

c. $\frac{4}{10}\text{ m} = \frac{40}{\_\_\_}\text{ m}$

3. Use the model to add the shaded parts as shown. Write a number bond with the total written in decimal form and the parts written as fractions. The first one has been done for you.

a.

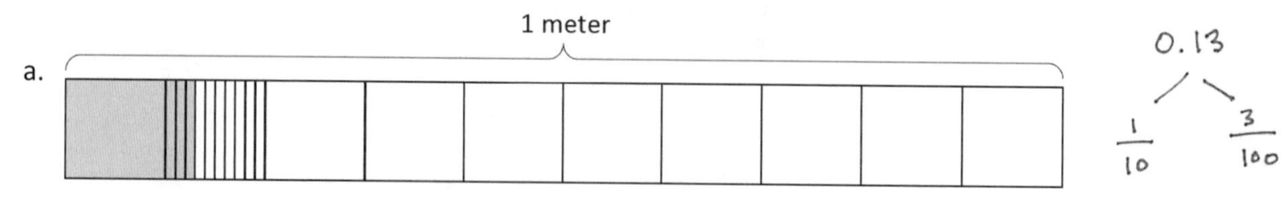

0.13

$\frac{1}{10}$ $\frac{3}{100}$

$\frac{1}{10}\text{ m} + \frac{3}{100}\text{ m} = \frac{13}{100}\text{ m} = 0.13\text{ m}$

© 2015 Great Minds. eureka-math.org
G4-M6-TE-B5-1.3.1-01.2016

EUREKA MATH

b.

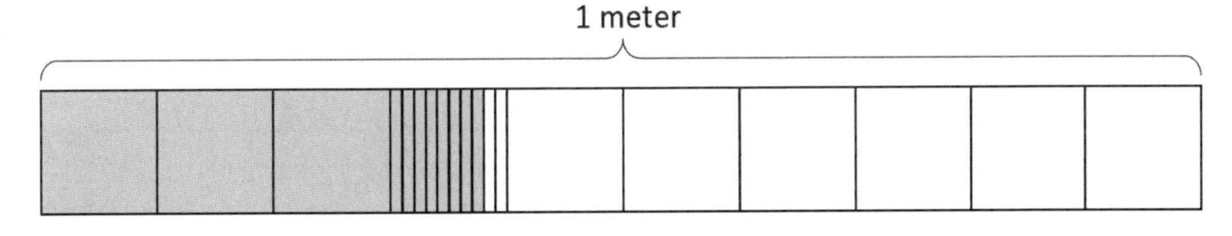

c.

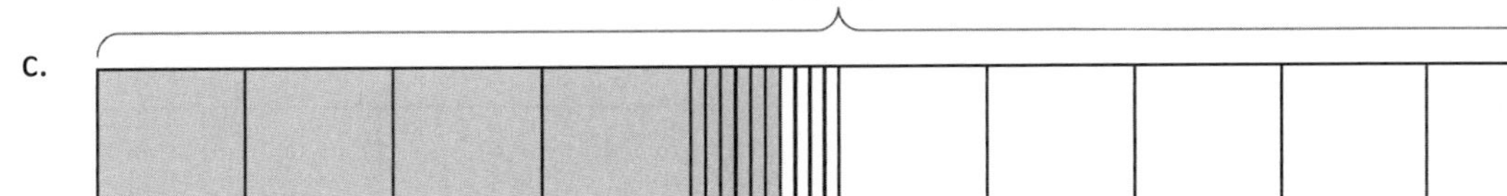

4. On each meter stick, shade in the amount shown. Then, write the equivalent decimal.

a. $\frac{9}{10}$ m

1 meter

b. $\frac{15}{100}$ m

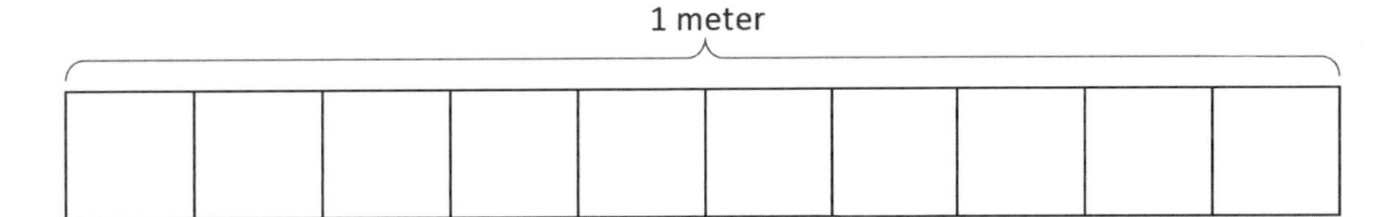

c. $\frac{41}{100}$ m

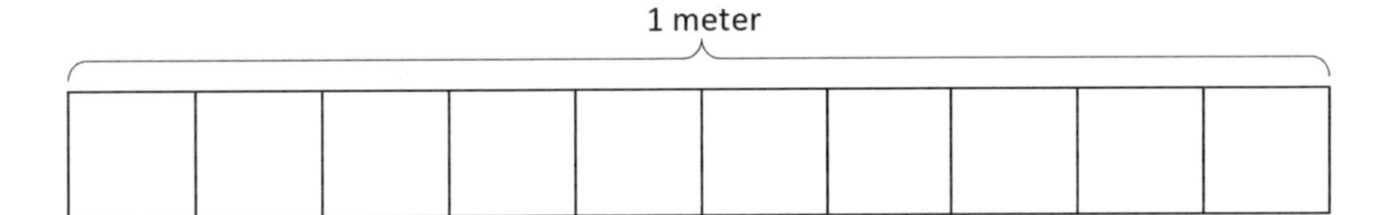

5. Draw a number bond, pulling out the tenths from the hundredths, as in Problem 3 of the Homework. Write the total as the equivalent decimal.

a. $\frac{23}{100}$ m

b. $\frac{38}{100}$ m

c. $\frac{82}{100}$

d. $\frac{76}{100}$

© 2015 Great Minds. eureka-math.org
G4-M6-TE-B5-1.3.1-01.2016

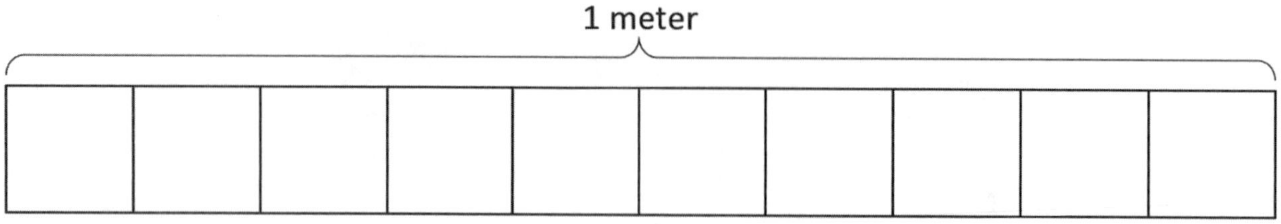

1 meter

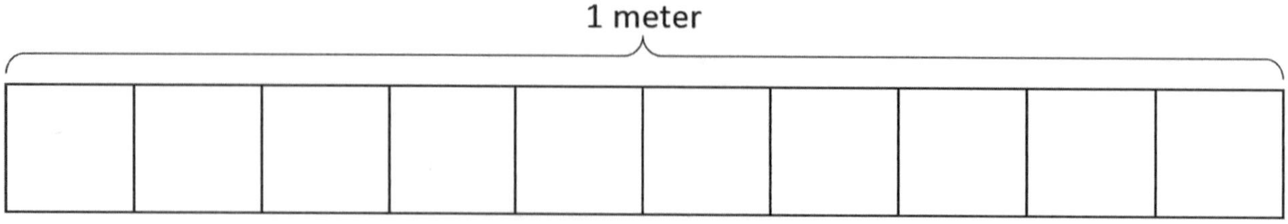

1 meter

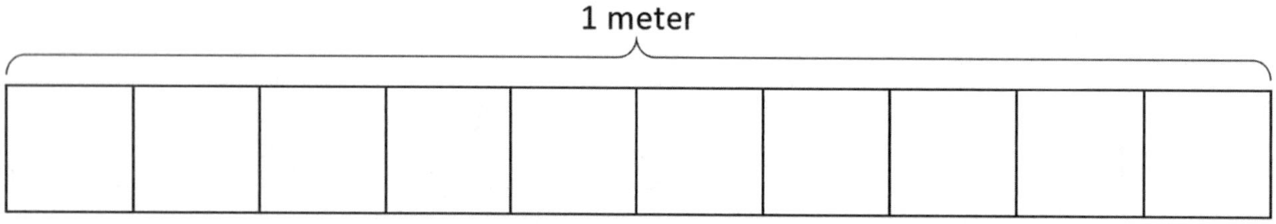

1 meter

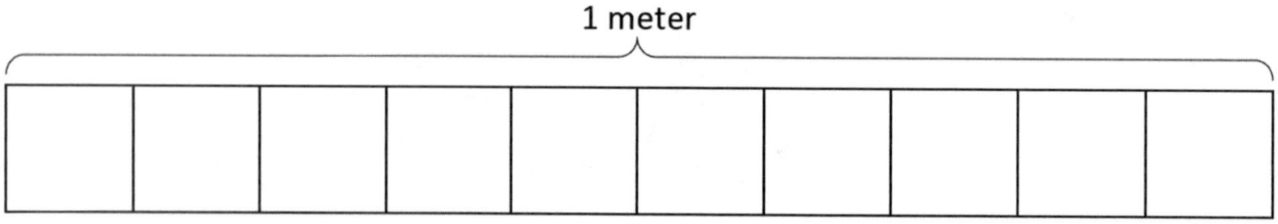

1 meter

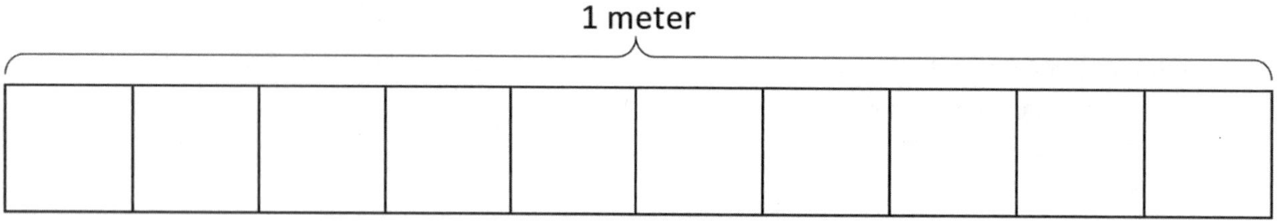

1 meter

tape diagram in tenths

© 2015 Great Minds. eureka-math.org
G4-M6-TE-B5-1.3.1-01.2016

Lesson 5

Objective: Model the equivalence of tenths and hundredths using the area model and place value disks.

Suggested Lesson Structure

■ Fluency Practice	(12 minutes)
■ Application Problem	(6 minutes)
■ Concept Development	(32 minutes)
■ Student Debrief	(10 minutes)
Total Time	**(60 minutes)**

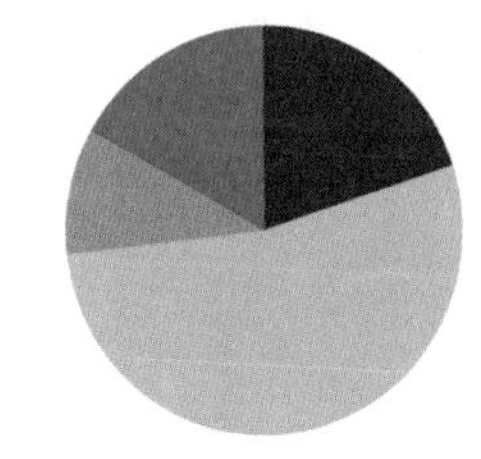

Fluency Practice (12 minutes)

- Divide by 10 **4.NF.7** (3 minutes)
- Write the Decimal or Fraction **4.NF.5** (4 minutes)
- Count by Tenths and Hundredths **4.NF.6** (5 minutes)

Divide by 10 (3 minutes)

Materials: (S) Personal white board

Note: This fluency activity reviews Lesson 4.

T: (Project one 1 hundred disk. Beneath it, write 100 = 10 ____.) 100 is the same as 10 of what unit? Write the number sentence.

S: (Write 100 = 10 tens.)

T: (Write 100 = 10 tens.)

Continue with the following possible sequence: 10 = 10 ones, 1 = 10 tenths, and $\frac{1}{10}$ = 10 hundredths

Write the Decimal or Fraction (4 minutes)

Materials: (S) Personal white board

Note: This fluency activity reviews Lesson 4.

T: (Write $\frac{1}{100}$.) Say the fraction.

S: 1 hundredth.

© 2015 Great Minds. eureka-math.org
G4-M6-TE-B5-1.3.1-01.2016

T: (Write $\frac{1}{100}$ = __.__.) Complete the number sentence.

S: (Write $\frac{1}{100} = 0.01$.)

Continue with the following possible sequence: $\frac{2}{100}, \frac{3}{100}, \frac{7}{100}$, and $\frac{17}{100}$.

T: (Write $\frac{17}{100} = \frac{10}{100} + \frac{}{100} = 0.17$.) Complete the number sentence.

S: (Write $\frac{17}{100} = \frac{10}{100} + \frac{7}{100} = 0.17$.)

Continue with the following possible sequence: $\frac{13}{100}$ and $\frac{19}{100}$.

T: (Write 0.05 = –.) Complete the number sentence.

S: (Write $0.05 = \frac{5}{100}$.)

Continue with the following possible sequence: 0.15, 0.03, and 0.13.

T: (Write $\frac{100}{100}$.) Say the fraction.

S: 100 hundredths.

T: Complete the number sentence, writing 100 hundredths as a whole number.

S: (Write $\frac{100}{100} = 1$.)

Count by Tenths and Hundredths (5 minutes)

Note: This fluency activity reviews Lessons 1 and 4.

T: 1 is the same as how many tenths?

S: 10 tenths.

T: Let's count to 10 tenths. When you come to 1, say 1.

S: $\frac{0}{10}, \frac{1}{10}, \frac{2}{10}, \frac{3}{10}, \frac{4}{10}, \frac{5}{10}, \frac{6}{10}, \frac{7}{10}, \frac{8}{10}, \frac{9}{10}, 1$.

T: Count by hundredths to 10 hundredths, starting at 0 hundredths.

S: $\frac{0}{100}, \frac{1}{100}, \frac{2}{100}, \frac{3}{100}, \frac{4}{100}, \frac{5}{100}, \frac{6}{100}, \frac{7}{100}, \frac{8}{100}, \frac{9}{100}, \frac{10}{100}$.

T: 10 hundredths is the same as 1 of what unit?

S: 1 tenth.

T: Let's count to 10 hundredths again. This time, when you come to 1 tenth, say 1 tenth.

S: $\frac{0}{100}, \frac{1}{100}, \frac{2}{100}, \frac{3}{100}, \frac{4}{100}, \frac{5}{100}, \frac{6}{100}, \frac{7}{100}, \frac{8}{100}, \frac{9}{100}, \frac{1}{10}$.

T: Count by hundredths again. This time, when I raise my hand, stop.

S: $\frac{0}{100}, \frac{1}{100}, \frac{2}{100}, \frac{3}{100}, \frac{4}{100}$.

NOTES ON MULTIPLE MEANS OF REPRESENTATION:

Distinguish *tenths* from *tens* for English language learners and others. Some students may not be able to differentiate the *th* sound at the end of the fraction words from the *s* sound at the end of *tens*. If possible, couple Count by Tenths and Hundredths with a visual aid, such as the fraction form, decimal form, or area model.

© 2015 Great Minds. eureka-math.org
G4-M6-TE-B5-1.3.1-01.2016

EUREKA MATH

T: (Raise hand.) Say 4 hundredths using digits.

S: Zero point zero 4.

T: Continue.

S: $\frac{5}{100}, \frac{6}{100}, \frac{7}{100}, \frac{8}{100}$.

T: (Raise hand.) Say 8 hundredths using digits.

S: Zero point zero 8.

T: Continue.

S: $\frac{9}{100}, \frac{1}{10}$.

T: Count backward by hundredths starting at 1 tenth.

Continue interrupting to express the hundredths using digits.

NOTES ON READING DECIMALS:

Students benefit from hearing decimal numbers read in both fraction form and as, for example, "zero point zero eight." Without the latter, it is hard to verify orally that students have written a decimal correctly. Furthermore, this manner of communicating decimals is used at times in the culture.

However, saying "zero point zero eight" is the exception rather than the rule because "8 hundredths" communicates the equality of the fraction and decimal forms. The general rule is that students should read 0.08 and $\frac{8}{100}$ as 8 hundredths.

Application Problem (6 minutes)

The perimeter of a square measures 0.48 m. What is the measure of each side length in centimeters?

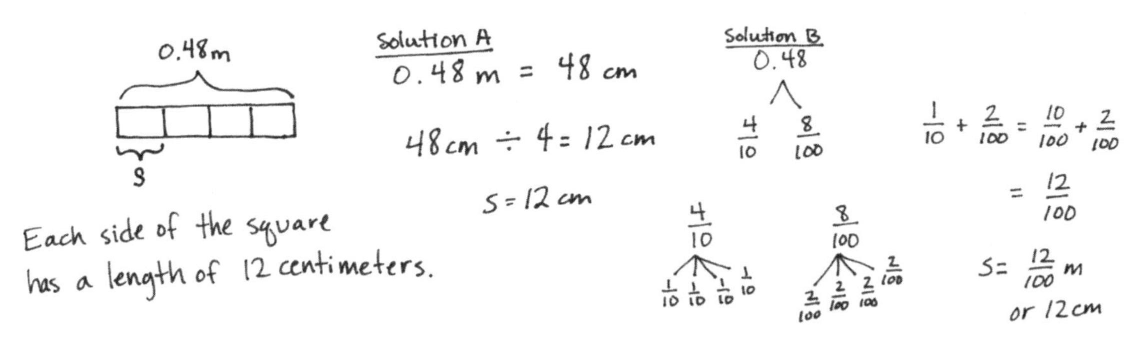

Note: The Application Problem reviews solving for an unknown side length (Module 4) and metric conversions (Module 2). Division of decimals is a Grade 5 standard, so instead, students might convert to centimeters (as in Solution A), use their fraction knowledge to decompose 48 hundredths into 4 equal parts (as in Solution B), or simply think in unit form (i.e., 48 hundredths ÷ 4 = 12 hundredths).

Concept Development (32 minutes)

Materials: (T) Tenths and hundredths area model (Template), tape diagram in tenths (Lesson 4 Template), decimal place value disks (S) Tenths and hundredths area model (Template), personal white board

© 2015 Great Minds. eureka-math.org
G4-M6-TE-B5-1.3.1-01.2016

Problem 1: Simplify hundredths by division.

T: We can show the equivalence of 10 hundredths and 1 tenth in the same way we showed the equivalence of 2 fourths and 1 half by using division.

T: Shade 1 tenth of the first area model. Next, shade 10 hundredths on the second area model. Label each area model. What do you notice?

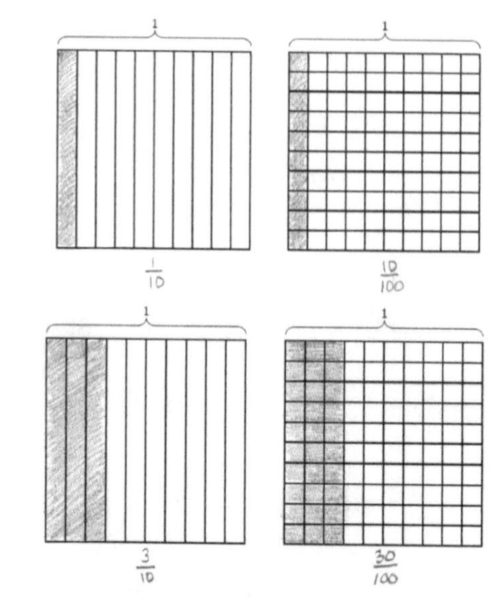

S: The same amount is shaded for each. → One area is decomposed into tenths and the other into hundredths, but the same amount is selected. That means they are equivalent.

T: (Write $\frac{1}{10} = \frac{10}{100}$.) Write the equivalent statement using decimals.

S: (Write 0.1 = 0.10.)

T: Show in the next area models how many tenths are equal to 30 hundredths. Write two equivalent statements using fractions and decimals.

S: (Shade area models.) $\frac{3}{10} = \frac{30}{100}$. 0.3 = 0.30.

T: Let's show those as equivalent fractions using division. (Write $\frac{10}{100} = \frac{10 \div 10}{100 \div 10} = \frac{1}{10}$.) Why did I divide by 10?

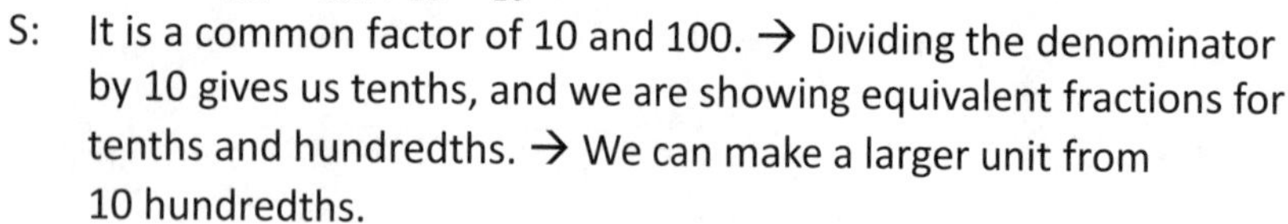

S: It is a common factor of 10 and 100. → Dividing the denominator by 10 gives us tenths, and we are showing equivalent fractions for tenths and hundredths. → We can make a larger unit from 10 hundredths.

$$\frac{10}{100} = \frac{10 \div 10}{100 \div 10} = \frac{1}{10}$$

$$\frac{30}{100} = \frac{30 \div 10}{100 \div 10} = \frac{3}{10}$$

$$\frac{3}{10} = \frac{3 \times 10}{10 \times 10} = \frac{30}{100}$$

T: With your partner, use division to find how many tenths are equal to 30 hundredths.

S: (Record $\frac{30}{100} = \frac{30 \div 10}{100 \div 10} = \frac{3}{10}$.) 3 tenths.

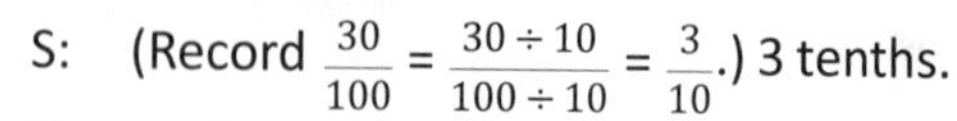

MP.8

T: With your partner, use multiplication to find how many hundredths are in 3 tenths.

S: (Record $\frac{3}{10} = \frac{3 \times 10}{10 \times 10} = \frac{30}{100}$.) 30 hundredths.

T: Is there a pattern as you find equivalent fractions for tenths and hundredths?

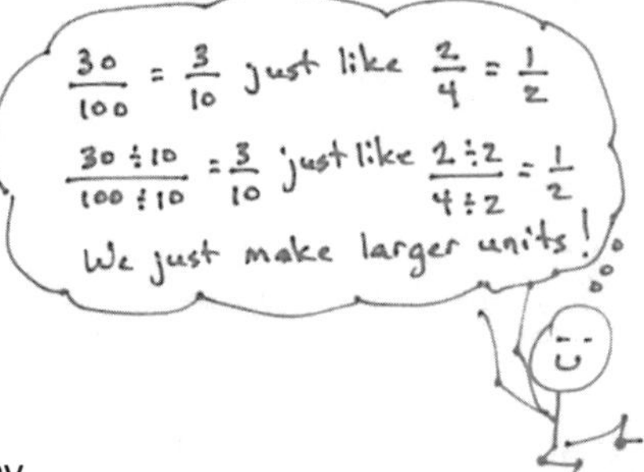

S: I multiply the number of tenths by 10 to get the number of hundredths, and I divide the number of hundredths by 10 to get the number of tenths. → I can convert tenths to hundredths in my head by putting a zero at the end of the numerator and denominator. I can convert hundredths to tenths by removing a zero from the numerator and denominator. → We are just changing the units, making either larger or smaller units. Both have the same value.

Have students convert 7 tenths to 70 hundredths using multiplication and 70 hundredths to 7 tenths using division.

© 2015 Great Minds. eureka-math.org
G4-M6-TE-B5-1.3.1-01.2016
EUREKA MATH

Problem 2: Model hundredths with an area model.

T: (Project a tape diagram, as was used in Lesson 4, with $\frac{25}{100}$ shaded.) Say the fractional part that is shaded.

S: 25 hundredths.

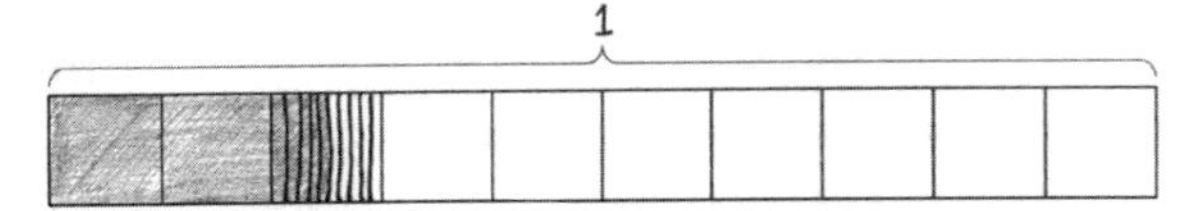

T: Say it as a decimal number.

S: 25 hundredths. We say it the same way.

T: Yes. Both the fraction and decimal number represent the same amount. What is different is the way that they are written. Write 25 hundredths as a fraction and then as a decimal number.

S: (Write $\frac{25}{100}$ and 0.25.)

T: Just as we can express 25 hundredths in different ways when we write it, we can also represent it in different ways pictorially, just like we did with tenths and other fractions from Module 5. (Project the area model.) How can we shade $\frac{25}{100}$?

S: We can draw horizontal lines to make smaller units. → We can decompose each tenth into 10 parts to make hundredths using horizontal lines.

T: Yes. Decimals like this are just fractions. We are doing exactly the same thing, but we are writing the number in a different way. Go ahead and make the hundredths.

S: (Partition the area model.)

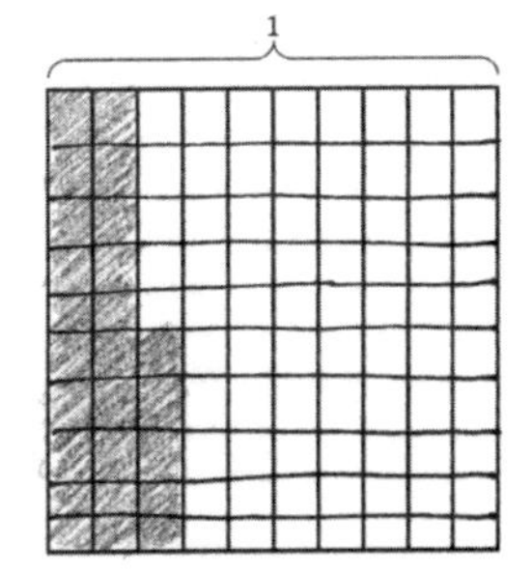

T: Shade $\frac{25}{100}$. (Allow students time to shade the area.)

T: What is a shortcut for shading 25 hundredths?

S: There are 10 hundredths in each column. I shaded 10 hundredths at a time. $\frac{10}{100}, \frac{20}{100}$. Then, I shaded 5 hundredths more. → I shaded 2 columns and then 5 more units. → A tenth, and a tenth and 5 hundredths. → I shaded two and a half columns.

T: In total, how many tenths are shaded?

S: 2 tenths and part of another tenth. → $2\frac{1}{2}$ tenths.

T: Both are correct: 2 complete tenths are shaded, and another half of a tenth is shaded. In total, how many hundredths are shaded?

S: 25 hundredths.

Repeat with $\frac{52}{100}$ and $\frac{35}{100}$.

Problem 3: Compose hundredths to tenths using place value disks, and then represent with a number bond.

T: Look at the area model we just drew. 1 tenth equals how many hundredths?

S: 10 hundredths.

T: Write it in decimal form.

S: 0.10. → 0.1.

© 2015 Great Minds. eureka-math.org
G4-M6-TE-B5-1.3.1-01.2016

T: (Project 16 hundredths with place value disks.) What is the value of each disk? How can you tell?

S: 1 hundredth. I see point zero one on each disk.

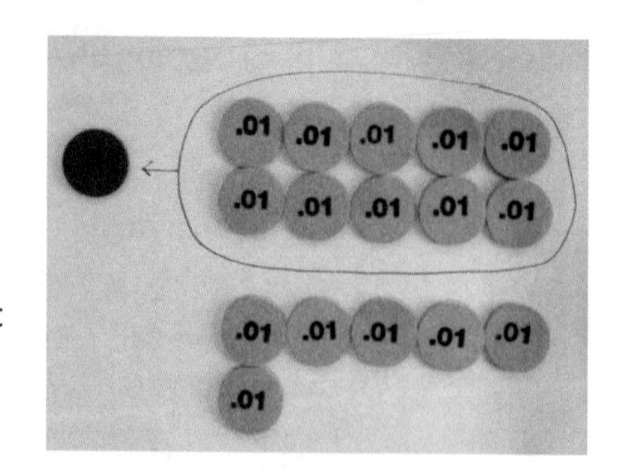

T: How many hundredths are there?

S: 16 hundredths.

T: Can we make a tenth? Talk to your partner.

S: 10 hundredths can be traded for 1 tenth. → Yes! We can compose 10 hundredths to 1 tenth since $\frac{1}{10} = \frac{10}{100}$. → It is just like place value: 10 ones make 1 ten, or 10 tens make 1 hundred.

T: Circle 10 hundredths to show 1 tenth. What is represented now?

S: 1 tenth and 6 hundredths.

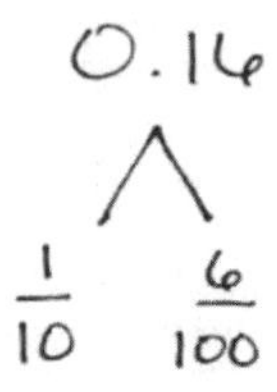

T: (Draw a number bond to show the parts of 1 tenth and 6 hundredths. Point to the number bond.) 16 hundredths can be represented as 1 tenth and 6 hundredths.

Repeat with 13 hundredths and 22 hundredths.

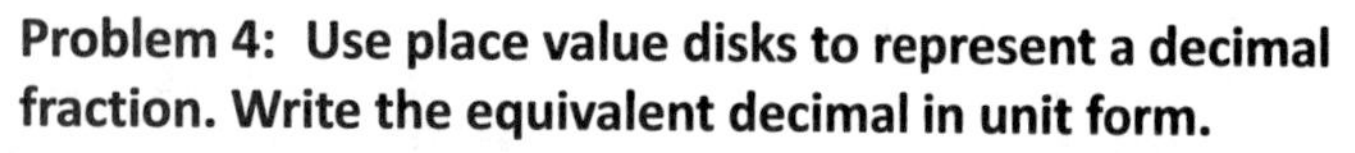

Problem 4: Use place value disks to represent a decimal fraction. Write the equivalent decimal in unit form.

T: (Write $\frac{5}{100}$.) Draw place value disks to represent this fraction.

S: (Draw 5 hundredths disks.)

T: Say it in unit form.

0.05

S: 5 hundredths.

T: Write it as a decimal. Be careful that your decimal notation shows hundredths.

S: (Write 0.05.)

T: (Write $\frac{25}{100}$.) Draw place value disks to represent this fraction.

S: That is 25 hundredths! → We can represent $\frac{25}{100}$ with 2 tenth disks and 5 hundredth disks.

T: I hope so, since it takes much too long to draw 25 hundredths. Say the number in unit form, and write it as a decimal.

S: 25 hundredths. → 0.25.

2 tenths 5 hundredths

0.25

Repeat with 32 hundredths and 64 hundredths.

NOTES ON MULTIPLE MEANS FOR ACTION AND EXPRESSION:

Students working below grade level and English language learners may benefit from additional practice reading and writing decimals. If students are confusing the decimal notation (for example, modeling 0.5 rather than 0.05), couple place value disks with the area model, and have students count and recount their disks.

© 2015 Great Minds. eureka-math.org
G4-M6-TE-B5-1.3.1-01.2016

Problem Set (10 minutes)

Students should do their personal best to complete the Problem Set within the allotted 10 minutes. For some classes, it may be appropriate to modify the assignment by specifying which problems they work on first. Some problems do not specify a method for solving. Students should solve these problems using the RDW approach used for Application Problems.

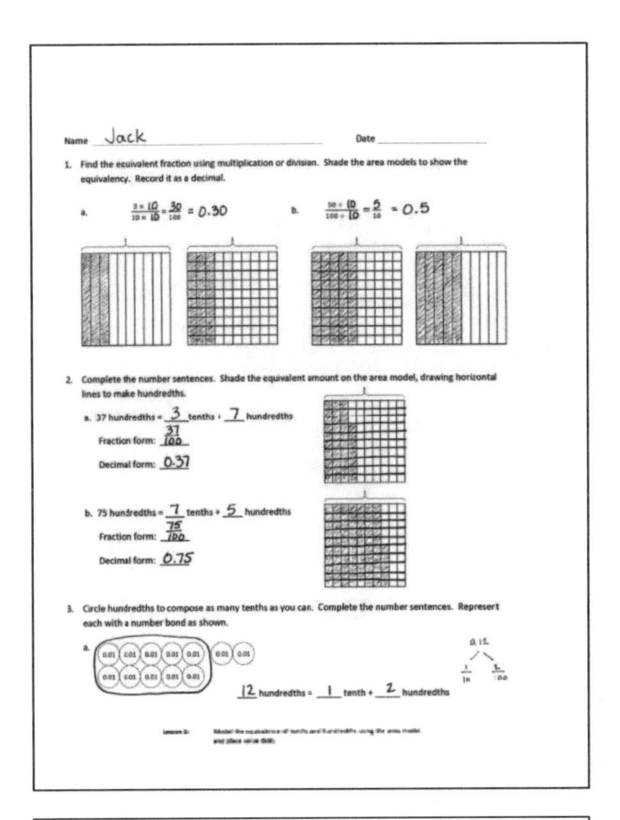
Name Jack Date

1. Find the equivalent fraction using multiplication or division. Shade the area models to show the equivalency. Record it as a decimal.

a. $\frac{3 \times 10}{10 \times 10} = \frac{30}{100} = 0.30$ b. $\frac{50 \div 10}{100 \div 10} = \frac{5}{10} = 0.5$

2. Complete the number sentences. Shade the equivalent amount on the area model, drawing horizontal lines to make hundredths.

a. 37 hundredths = 3 tenths + 7 hundredths
Fraction form: $\frac{37}{100}$
Decimal form: 0.37

b. 75 hundredths = 7 tenths + 5 hundredths
Fraction form: $\frac{75}{100}$
Decimal form: 0.75

3. Circle hundredths to compose as many tenths as you can. Complete the number sentences. Represent each with a number bond as shown.

a. 12 hundredths = 1 tenth + 2 hundredths

Student Debrief (10 minutes)

Lesson Objective: Model the equivalence of tenths and hundredths using the area model and place value disks.

The Student Debrief is intended to invite reflection and active processing of the total lesson experience.

Invite students to review their solutions for the Problem Set. They should check work by comparing answers with a partner before going over answers as a class. Look for misconceptions or misunderstandings that can be addressed in the Debrief. Guide students in a conversation to debrief the Problem Set and process the lesson.

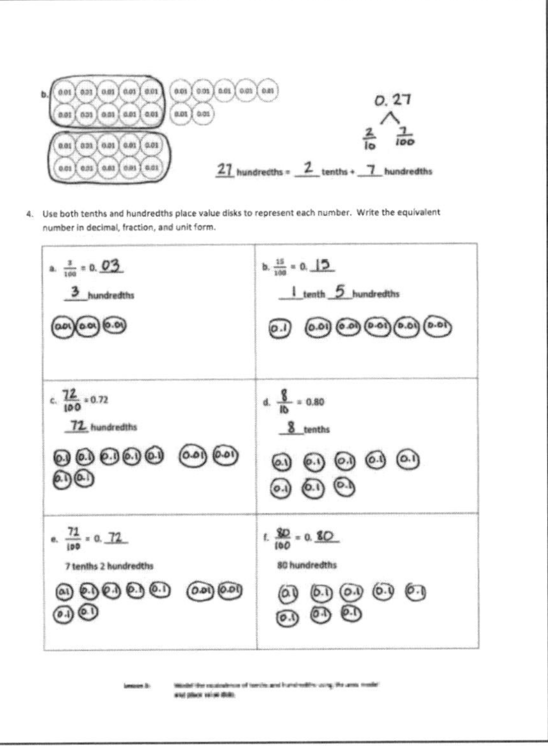
b. 27 hundredths = 2 tenths + 7 hundredths

4. Use both tenths and hundredths place value disks to represent each number. Write the equivalent number in decimal, fraction, and unit form.

a. $\frac{3}{100}$ = 0.03 3 hundredths	b. $\frac{15}{100}$ = 0.15 1 tenth 5 hundredths
c. $\frac{72}{100}$ = 0.72 72 hundredths	d. $\frac{8}{10}$ = 0.80 8 tenths
e. $\frac{72}{100}$ = 0.72 7 tenths 2 hundredths	f. $\frac{80}{100}$ = 0.80 80 hundredths

Any combination of the questions below may be used to lead the discussion.

- How does solving Problem 1(a) help you solve Problem 2(a)?
- In Problem 3(a), how does circling groups of 10 hundredths help you find how many tenths are in the number?
- In Problem 4(a), how did you write 3 hundredths in decimal form? A student wrote 0.3 (zero point 3). What number did she write? Use your disks to explain how to properly express 3 hundredths in decimal form.
- With your partner, compare the answers to Problem 4 (d) and (f). Did you write the same equivalent numbers? Why are there several possibilities for answers in these two problems? Where have we seen that before?
- How is using the area model to show tenths and hundredths similar to or different from using place value disks to show tenths and hundredths? Which model do you prefer and why?

© 2015 Great Minds. eureka-math.org
G4-M6-TE-B5-1.3.1-01.2016

- How is exchanging 10 hundredths for 1 tenth like exchanging 10 tens for 1 hundred? How is it different?
- Use an area model to model both renaming 3 sixths as 1 half and renaming 30 hundredths as 3 tenths. What is happening to the units in both renamings?

Exit Ticket (3 minutes)

After the Student Debrief, instruct students to complete the Exit Ticket. A review of their work will help with assessing students' understanding of the concepts that were presented in today's lesson and planning more effectively for future lessons. The questions may be read aloud to the students.

© 2015 Great Minds. eureka-math.org
G4-M6-TE-B5-1.3.1-01.2016

Name _______________________________ Date _______________

1. Find the equivalent fraction using multiplication or division. Shade the area models to show the equivalency. Record it as a decimal.

a. $\frac{3\times}{10\times} = \frac{}{100}$

b. $\frac{50\div}{100\div} = \frac{}{10}$

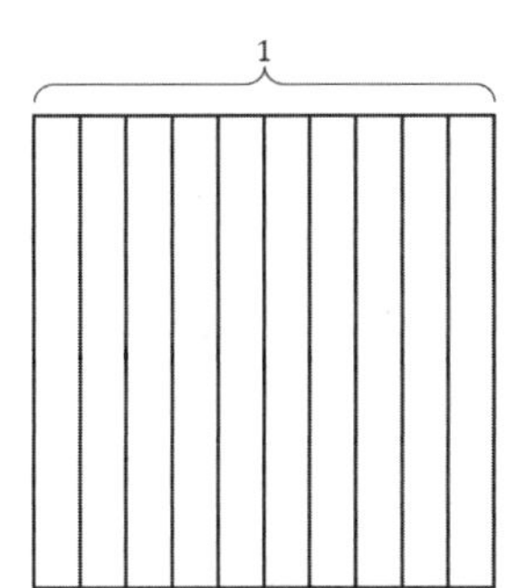
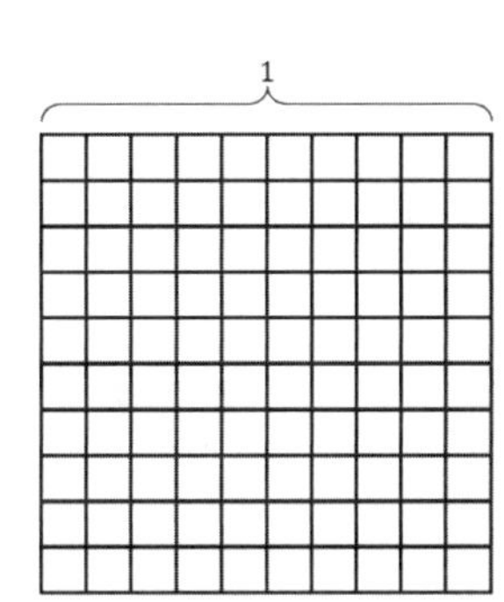
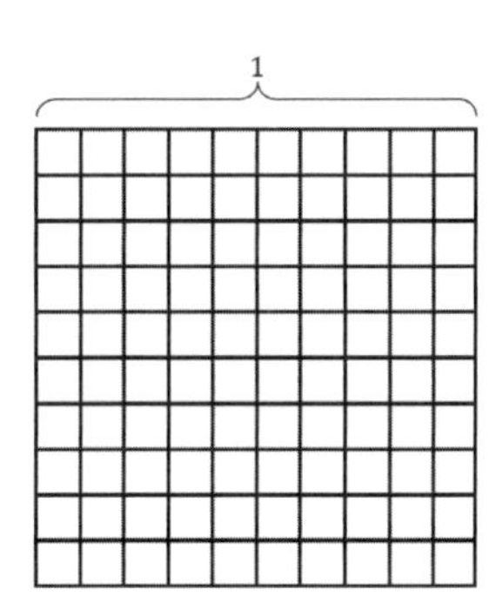
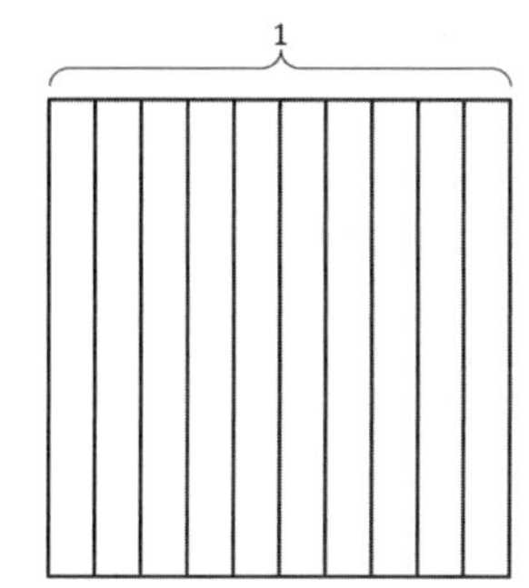

2. Complete the number sentences. Shade the equivalent amount on the area model, drawing horizontal lines to make hundredths.

a. 37 hundredths = _____ tenths + _____ hundredths

Fraction form: ______

Decimal form: ______

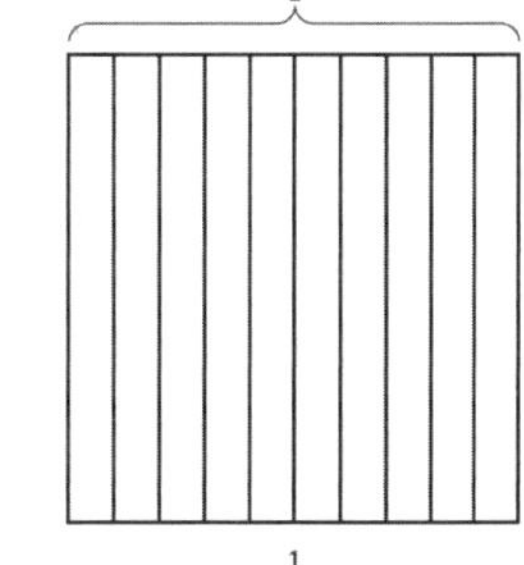

b. 75 hundredths = ____ tenths + ____ hundredths

Fraction form: ______

Decimal form: ______

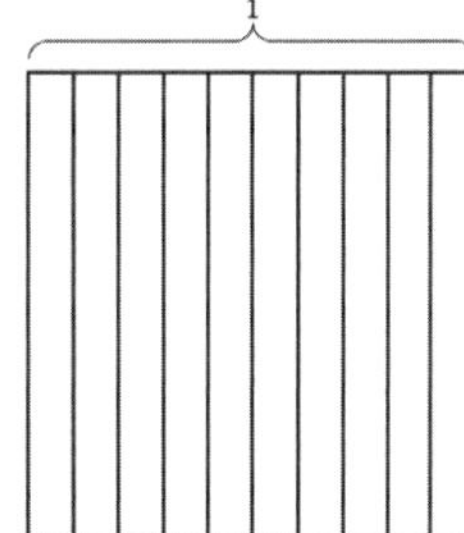

3. Circle hundredths to compose as many tenths as you can. Complete the number sentences. Represent each with a number bond as shown.

a. 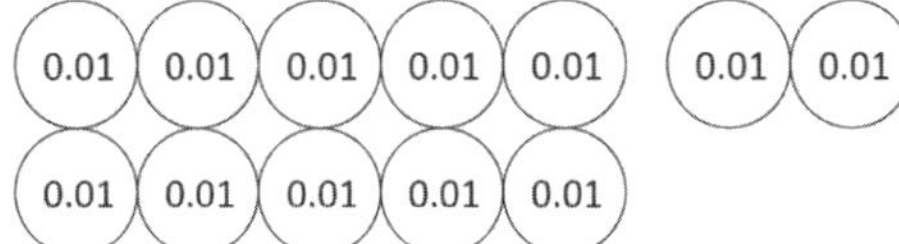

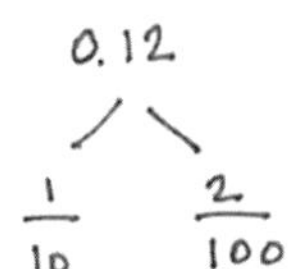

____ hundredths = _____ tenth + _____ hundredths

© 2015 Great Minds. eureka-math.org
G4-M6-TE-B5-1.3.1-01.2016

b.

0.01	0.01	0.01	0.01	0.01		0.01	0.01	0.01	0.01	0.01
0.01	0.01	0.01	0.01	0.01		0.01	0.01			

0.01	0.01	0.01	0.01	0.01
0.01	0.01	0.01	0.01	0.01

____ hundredths = _____ tenths + _____ hundredths

4. Use both tenths and hundredths place value disks to represent each number. Write the equivalent number in decimal, fraction, and unit form.

a. $\frac{3}{100}$ = 0. _____ _____ hundredths	b. $\frac{15}{100}$ = 0. _____ _____ tenth _____ hundredths
c. —— = 0.72 _____ hundredths	d. —— = 0.80 _____ tenths
e. —— = 0. _____ 7 tenths 2 hundredths	f. —— = 0. _____ 80 hundredths

© 2015 Great Minds. eureka-math.org
G4-M6-TE-B5-1.3.1-01.2016

Name ______________________________ Date ________________

Use both tenths and hundredths place value disks to represent each fraction. Write the equivalent decimal, and fill in the blanks to represent each in unit form.

1. $\frac{7}{100}$ = 0.____

___ hundredths

2. $\frac{34}{100}$ = 0.____

___ tenths ___ hundredths

© 2015 Great Minds. eureka-math.org
G4-M6-TE-B5-1.3.1-01.2016

Name ______________________________ Date ______________

1. Find the equivalent fraction using multiplication or division. Shade the area models to show the equivalency. Record it as a decimal.

a. $\frac{4 \times}{10 \times} = \frac{}{100}$

b. $\frac{60 \div}{100 \div} = \frac{}{10}$

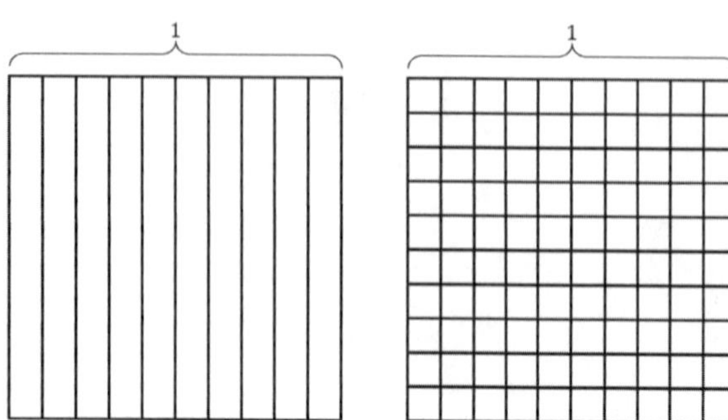

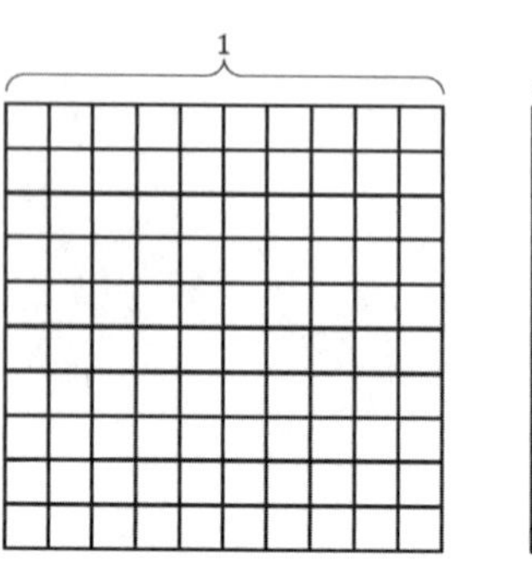

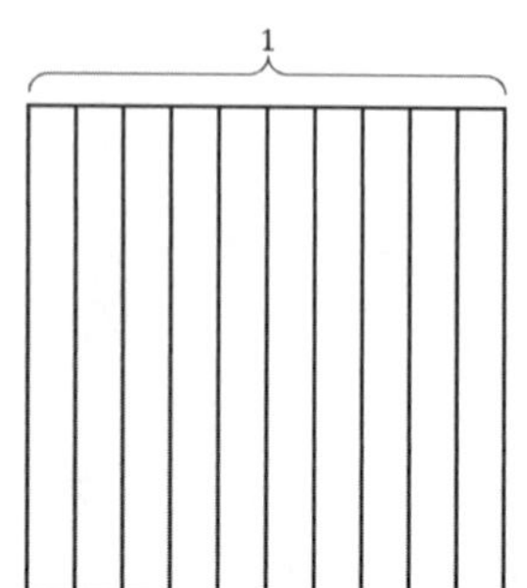

2. Complete the number sentences. Shade the equivalent amount on the area model, drawing horizontal lines to make hundredths.

a. 36 hundredths = _____ tenths + _____ hundredths

Decimal form: ________

Fraction form: ________

b. 82 hundredths = _____ tenths + _____ hundredths

Decimal form: ________

Fraction form: ________

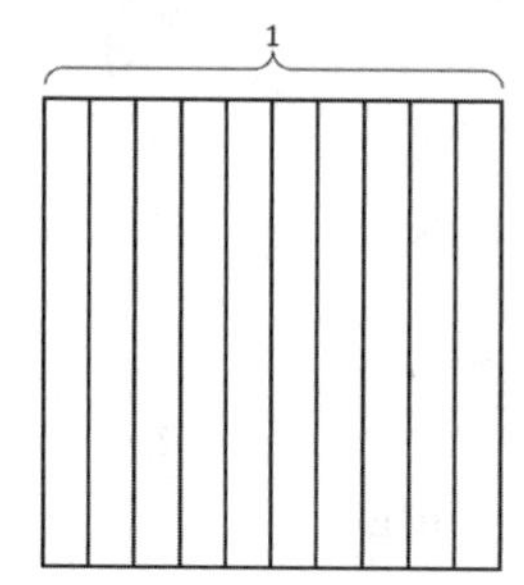

3. Circle hundredths to compose as many tenths as you can. Complete the number sentences. Represent each with a number bond as shown.

a.

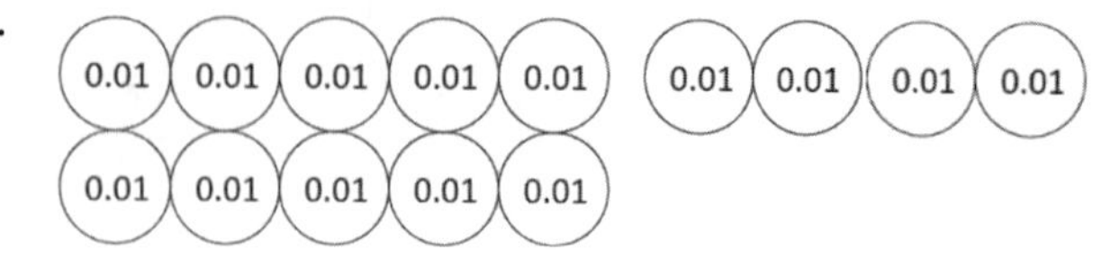

0.14

$\frac{1}{10}$ $\frac{4}{100}$

_____ hundredths = _____ tenth + _____ hundredths

EUREKA MATH

© 2015 Great Minds. eureka-math.org
G4-M6-TE-B5-1.3.1-01.2016

b. 0.01 0.01 0.01 0.01 0.01 0.01 0.01 0.01 0.01
0.01 0.01 0.01 0.01 0.01
0.01 0.01 0.01 0.01 0.01
0.01 0.01 0.01 0.01 0.01

____ hundredths = _____ tenths + _____ hundredths

4. Use both tenths and hundredths place value disks to represent each number. Write the equivalent number in decimal, fraction, and unit form.

a. $\frac{4}{100}$ = 0. _____ _____ hundredths	b. $\frac{13}{100}$ = 0. _____ _____ tenth _____ hundredths
c. —— = 0.41 _____ hundredths	d. —— = 0.90 _____ tenths
e. —— = 0. _____ 6 tenths 3 hundredths	f. —— = 0. _____ 90 hundredths

© 2015 Great Minds. eureka-math.org
G4-M6-TE-B5-1.3.1-01.2016

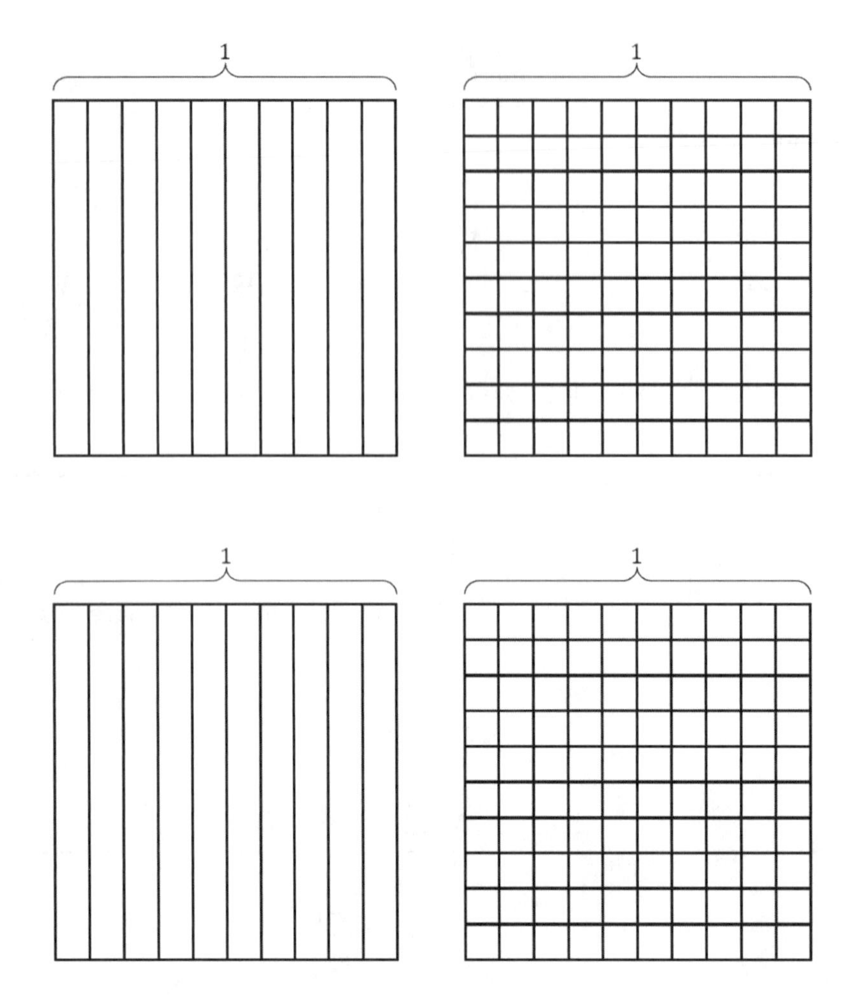

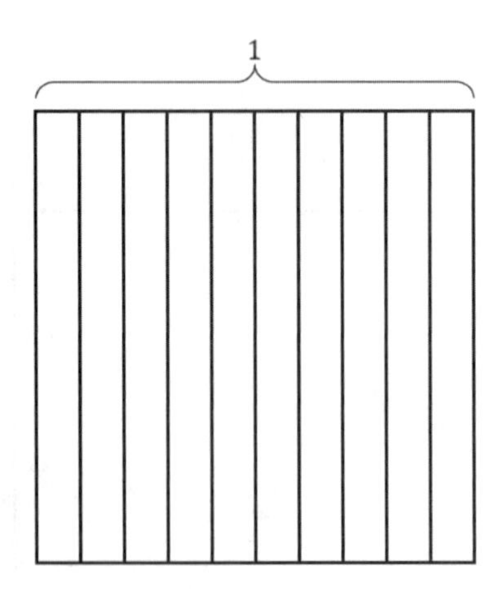

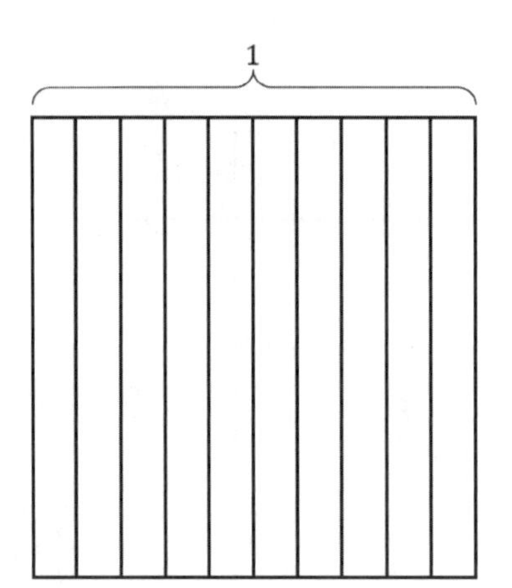

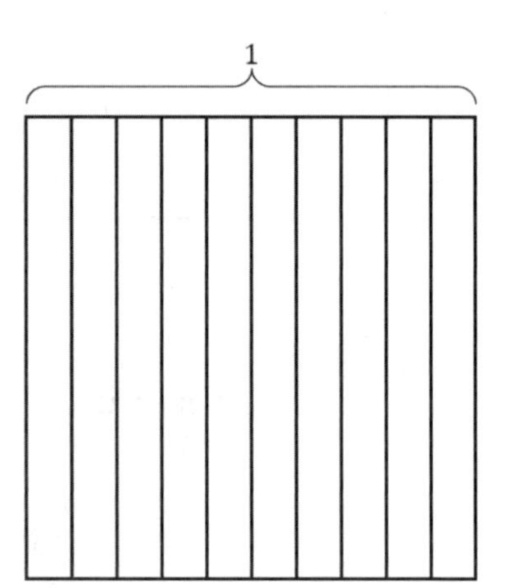

tenths and hundredths area model

© 2015 Great Minds. eureka-math.org
G4-M6-TE-B5-1.3.1-01.2016

Lesson 6

Objective: Use the area model and number line to represent mixed numbers with units of ones, tenths, and hundredths in fraction and decimal forms.

Suggested Lesson Structure

■ Fluency Practice	(12 minutes)
■ Application Problem	(5 minutes)
■ Concept Development	(33 minutes)
■ Student Debrief	(10 minutes)
Total Time	**(60 minutes)**

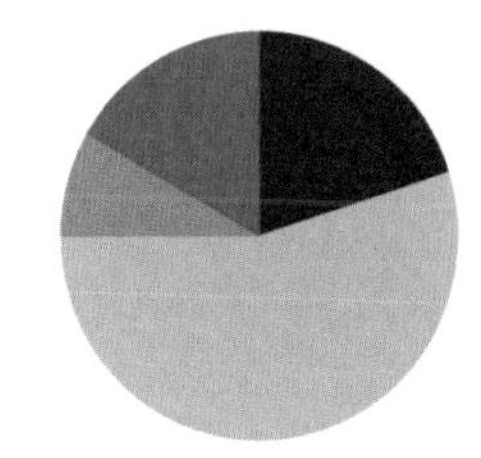

Fluency Practice (12 minutes)

- Count by Hundredths **4.NF.5** (5 minutes)
- Write the Decimal or Fraction **4.NF.5** (4 minutes)
- Break Apart Hundredths **4.NF.5** (3 minutes)

Count by Hundredths (5 minutes)

Note: This fluency activity reviews Lessons 4–5.

$\frac{0}{100}$	$\frac{5}{100}$	$\frac{10}{100}$	$\frac{15}{100}$	$\frac{20}{100}$	$\frac{25}{100}$	$\frac{30}{100}$
$\frac{0}{10}$		$\frac{1}{10}$		$\frac{2}{10}$		$\frac{3}{10}$

T: Count by fives to 30, starting at zero.

S: 0, 5, 10, 15, 20, 25, 30.

T: Count by 5 hundredths to 30 hundredths, starting at 0 hundredths. (Write as students count.)

S: $\frac{0}{100}, \frac{5}{100}, \frac{10}{100}, \frac{15}{100}, \frac{20}{100}, \frac{25}{100}, \frac{30}{100}$.

T: 1 tenth is the same as how many hundredths?

S: 10 hundredths.

T: (Beneath $\frac{10}{100}$, write $\frac{1}{10}$.)

Continue the process for $\frac{2}{10}$ and $\frac{3}{10}$.

T: Let's count by 5 hundredths again. This time, when you come to a tenth, say the tenth. Try not to look at the board.

S: $\frac{0}{100}, \frac{5}{100}, \frac{1}{10}, \frac{15}{100}, \frac{2}{10}, \frac{25}{100}, \frac{3}{10}$.

© 2015 Great Minds. eureka-math.org
G4-M6-TE-B5-1.3.1-01.2016

T: Count backward by 5 hundredths, starting at 3 tenths.

S: $\frac{3}{10}, \frac{25}{100}, \frac{2}{10}, \frac{15}{100}, \frac{1}{10}, \frac{5}{100}, \frac{0}{100}$.

T: Count by 5 hundredths again. This time, when I raise my hand, stop.

S: $\frac{0}{100}, \frac{5}{100}, \frac{1}{10}, \frac{15}{100}$.

T: (Raise hand.) Say 15 hundredths using digits.

S: Zero point one five.

T: Continue.

S: $\frac{2}{10}, \frac{25}{100}, \frac{3}{10}$.

T: (Raise hand.) Say 3 tenths in digits.

S: Zero point three.

T: Count backward starting at 3 tenths.

S: $\frac{3}{10}, \frac{25}{100}$.

T: (Raise hand.) Say 25 hundredths in digits.

S: Zero point two five.

T: Continue.

S: $\frac{2}{10}, \frac{15}{100}, \frac{1}{10}$.

T: (Raise hand.) Say 1 tenth in digits.

S: Zero point one.

T: Continue.

S: $\frac{5}{100}, \frac{0}{100}$.

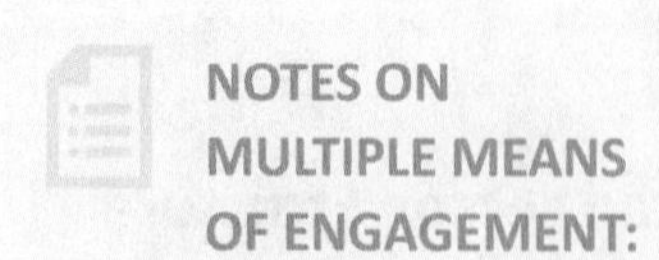

Students working below grade level and others may find it challenging to integrate equivalent fractions (such as $\frac{1}{10}$) into the Count by Hundredths fluency activity. Ease the task by chunking. Count a little at a time, and repeat the count so that students are comfortable, confident, and excited. For example, lead students to count from $\frac{1}{100}$ to $\frac{1}{10}$, repeat a few times, and then add onto the count $\frac{15}{100}$, and so on.

Write the Decimal or Fraction (4 minutes)

Materials: (T) Hundredths area model (Fluency Template), personal white board (S) Personal white board

Note: This fluency activity reviews Lessons 4–5.

T: (Project the hundredths area model. Shade 3 units.) 1 whole is decomposed into 100 equal units. Write the fraction of the grid that is shaded.

S: (Write $\frac{3}{100}$.)

T: (Write $\frac{3}{100}$ = ___.___.) Complete the number sentence.

S: (Write $\frac{3}{100}$ = 0.03.)

Continue the process for $\frac{5}{100}$, $\frac{8}{100}$, $\frac{4}{100}$, and $\frac{14}{100}$.

© 2015 Great Minds. eureka-math.org
G4-M6-TE-B5-1.3.1-01.2016

T: (Write $\frac{14}{100} = \frac{10}{100} + \frac{\quad}{100} = 0.14$.) Complete the number sentence.

S: (Write $\frac{14}{100} = \frac{10}{100} + \frac{4}{100} = 0.14$.)

Continue with the following possible sequence: $\frac{17}{100}$ and $\frac{53}{100}$.

T: (Shade 4 units.) Write the amount of the grid that is shaded as a decimal.

S: (Write 0.04.)

T: (Write $0.04 = \frac{\quad}{100}$.) Complete the number sentence.

S: (Write $0.04 = \frac{4}{100}$.)

Continue with the following possible sequence: 0.14, 0.06, and 0.16.

T: (Shade in the entire grid.) Write the amount of the grid that is shaded as a fraction and as a digit.

S: (Write $\frac{100}{100} = 1$.)

Break Apart Hundredths (3 minutes)

Materials: (T/S) Personal white board

Note: This fluency activity reviews Lesson 5.

T: (Project 13 hundredths disks.) Say the value.

S: 13 hundredths.

T: Write the value of the disks as a decimal.

S: (Write 0.13.)

T: (Write 0.13 = —.) Write 13 hundredths as a fraction.

S: (Write $0.13 = \frac{13}{100}$.)

T: How many hundredths are in 1 tenth?

S: 10 hundredths.

T: Draw place value disks to represent the 13 hundredths after composing 1 tenth.

S: (Draw 1 tenth disk and 3 hundredth disks.)

T: (Write $0.13 = \frac{13}{100} = \frac{\quad}{10} + \frac{\quad}{100}$.) Complete the number sentence.

S: (Write $0.13 = \frac{13}{100} = \frac{1}{10} + \frac{3}{100}$.)

Continue with the following possible sequence: 0.21 and 0.14.

© 2015 Great Minds. eureka-math.org
G4-M6-TE-B5-1.3.1-01.2016

Application Problem (5 minutes)

The table shows the perimeter of four rectangles.

a. Which rectangle has the smallest perimeter?
b. The perimeter of Rectangle C is how many meters less than a kilometer?
c. Compare the perimeters of Rectangles B and D. Which rectangle has the greater perimeter? How much greater?

Rectangle	Perimeter
A	54 cm
B	$\frac{69}{100}$ m
C	54 m
D	0.8 m

a) Rectangle A has the smallest perimeter.
A: 54 cm = $\frac{54}{100}$ m
B: $\frac{69}{100}$ m
C: 54 m
D: 0.8 m = $\frac{8}{10}$ m = $\frac{80}{100}$ m

b) The perimeter of Rectangle C is 946 meters less than a kilometer.
1 km = 1,000 m
$1000 - 54 = 946$

c) Rectangle D's perimeter is $\frac{11}{100}$ m greater than Rectangle B's perimeter.
$\frac{80}{100} - \frac{69}{100} = \frac{11}{100}$

Note: This Application Problem reviews related metric units (Module 2) and comparing measurements expressed as fractions and decimals in preparation for work with mixed numbers, metric units, and place value in today's Concept Development.

Concept Development (33 minutes)

Materials: (T/S) Area model (Template 1), number line (Template 2), pencil, personal white board

Problem 1: Represent mixed numbers with units of ones, tenths, and hundredths using area models.

T: (Write $1\frac{22}{100}$.) How many ones?
S: 1 one.
T: How many hundredths more than 1?
S: 22 hundredths.
T: (Distribute Template 1, area model.) Use the area models to shade $1\frac{22}{100}$.

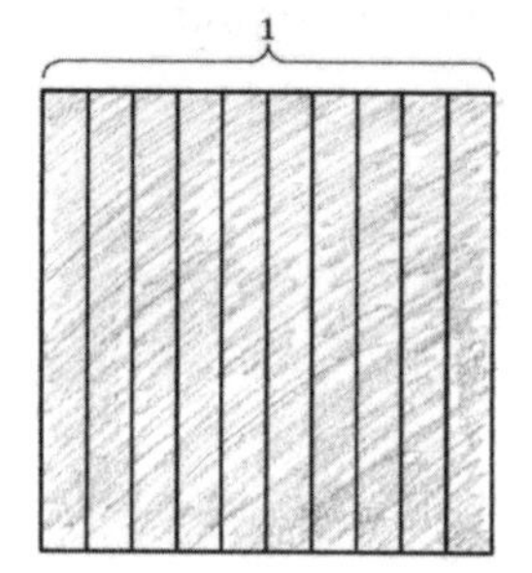

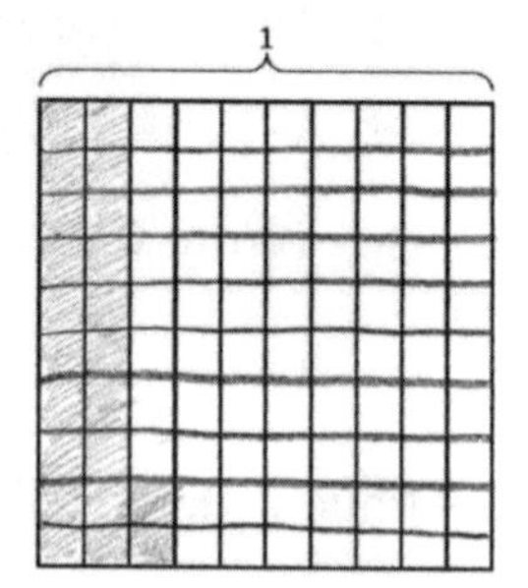

S: (Shade the area models.)
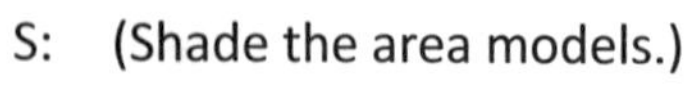
T: How many ones are shaded?
S: 1 one.

EUREKA MATH
© 2015 Great Minds. eureka-math.org
G4-M6-TE-B5-1.3.1-01.2016

T: What fraction of another one is shaded?

S: 22 hundredths.

T: Write $1\frac{22}{100}$ as a decimal number.

S: (Write 1.22.)

Continue with $1\frac{38}{100}$, $1\frac{60}{100}$, and $1\frac{81}{100}$.

Problem 2: Represent mixed numbers with units of ones, tenths, and hundredths on a number line.

T: (Refer to the area models representing 1.22.) We have used tape diagrams, area models, and place value disks to represent decimal numbers. We can also use a number line. (Distribute Template 2, number line, and label the intervals of 0, 1, 2, and 3.) To find 1.22 on a number line, we can start with the largest unit. What is the largest unit?

S: Ones.

T: Start at zero, and slide 1 one. What is remaining?

S: 22 hundredths.

T: What is the next largest unit?

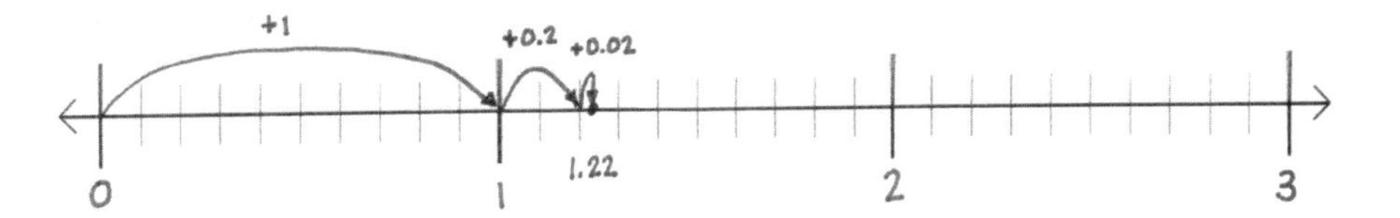

S: Tenths.

T: How many tenths?

S: 2 tenths.

T: From 1 one, slide 2 tenths. What remains?

S: 2 hundredths.

T: Can we show hundredths? How do we partition tenths into hundredths?

S: Each tenth would be split into 10 parts, just like on a tape diagram or an area model. It's hard to do that here because the tenths are so small.

T: Let's estimate where the hundredths would be. We need to show 2 hundredths. If I imagine each tenth partitioned into ten parts, where would 2 hundredths be? I will move very slowly. Say, "Stop!" when I get to 1 and 22 hundredths. (Slide very slowly from 1.2.)

S: Stop! (This should be at a place just beyond 1 and 2 tenths.)

T: Draw an arrow to show this very small slide. Discuss with a partner. How did we move from zero to 1.22?

S: We began with moving 1 one. Then, we moved 2 tenths, and then we moved 2 hundredths. → We started at zero and went up, beginning with the largest unit, the ones, the tenths, and then the hundredths. → We slid units from left to right, largest to smallest, but we estimated the 2 hundredths.

T: Draw a point to show where 1.22 is located. Write the number in decimal form.

T: Let's locate $3\frac{46}{100}$ on the next number line. Can we label the intervals the same?

S: No, because this point will come after 3.

© 2015 Great Minds. eureka-math.org
G4-M6-TE-B5-1.3.1-01.2016

T: Start the number line at 3 ones. We will locate $\frac{46}{100}$ more than 3. Decompose $\frac{46}{100}$ into tenths and hundredths.

S: $\frac{46}{100} = \frac{4}{10} + \frac{6}{100}$.

+0.4 +0.06 3 3.46 4 5 6

T: Which unit is larger: tenths or hundredths?

S: Tenths.

T: Let's count up 4 tenths. Draw an arrow, or keep track of the movement with your pencil. Now, what unit is left?

S: Hundredths. We have 6 hundredths. 6 hundredths is one hundredth more than 5 hundredths, so 4 tenths 6 hundredths would be just past the midpoint of 4 tenths and 5 tenths.

T: Draw a point to show where $3\frac{46}{100}$ is located. Write the number in decimal form.

S: (Draw and write 3.46.)

NOTES ON MULTIPLE MEANS OF ENGAGEMENT:

Students working above grade level or others may present alternative ways of locating $3\frac{46}{100}$ on the number line, such as reasoning that half of 100 is 50 and then counting back to 46. Efficiency and variety in strategies are always welcome.

Repeat with 2.34 and 3.70.

Problem 3: Match the unit form of a mixed number to its decimal and fraction forms.

MP.6

T: When we write decimal numbers, the decimal point separates the whole number part on the left from the decimal fraction part on the right.

T: Write 3 ones 8 tenths as a decimal.

S: (Write 3.8.)

ones tenths
3.8

T: The ones and the tenths each have a special place. (Label each place value.)

T: Write 3 ones 8 hundredths in decimal form. Show your partner what you have written. Are your answers the same?

ones tenths hundredths
3.08

S: The answer is 3.8. → I disagree. That would be 3 ones 8 tenths. We want hundredths. It's 3.08. There are no tenths. We need to put a zero to show that. It's just like when we write whole numbers. The zero holds a place value.

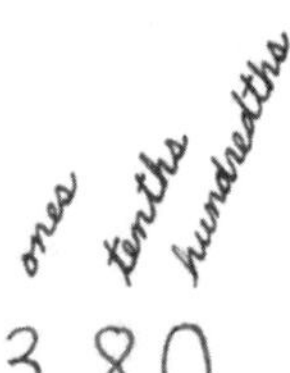

T: Look again at 3 ones 8 tenths.

T: Place a zero to the right of the digit eight. Say that number in unit form.

S: 3 ones 80 hundredths.

T: Express 80 hundredths as tenths.

S: 8 tenths.

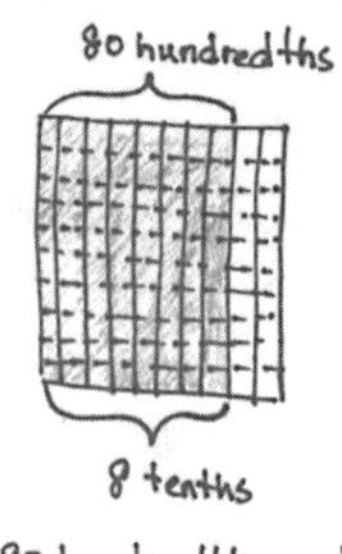

© 2015 Great Minds. eureka-math.org
G4-M6-TE-B5-1.3.1-01.2016

T: Yes. 0.80 and 0.8 are equivalent. We have shown this using an area model and using division, too, when the number was in fraction form.

T: Let's practice writing fractions and decimals. Be mindful of each digit's place in the number.

T: Write 2 ones 8 hundredths as a mixed number and then as a decimal number.

S: $2\frac{8}{100}$, 2.08.

T: Write 8 ones 2 hundredths as a mixed number and a decimal number.

S: $8\frac{2}{100}$, 8.2. Wait! That decimal is not right. That would be 8 and 2 tenths. It is 8.02. There are 8 ones, 0 tenths, and 2 hundredths.

Repeat, as needed, with 9 ones 80 hundredths, 2 ones 2 tenths, and 4 ones 7 hundredths.

Problem Set (10 minutes)

Students should do their personal best to complete the Problem Set within the allotted 10 minutes. For some classes, it may be appropriate to modify the assignment by specifying which problems they work on first. Some problems do not specify a method for solving. Students should solve these problems using the RDW approach used for Application Problems.

Student Debrief (10 minutes)

Lesson Objective: Use the area model and number line to represent mixed numbers with units of ones, tenths, and hundredths in fraction and decimal forms.

The Student Debrief is intended to invite reflection and active processing of the total lesson experience.

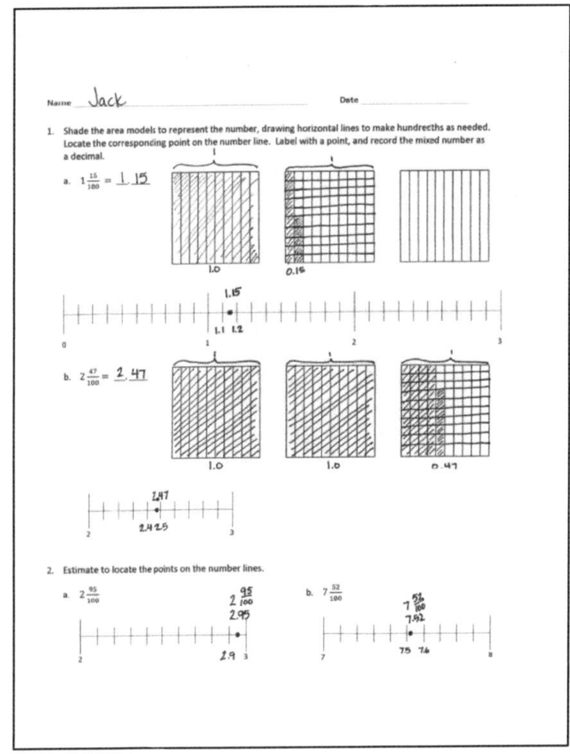
Name Jack Date

1. Shade the area models to represent the number, drawing horizontal lines to make hundredths as needed. Locate the corresponding point on the number line. Label with a point, and record the mixed number as a decimal.

a. $1\frac{15}{100}$ = 1.15

b. $2\frac{47}{100}$ = 2.47

2. Estimate to locate the points on the number lines.

a. $2\frac{95}{100}$

b. $7\frac{52}{100}$

Invite students to review their solutions for the Problem Set. They should check work by comparing answers with a partner before going over answers as a class. Look for misconceptions or misunderstandings that can be addressed in the Debrief. Guide students in a conversation to debrief the Problem Set and process the lesson.

Any combination of the questions below may be used to lead the discussion.

- How could you count backward to locate 2.47 on the number line in Problem 1(b)?
- In Problem 2(a), how did you estimate the location of your point?
- In Problem 3(a), the units are ones and hundredths. If I had 1.02 liters of water and you had 1.02 kilograms of rice, how do the measurement units change the meaning of that number?

© 2015 Great Minds. eureka-math.org
G4-M6-TE-B5-1.3.1-01.2016

- In Problem 3(f), express this number in ones and tenths. Use a model to show that this new representation is equivalent to 7 ones 70 hundredths.
- Simplify $7\frac{70}{100}$ using division to show it is equal to $7\frac{7}{10}$. Explain to your partner how that relates to $7.70 = 7.7$.
- Explain to your partner why there is one less item in the left and right columns of Problem 4 than in the center column.
- Compare. (Write 1.4 meters ______ 1.7 grams.) Does it make sense to compare meters with grams? Why not?
- Talk with your partner about the importance of the number zero. Use the number 100 and the number 0.01 in your discussion. (Provide Hide Zero cards to strengthen the conversation.)

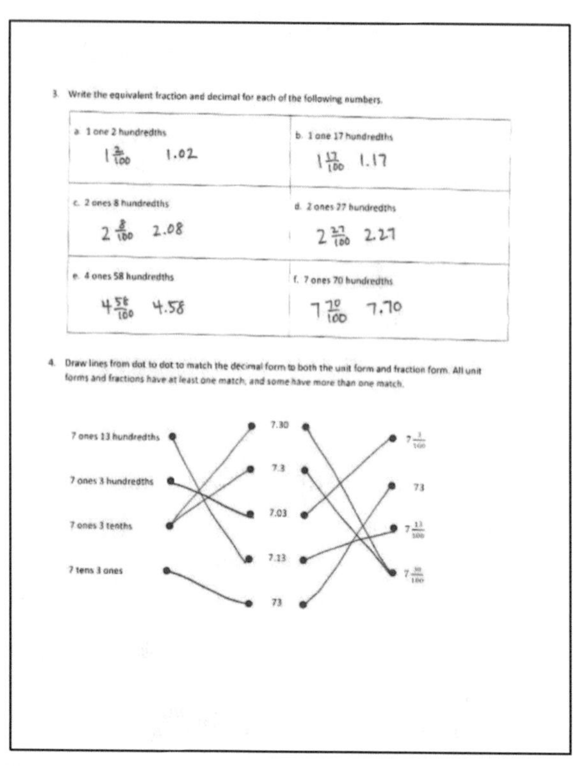

3. Write the equivalent fraction and decimal for each of the following numbers.

a. 1 one 2 hundredths $1\frac{2}{100}$ 1.02	b. 1 one 17 hundredths $1\frac{17}{100}$ 1.17
c. 2 ones 8 hundredths $2\frac{8}{100}$ 2.08	d. 2 ones 27 hundredths $2\frac{27}{100}$ 2.27
e. 4 ones 58 hundredths $4\frac{58}{100}$ 4.58	f. 7 ones 70 hundredths $7\frac{70}{100}$ 7.70

4. Draw lines from dot to dot to match the decimal form to both the unit form and fraction form. All unit forms and fractions have at least one match, and some have more than one match.

Exit Ticket (3 minutes)

After the Student Debrief, instruct students to complete the Exit Ticket. A review of their work will help with assessing students' understanding of the concepts that were presented in today's lesson and planning more effectively for future lessons. The questions may be read aloud to the students.

© 2015 Great Minds. eureka-math.org
G4-M6-TE-B5-1.3.1-01.2016

Name ____ Date ______________________

1. Shade the area models to represent the number, drawing horizontal lines to make hundredths as needed. Locate the corresponding point on the number line. Label with a point, and record the mixed number as a decimal.

   a. $1\frac{15}{100}$ = ___.____

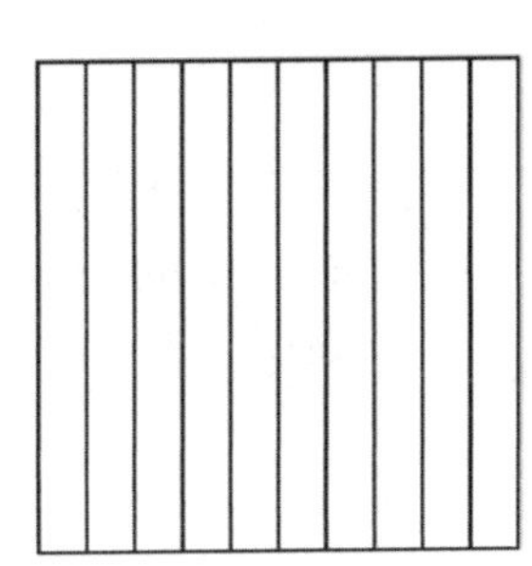

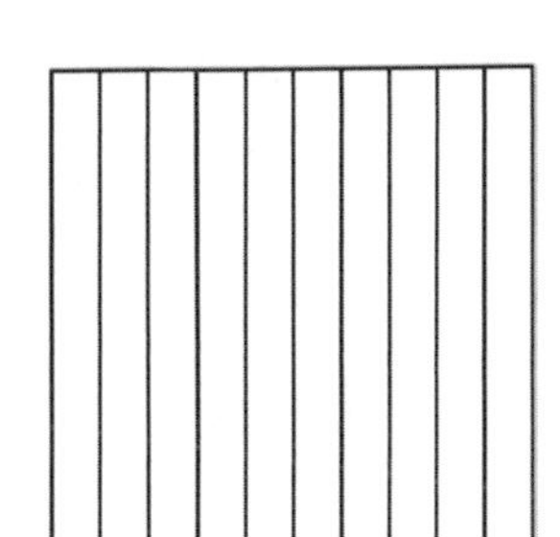

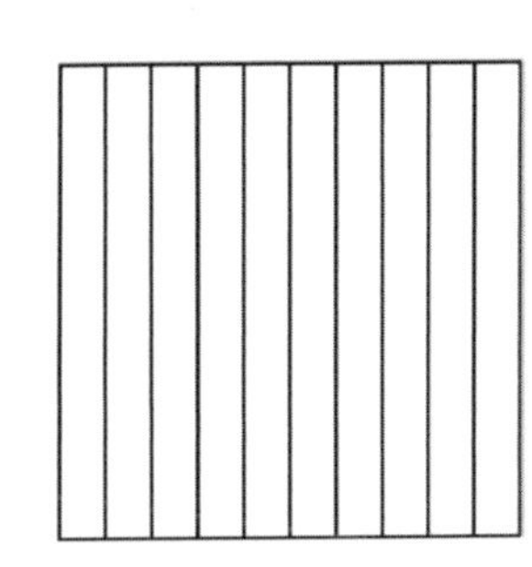

0 1 2 3

   b. 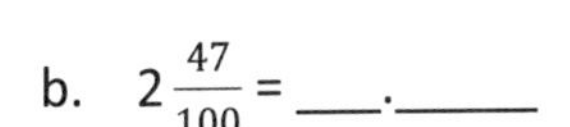

$2\frac{47}{100}$ = ___.____

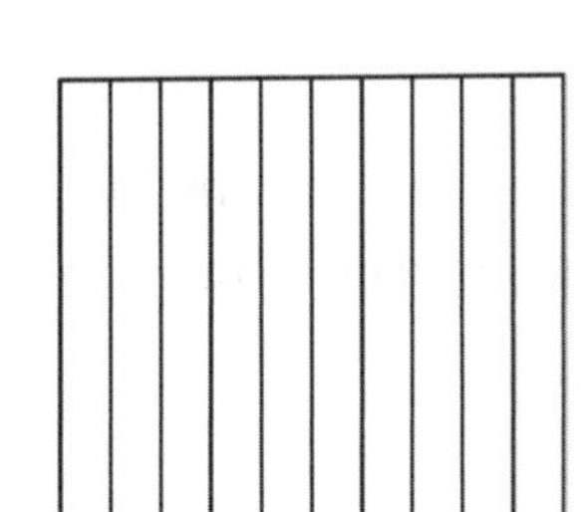

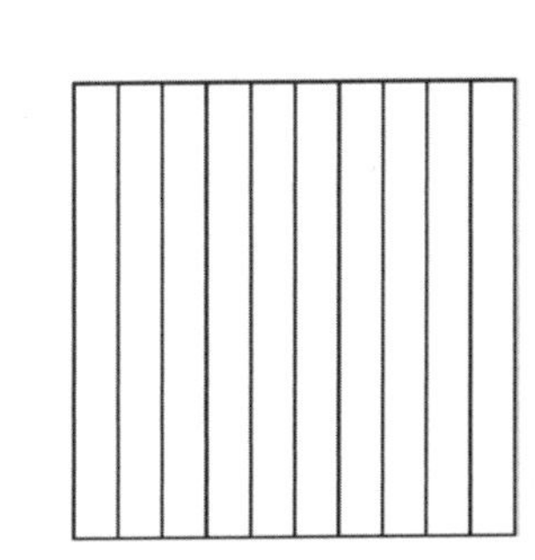

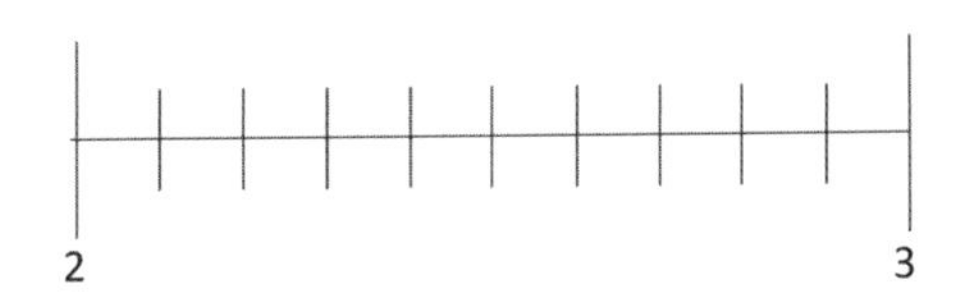

2. Estimate to locate the points on the number lines.

   a. $2\frac{95}{100}$

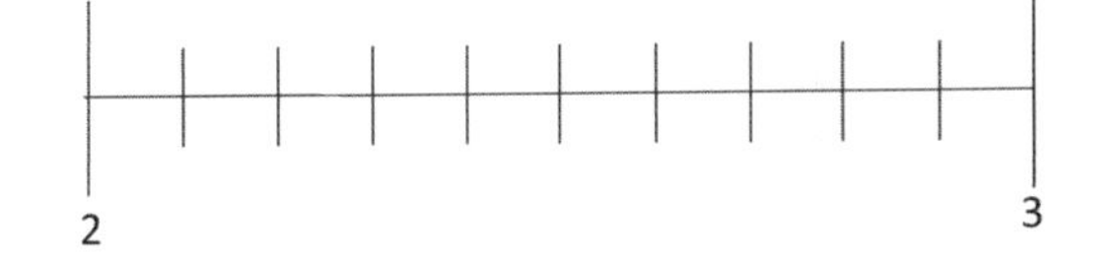

   b. $7\frac{52}{100}$

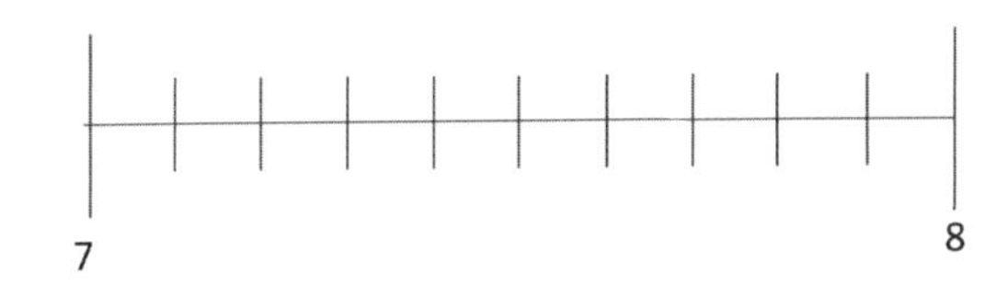

© 2015 Great Minds. eureka-math.org
G4-M6-TE-B5-1.3.1-01.2016

3. Write the equivalent fraction and decimal for each of the following numbers.

a. 1 one 2 hundredths	b. 1 one 17 hundredths
c. 2 ones 8 hundredths	d. 2 ones 27 hundredths
e. 4 ones 58 hundredths	f. 7 ones 70 hundredths

4. Draw lines from dot to dot to match the decimal form to both the unit form and fraction form. All unit forms and fractions have at least one match, and some have more than one match.

Unit form	Decimal form	Fraction form
7 ones 13 hundredths ●	● 7.30 ●	● $7\frac{3}{100}$
7 ones 3 hundredths ●	● 7.3 ●	● 73
7 ones 3 tenths ●	● 7.03 ●	● $7\frac{13}{100}$
7 tens 3 ones ●	● 7.13 ●	● $7\frac{30}{100}$
	● 73 ●	

© 2015 Great Minds. eureka-math.org
G4-M6-TE-B5-1.3.1-01.2016

Name ______________________________ Date ________________

1. Estimate to locate the points on the number lines. Mark the point, and label it as a decimal.

   a. $7\frac{20}{100}$

   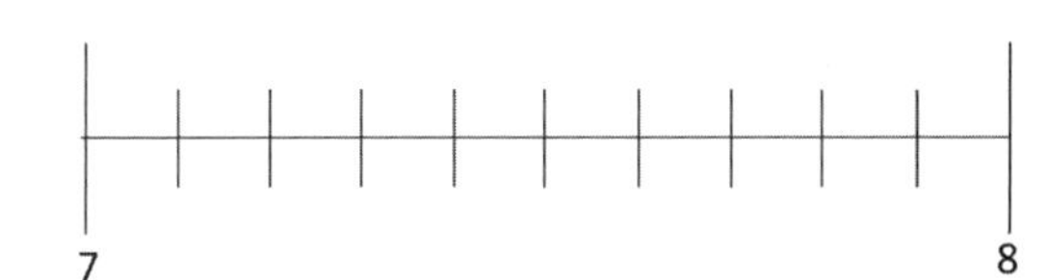

   b. $1\frac{75}{100}$

   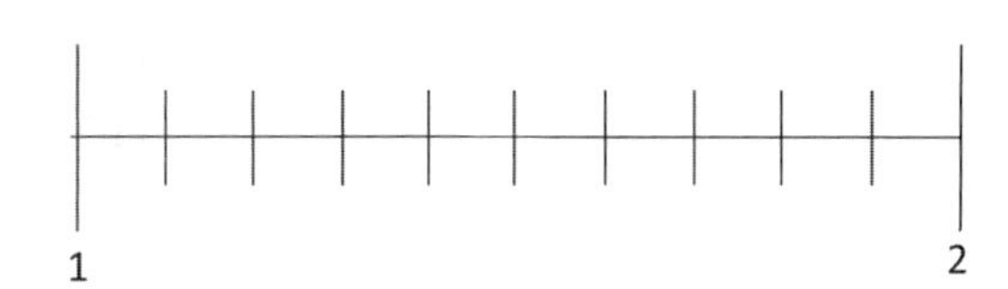

2. Write the equivalent fraction and decimal for each number.

   a. 8 ones 24 hundredths

   b. 2 ones 6 hundredths

© 2015 Great Minds. eureka-math.org
G4-M6-TE-B5-1.3.1-01.2016

Name ______________________________ Date ________________

1. Shade the area models to represent the number, drawing horizontal lines to make hundredths as needed. Locate the corresponding point on the number line. Label with a point, and record the mixed number as a decimal.

 a. $2\frac{35}{100}$ = ___.____

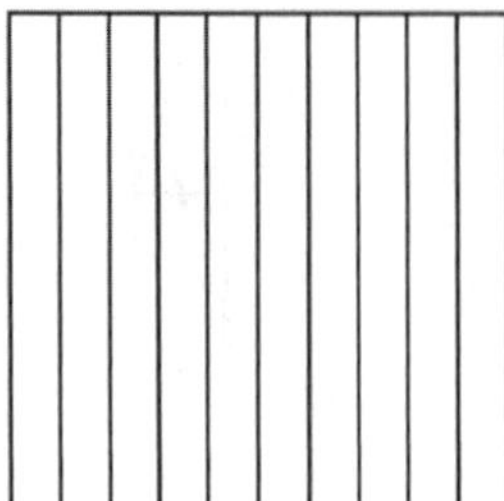
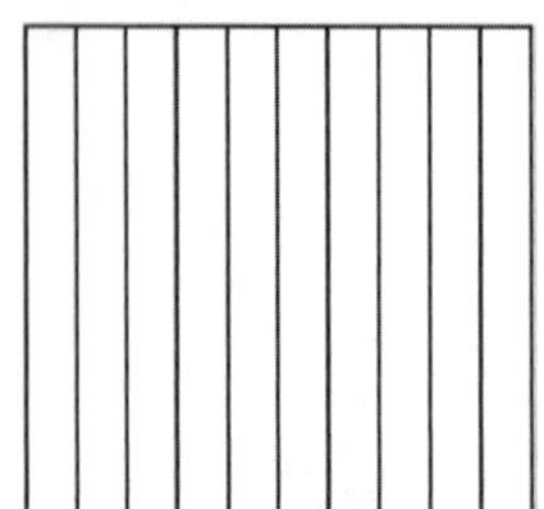
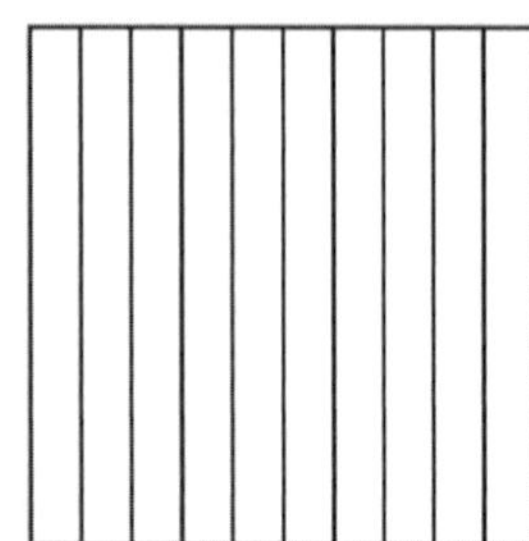

0 1 2 3

 b. $3\frac{17}{100}$ = ___.____

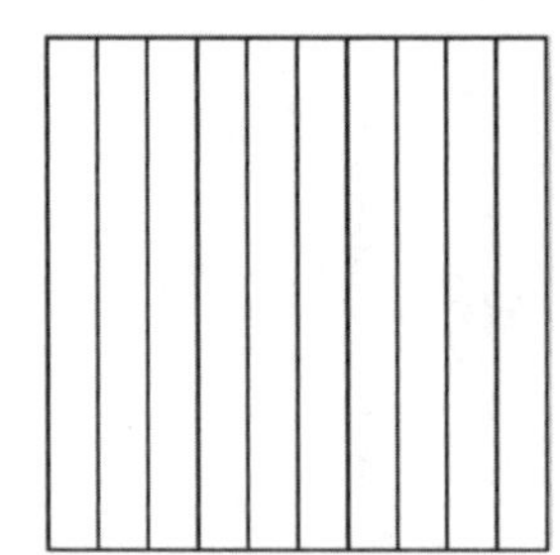
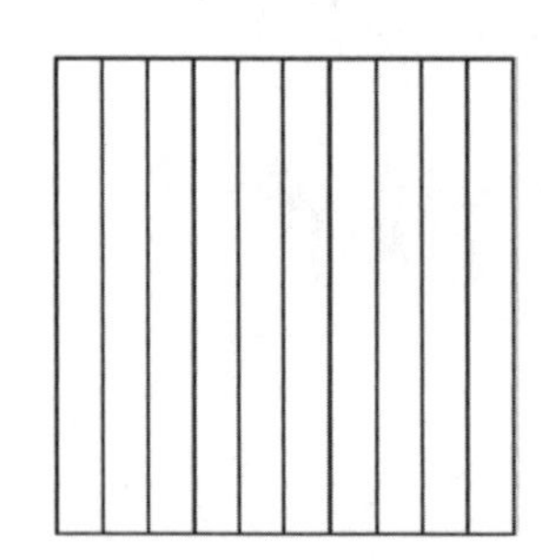
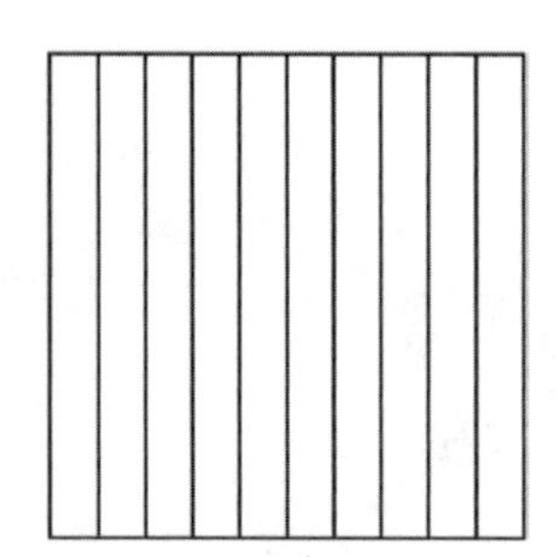
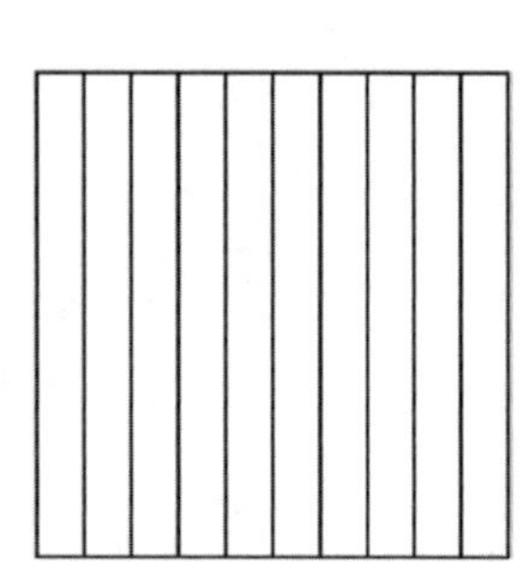

3 4

2. Estimate to locate the points on the number lines.

 a. $5\frac{90}{100}$

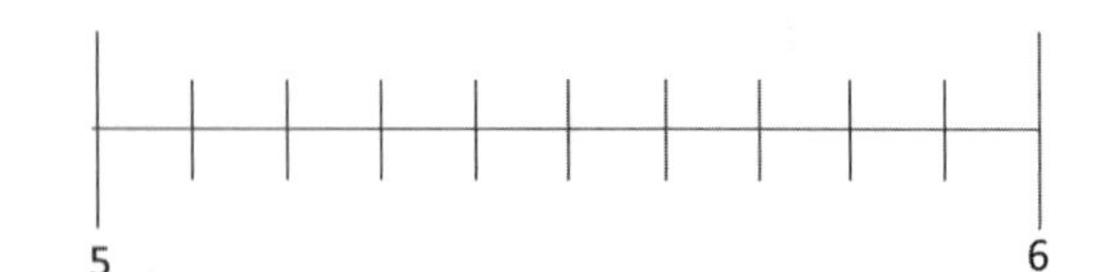

 b. $3\frac{25}{100}$

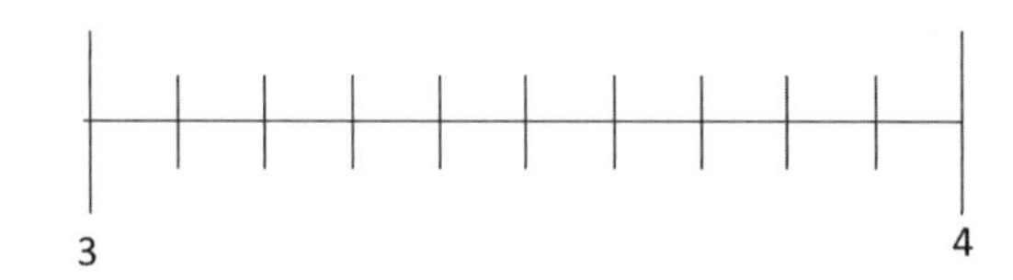

EUREKA MATH
© 2015 Great Minds. eureka-math.org
G4-M6-TE-B5-1.3.1-01.2016

3. Write the equivalent fraction and decimal for each of the following numbers.

a. 2 ones 2 hundredths	b. 2 ones 16 hundredths
c. 3 ones 7 hundredths	d. 1 one 18 hundredths
e. 9 ones 62 hundredths	f. 6 ones 20 hundredths

4. Draw lines from dot to dot to match the decimal form to both the unit form and fraction form. All unit forms and fractions have at least one match, and some have more than one match.

Unit form	Decimal form	Fraction form
4 ones 18 hundredths ●	● 4.80 ●	● $4\frac{18}{100}$
4 ones 8 hundredths ●	● 4.8 ●	● 48
4 ones 8 tenths ●	● 4.18 ●	● $4\frac{8}{100}$
4 tens 8 ones ●	● 4.08 ●	● $4\frac{80}{100}$
	● 48 ●	

© 2015 Great Minds. eureka-math.org
G4-M6-TE-B5-1.3.1-01.2016

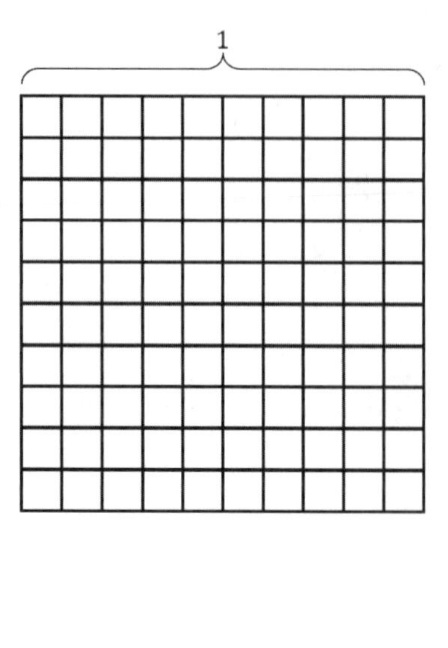

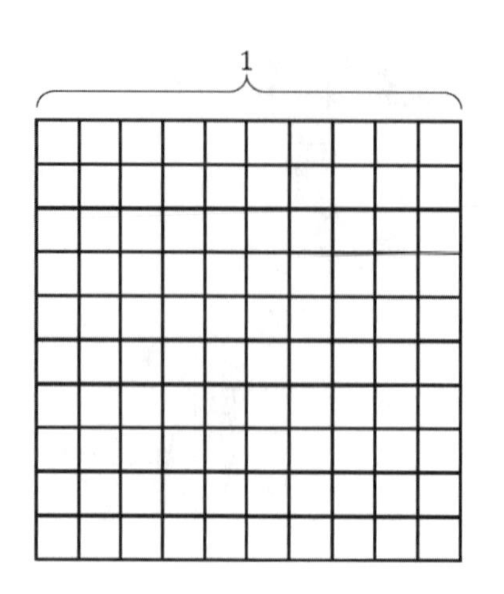

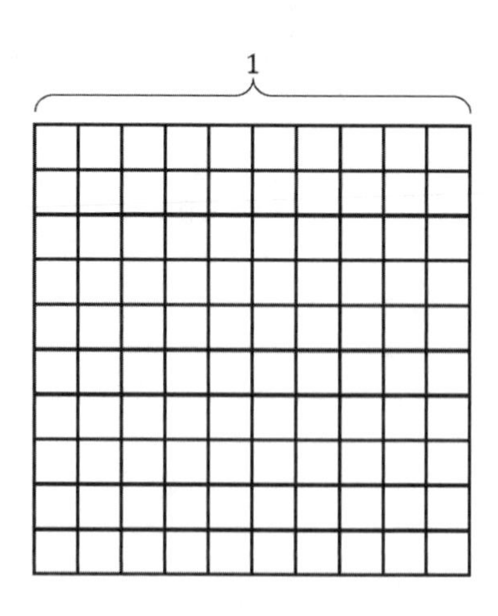

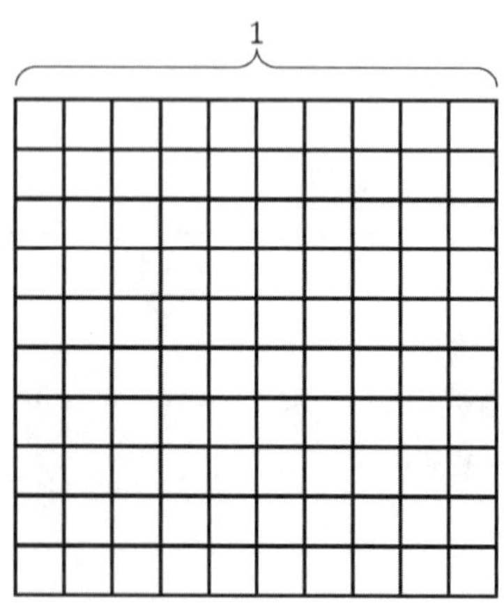

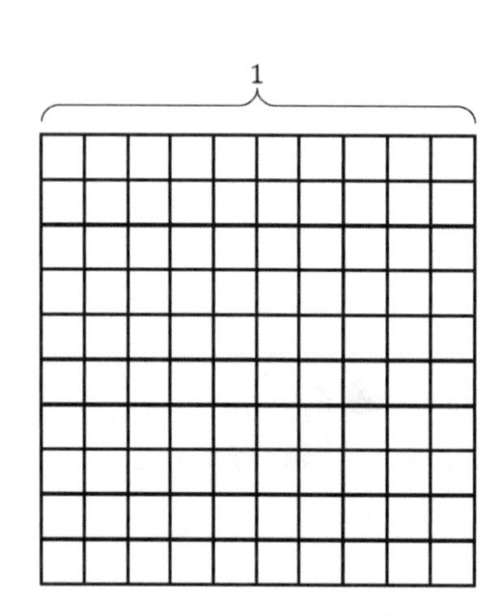

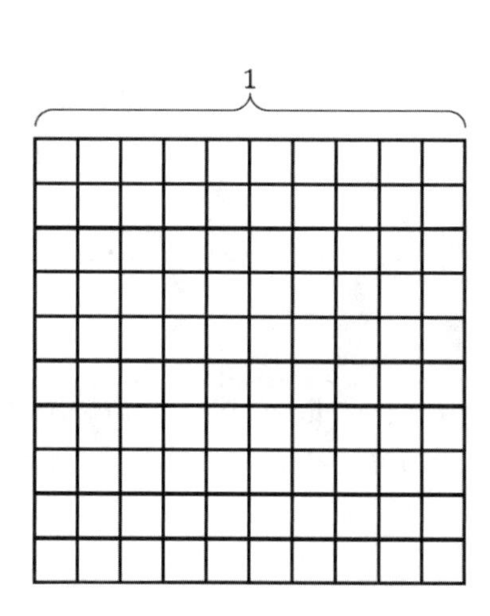

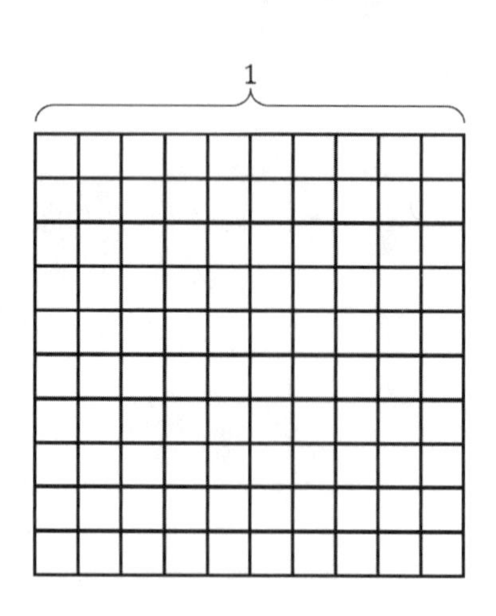

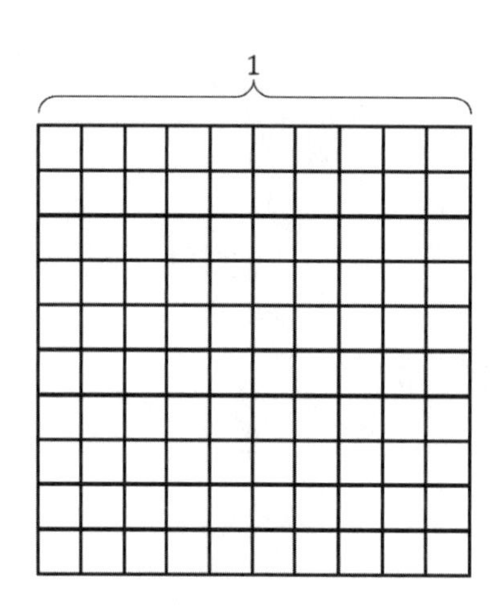

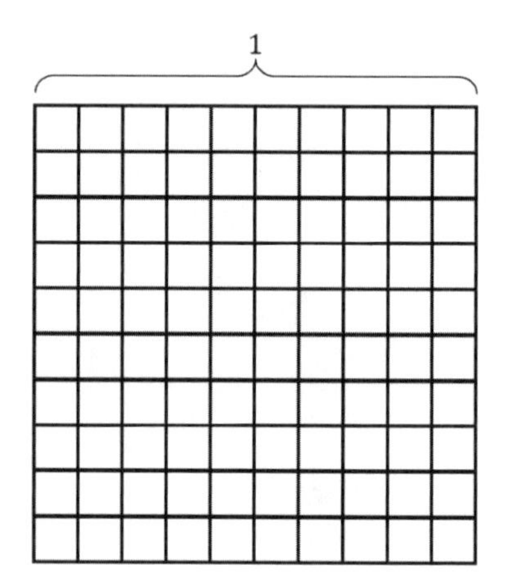

hundredths area model

© 2015 Great Minds. eureka-math.org
G4-M6-TE-B5-1.3.1-01.2016
EUREKA MATH

area model

© 2015 Great Minds. eureka-math.org
G4-M6-TE-B5-1.3.1-01.2016

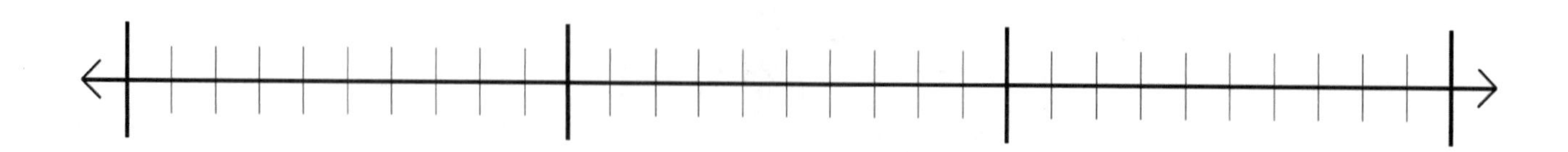

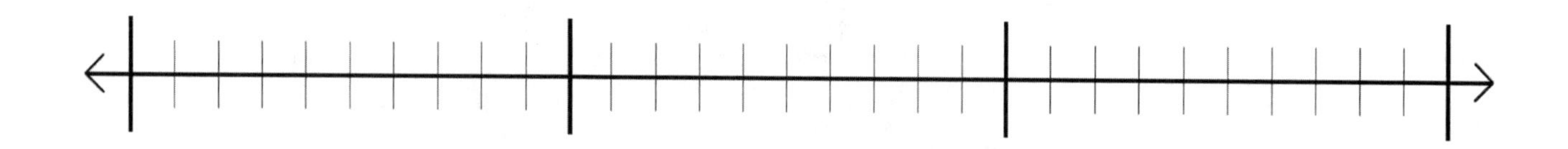

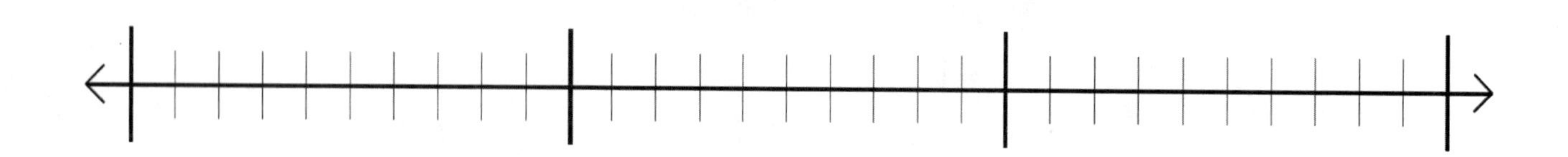

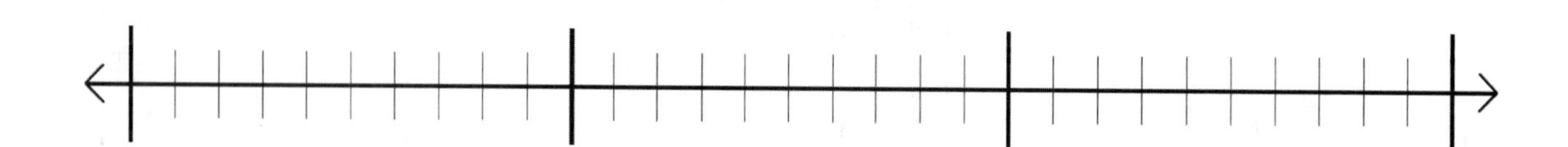

number line

EUREKA MATH
© 2015 Great Minds. eureka-math.org
G4-M6-TE-B5-1.3.1-01.2016

Lesson 7

Objective: Model mixed numbers with units of hundreds, tens, ones, tenths, and hundredths in expanded form and on the place value chart.

Suggested Lesson Structure

- Fluency Practice (11 minutes)
- Application Problem (5 minutes)
- Concept Development (34 minutes)
- Student Debrief (10 minutes)

Total Time (60 minutes)

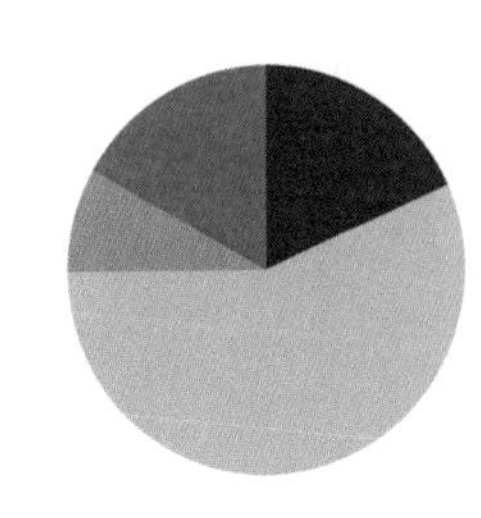

Fluency Practice (11 minutes)

- Count by Hundredths **4.NF.6** (5 minutes)
- Write the Decimal or Fraction **4.NF.5** (3 minutes)
- Write the Mixed Number **4.NF.5** (3 minutes)

Count by Hundredths (5 minutes)

Note: This fluency activity reviews Lessons 4–5.

T: Count by twos to 20, starting at zero.

S: 0, 2, 4, 6, 8, 10, 12, 14, 16, 18, 20.

T: Count by 2 hundredths to 20 hundredths, starting at 0 hundredths. (Write as students count.)

S: $\frac{0}{100}, \frac{2}{100}, \frac{4}{100}, \frac{6}{100}, \frac{8}{100}, \frac{10}{100}, \frac{12}{100}, \frac{14}{100}, \frac{16}{100}, \frac{18}{100}, \frac{20}{100}$.

$\frac{0}{100}$	$\frac{2}{100}$	$\frac{4}{100}$	$\frac{6}{100}$	$\frac{8}{100}$	$\frac{10}{100}$	$\frac{12}{100}$	$\frac{14}{100}$	$\frac{16}{100}$	$\frac{18}{100}$	$\frac{20}{100}$
$\frac{0}{10}$					$\frac{1}{10}$					$\frac{2}{10}$

T: 1 tenth is the same as how many hundredths?

S: 10 hundredths.

T: (Beneath $\frac{10}{100}$, write $\frac{1}{10}$.)

Continue this process for $\frac{2}{10}$.

T: Let's count by 2 hundredths again. This time, when you come to a tenth, say the tenth. Try not to look at the board.

© 2015 Great Minds. eureka-math.org
G4-M6-TE-B5-1.3.1-01.2016

S: $\frac{0}{100}, \frac{2}{100}, \frac{4}{100}, \frac{6}{100}, \frac{8}{100}, \frac{1}{10}, \frac{12}{100}, \frac{14}{100}, \frac{16}{100}, \frac{18}{100}, \frac{2}{10}$.

T: Count backward by 2 hundredths, starting at 2 tenths.

S: $\frac{2}{10}, \frac{18}{100}, \frac{16}{100}, \frac{14}{100}, \frac{12}{100}, \frac{1}{10}, \frac{8}{100}, \frac{6}{100}, \frac{4}{100}, \frac{2}{100}, \frac{0}{100}$.

T: Count by 2 hundredths again. This time, when I raise my hand, stop.

S: $\frac{0}{100}, \frac{2}{100}, \frac{4}{100}, \frac{6}{100}$.

T: (Raise hand.) Say 6 hundredths using digits.

S: Zero point zero six.

T: Continue.

S: $\frac{8}{100}, \frac{1}{10}, \frac{12}{100}, \frac{14}{100}$.

T: (Raise hand.) Say 14 hundredths in digits.

S: Zero point one four.

T: Continue.

S: $\frac{16}{100}, \frac{18}{100}, \frac{2}{10}$.

T: (Raise hand.) Say 2 tenths in digits.

S: Zero point 2.

Write the Decimal or Fraction (3 minutes)

Materials: (T) Hundredths area model (Lesson 6 Fluency Template) (S) Personal white board

Note: This fluency activity reviews Lessons 4–5.

T: (Project hundredths area model. Shade 7 units.) This 1 square is divided into 100 equal parts. Write the fraction of the area that is shaded.

S: (Write $\frac{7}{100}$.)

T: (Write $\frac{7}{100}$ = ___.___.) Complete the number sentence.

S: (Write $\frac{7}{100}$ = 0.07.)

T: (Project 2 hundredths area models as pictured to the right. Shade one in completely. Shade 7 units in the other area.) Write a fraction to express the area shaded.

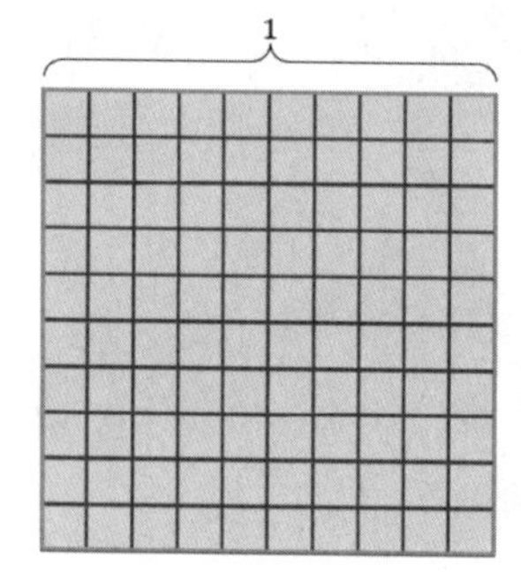

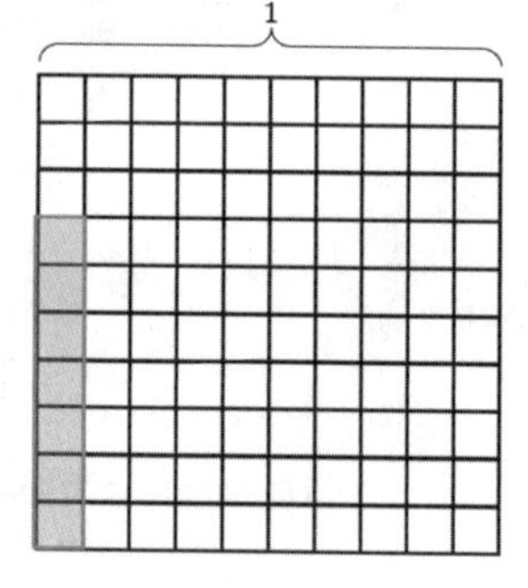

S: (Write $1\frac{7}{100}$.)

© 2015 Great Minds. eureka-math.org
G4-M6-TE-B5-1.3.1-01.2016
EUREKA MATH

T: (Write $1\frac{7}{100}$ = ___.___.) Complete the number sentence.

S: (Write $1\frac{7}{100}$ = 1.07.)

Continue with the following possible sequence: $2\frac{7}{100}$, $\frac{5}{100}$, $1\frac{5}{100}$, $\frac{3}{100}$, and $2\frac{3}{100}$.

T: (Write $3\frac{16}{100} = 3 + \frac{}{10} + \frac{}{100}$ = 3.16.) Complete the number sentence.

S: (Write $3\frac{16}{100} = 3 + \frac{1}{10} + \frac{6}{100}$ = 3.16.)

Continue with the following possible sequence: $2\frac{15}{100}$ and $1\frac{47}{100}$.

Write the Mixed Number (3 minutes)

Materials: (S) Personal white board

Note: This fluency activity reviews Lesson 6.

T: (Write 1 one 7 hundredths.) Write 1 one 7 hundredths as a mixed number.

S: (Write $1\frac{7}{100}$.)

Continue with the following possible sequence: 1 one 17 hundredths, 3 ones 37 hundredths, 7 ones 64 hundredths, and 9 ones 90 hundredths.

Application Problem (5 minutes)

Materials: (S) Pattern blocks

Use pattern blocks to create at least 1 figure with at least 1 line of symmetry.

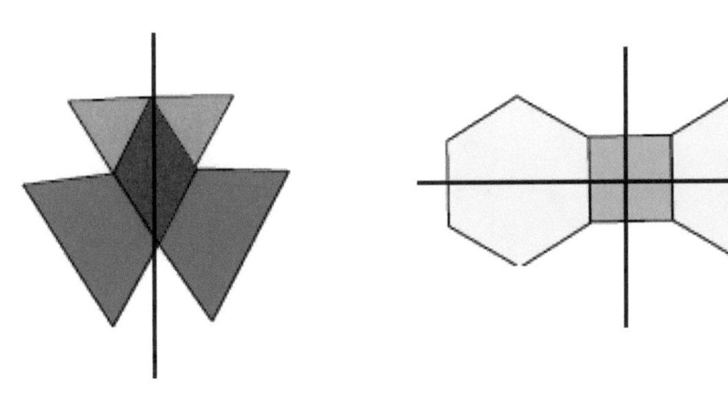

Note: This Application Problem reviews the concept of symmetry (Module 4) to prepare students to explore symmetry in the place value chart in today's Concept Development.

© 2015 Great Minds. eureka-math.org
G4-M6-TE-B5-1.3.1-01.2016

Concept Development (34 minutes)

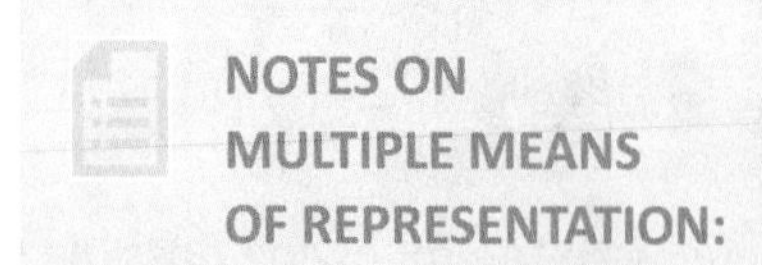

As learners begin to write numbers with decimal points, some students may need to be explicitly told to write a zero in the ones place as a placeholder, for example, in the number 0.7.

Materials: (T/S) Place value chart (Template), personal white board

Problem 1: Use place value disks to model mixed numbers with units of hundreds, tens, ones, tenths, and hundredths on the place value chart.

T: (Write 378.73.) Draw place value disks to show 378.73.

S: (Work.)

T: Write 378.73 in unit form.

S: (Write 3 hundreds 7 tens 8 ones 7 tenths 3 hundredths.)

3 hundreds 7 tens 8 ones 7 tenths 3 hundredths

T: (Project a place value chart showing hundreds to hundredths, including a decimal point as modeled below.) How is this place value chart different from the charts we have used this year?

S: It has a decimal point and places for tenths and hundredths.

T: Let's show 378.73 on the place value chart. (Distribute the place value chart template, and write 378.73 in the chart.) The digit 3 is written in which places? Tell me the largest place value first.

S: The hundreds and the hundredths.

Hundreds	Tens	Ones	•	Tenths	Hundredths
3	7	8		7	3

T: The digit 7 is written in which places? Tell me the largest place value first.

S: The tens and the tenths.

T: How about the 8?

S: The ones.

Repeat this process with 301.56 and 200.09.

EUREKA MATH
© 2015 Great Minds. eureka-math.org
G4-M6-TE-B5-1.3.1-01.2016

Problem 2: Say the value of each digit.

MP.8

T: (Show the place value chart with the number 378.73.) As with any place value chart, the value of each digit is determined by the place value unit.
T: Say the value of the digit in the hundreds place.
S: 3 hundreds.
T: Say the value of the digit in the hundredths place.
S: 3 hundredths.
T: These values sound so much alike. Discuss with your partner how to tell them apart.
S: One is hundreds, and one is hundredths. You have to be careful to say *th*. → One is a whole number, a hundred, and one is a fraction, a hundredth. → It's easier to see how different the values are when you write them as numbers 100 and 0.01. → There are 100 hundredths in one and 100 ones in a hundred. 100 × 100 is 10,000. There are 10,000 hundredths in a hundred.
T: The digit 3 has a greater value in which place?
S: The hundreds!
T: Say the value of the digit in the tens place.
S: 7 tens.
T: Say the value of the digit in the tenths place.
S: 7 tenths.
T: These values also sound so much alike. Discuss the difference with your partner.
S: One is tens, and one is tenths. →One is 10, and one is a tenth. → It's easier to see when you write them as numbers: 10 and 0.1.
T: The digit 7 would have agreater value in which place?
S: The tens!
T: Say the value of the 8.
S: 8 ones.

Hundreds	Tens	Ones	•	Tenths	Hundredths
3	7	8		7	3

3 hundreds + 7 tens + 8 ones + 7 tenths + 3 hundredths

NOTES ON MULTIPLE MEANS OF ENGAGEMENT:

Students working above grade level and others may enjoy an independent exploration of symmetry in the place value chart around 1. Ask students to search for patterns in our newly expanded place value chart. Students may find word patterns, such as *tenths* and *tens*, or patterns of ten—multiplying to increase values greater than 1 and dividing to decrease values greater than 1. Students can extend their expression of numbers in expanded form to include their observations of division. This work reaches beyond the scope of Grade 4 standards.

Repeat this process with 920.37.

© 2015 Great Minds. eureka-math.org
G4-M6-TE-B5-1.3.1-01.2016

Problem 3: Express a decimal number in decimal and fraction expanded form.

$$(3 \times 100) + (7 \times 10) + (8 \times 1) + \left(7 \times \frac{1}{10}\right) + \left(3 \times \frac{1}{100}\right) = 378\frac{73}{100}$$

$$(3 \times 100) + (7 \times 10) + (8 \times 1) + (7 \times 0.1) + (3 \times 0.01) = 378.73$$

T: Work with a partner to write 378.73 in expanded form, representing the value of each digit as a multiplication expression.

T: So, some of you expanded it in decimal form (point) and some in fraction form (point). How would you describe to someone what you just did?

S: We took the number apart, one place value at a time. → We decomposed the number by its units. → There are 5 place values and 5 addends. Each addend is an expression that shows the product of the number of units and the size of the unit. → When it came to the tenths and hundredths, you didn't tell us if you wanted decimal form or fraction form, so we could write it either way.

T: In order from largest to smallest, tell me the place value units for this number.

S: Hundreds, tens, ones, tenths, and hundredths.

T: Which digits represent the number of units, in order from left to right?

S: 3, 7, 8, 7, and 3.

T: What do we know about $378\frac{73}{100}$ and 378.73?

S: One is in fraction form, and the other is in decimal form. → They are made of the same 5 units. → They are the same amount. They are just expressed in different forms.

Repeat this process for 340.83 and 456.08. (Point out that when there is a digit of 0 within a number, the digit need not be expressed in expanded form since it adds no value to the number sentence; however, when expressing the number in standard form, the zero is included as a placeholder.)

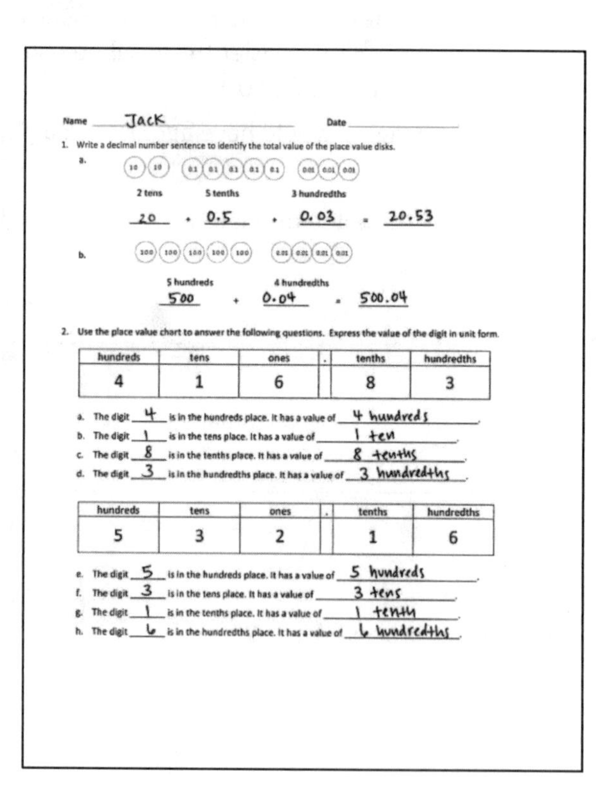

Name Jack Date

1. Write a decimal number sentence to identify the total value of the place value disks.

a. (10)(10) (0.1)(0.1)(0.1)(0.1)(0.1) (0.01)(0.01)(0.01)

2 tens + 5 tenths + 3 hundredths

20 + 0.5 + 0.03 = 20.53

b. (100)(100)(100)(100)(100) (0.01)(0.01)(0.01)(0.01)

5 hundreds + 4 hundredths

500 + 0.04 = 500.04

2. Use the place value chart to answer the following questions. Express the value of the digit in unit form.

hundreds	tens	ones	.	tenths	hundredths
4	1	6		8	3

a. The digit 4 is in the hundreds place. It has a value of 4 hundreds.
b. The digit 1 is in the tens place. It has a value of 1 ten.
c. The digit 8 is in the tenths place. It has a value of 8 tenths.
d. The digit 3 is in the hundredths place. It has a value of 3 hundredths.

hundreds	tens	ones	.	tenths	hundredths
5	3	2		1	6

e. The digit 5 is in the hundreds place. It has a value of 5 hundreds.
f. The digit 3 is in the tens place. It has a value of 3 tens.
g. The digit 1 is in the tenths place. It has a value of 1 tenth.
h. The digit 6 is in the hundredths place. It has a value of 6 hundredths.

Problem Set (10 minutes)

Students should do their personal best to complete the Problem Set within the allotted 10 minutes. For some classes, it may be appropriate to modify the assignment by specifying which problems they work on first. Some problems do not specify a method for solving. Students should solve these problems using the RDW approach used for Application Problems.

EUREKA MATH

© 2015 Great Minds. eureka-math.org
G4-M6-TE-B5-1.3.1-01.2016

Student Debrief (10 minutes)

Lesson Objective: Model mixed numbers with units of hundreds, tens, ones, tenths, and hundredths in expanded form and on the place value chart.

The Student Debrief is intended to invite reflection and active processing of the total lesson experience.

Invite students to review their solutions for the Problem Set. They should check work by comparing answers with a partner before going over answers as aclass. Look for misconceptions or misunderstandings that can be addressed in the Debrief. Guide students in a conversation to debrief the Problem Set and process the lesson.

Any combination of the questions below may be used to lead the discussion.

- How do the place value disks in Problem 1 help to show the value of each digit? How did the unit language help you to write the total value of the place value disks?
- In Problem 2 of the Problem Set, how did the place value chart help to determine the value of each digit?
- Look at the place value charts in Problem 2. *Ten* is found in the word *tenths*, and *hundred* is found in the word *hundredths*. We say that these place values are symmetric. What are they symmetric around? (Note: They are *not* symmetric about the decimal point.) I will shade the ones place to show the symmetry more dramatically.
- In Problem 3, we can write the expanded notation of a number in different ways. What is similar about each of the ways? What is different?
- How did the Application Problem connect to today's lesson?

Symmetry with respect to the ones place

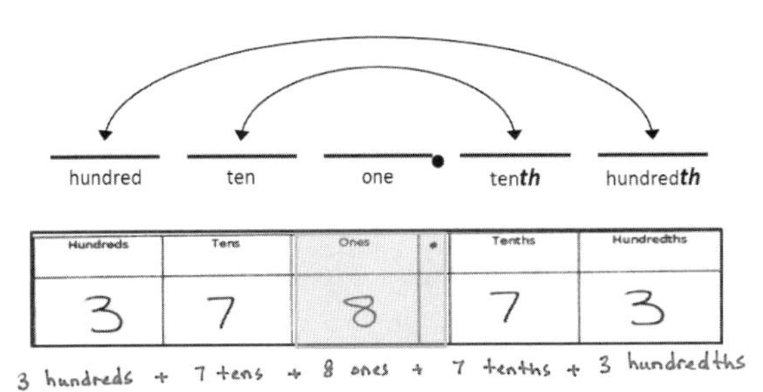

3. Write each decimal as an equivalent fraction. Then, write each number in expanded form, using both decimal and fraction notation. The first one has been done for you.

	Expanded Form	
Decimal and Fraction Form	Fraction Notation	Decimal Notation
$15.43 = 15\frac{43}{100}$	$(1 \times 10) + (5 \times 1) + (4 \times \frac{1}{10}) + (3 \times \frac{1}{100})$ $10 + 5 + \frac{4}{10} + \frac{3}{100}$	$(1 \times 10) + (5 \times 1) + (4 \times 0.1) + (3 \times 0.01)$ $10 + 5 + 0.4 + 0.03$
$21.4 = 21\frac{4}{10}$	$(2 \times 10) + (1 \times 1) + (4 \times \frac{1}{10})$ $20 + 1 + \frac{4}{10}$	$(2 \times 10) + (1 \times 1) + (4 \times 0.1)$ $20 + 1 + 0.4$
$38.09 = 38\frac{9}{100}$	$(3 \times 10) + (8 \times 1) + (9 \times \frac{1}{100})$ $30 + 8 + \frac{9}{100}$	$(3 \times 10) + (8 \times 1) + (9 \times 0.01)$ $30 + 8 + 0.09$
$50.2 = 50\frac{2}{10}$	$(5 \times 10) + (2 \times \frac{1}{10})$ $50 + \frac{2}{10}$	$(5 \times 10) + (2 \times 0.1)$ $50 + 0.2$
$301.07 = 301\frac{7}{100}$	$(3 \times 100) + (1 \times 1) + (7 \times \frac{1}{100})$ $300 + 1 + \frac{7}{100}$	$(3 \times 100) + (1 \times 1) + (7 \times 0.01)$ $300 + 1 + 0.07$
$620.80 = 620\frac{8}{10}$	$(6 \times 100) + (2 \times 10) + (8 \times \frac{1}{10})$ $600 + 20 + \frac{8}{10}$	$(6 \times 100) + (2 \times 10) + (8 \times 0.1)$ $600 + 20 + 0.8$
$800.08 = 800\frac{8}{100}$	$(8 \times 100) + (8 \times \frac{1}{100})$ $800 + \frac{8}{100}$	$(8 \times 100) + (8 \times 0.01)$ $800 + 0.08$

Exit Ticket (3 minutes)

After the Student Debrief, instruct students to complete the Exit Ticket. A review of their work will help with assessing students' understanding of the concepts that were presented in today's lesson and planning more effectively for future lessons. The questions may be aloud to the students.

© 2015 Great Minds. eureka-math.org
G4-M6-TE-B5-1.3.1-01.2016

Name ______________________________ Date ______________

1. Write a decimal number sentence to identify the total value of the place value disks.

a.

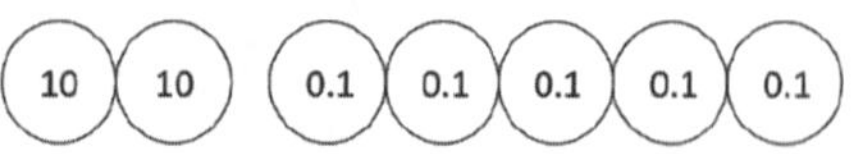

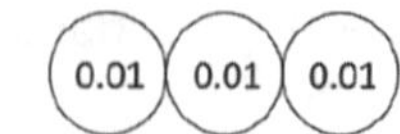

2 tens 5 tenths 3 hundredths

_______ + _______ + _______ = _______

b.

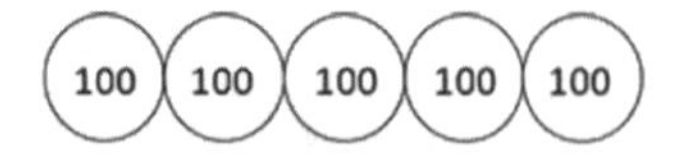

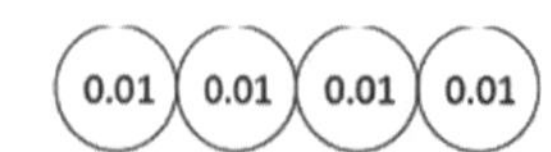

5 hundreds 4 hundredths

_______ + _______ = _______

2. Use the place value chart to answer the following questions. Express the value of the digit in unit form.

hundreds	tens	ones	.	tenths	hundredths
4	1	6		8	3

a. The digit_______ is in the hundreds place. It has a value of ______________________

b. The digit_______ is in the tens place. It has a value of ______________________

c. The digit_______ is in the tenths place. It has a value of ______________________

d. The digit_______ is in the hundredths place. It has a value of ______________________.

hundreds	tens	ones	.	tenths	hundredths
5	3	2		1	6

e. The digit_______ is in the hundreds place. It has a value of______________________.

f. The digit_______ is in the tens place. It has a value of______________________.

g. The digit_______ is in the tenths place. It has a value of______________________.

h. The digit_______ is in the hundredths place. It has a value of______________________.

© 2015 Great Minds. eureka-math.org
G4-M6-TE-B5-1.3.1-01.2016

3. Write each decimal as an equivalent fraction. Then, write each number in expanded form, using both decimal and fraction notation. The first one has been done for you.

Decimal and Fraction Form	Expanded Form	
	Fraction Notation	Decimal Notation
$15.43 = 15\frac{43}{100}$	$(1 \times 10) + (5 \times 1) + (4 \times \frac{1}{10}) + (3 \times \frac{1}{100})$ $10 + 5 + \frac{4}{10} + \frac{3}{100}$	$(1 \times 10) + (5 \times 1) + (4 \times 0.1) + (3 \times 0.01)$ $10 + 5 + 0.4 + 0.03$
21.4 = ________		
38.09 = _______		
50.2 = ________		
301.07 = ______		
620.80 = ______		
800.08 = ______		

© 2015 Great Minds. eureka-math.org
G4-M6-TE-B5-1.3.1-01.2016

Name ______________________________ Date ______________

1. Use the place value chart to answer the following questions. Express the value of the digit in unit form.

hundreds	tens	ones	.	tenths	hundredths
8	2	7		6	4

a. The digit _______ is in the hundreds place. It has a value of ______________________.

b. The digit _______ is in the tens place. It has a value of ______________________.

c. The digit _______ is in the tenths place. It has a value of ______________________.

d. The digit _______ is in the hundredths place. It has a value of ______________________.

2. Complete the following chart.

Fraction	Expanded Form		Decimal
	Fraction Notation	Decimal Notation	
$422\frac{8}{100}$			
	$(3 \times 100) + (9 \times \frac{1}{10}) + (2 \times \frac{1}{100})$		

© 2015 Great Minds. eureka-math.org
G4-M6-TE-B5-1.3.1-01.2016

Name ______________________________ Date ________________

1. Write a decimal number sentence to identify the total value of the place value disks.

a. 10 10 10 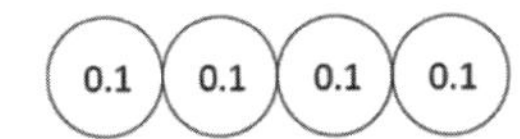

0.01 0.01

3 tens 4 tenths 2 hundredths

_______ + _______ + _______ = _______

b. 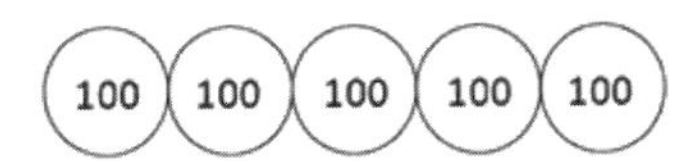

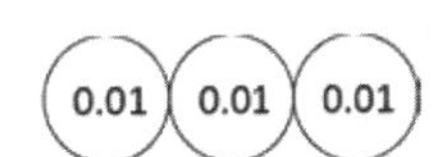

4 hundreds 3 hundredths

_______ + _______ = _______

2. Use the place value chart to answer the following questions. Express the value of the digit in unit form.

hundreds	tens	ones	.	tenths	hundredths
8	2	7		6	4

a. The digit _______ is in the hundreds place. It has a value of ______________________.

b. The digit _______ is in the tens place. It has a value of ______________________.

c. The digit _______ is in the tenths place. It has a value of ______________________.

d. The digit _______ is in the hundredths place. It has a value of ______________________.

hundreds	tens	ones	.	tenths	hundredths
3	4	5		1	9

e. The digit _______ is in the hundreds place. It has a value of ______________________.

f. The digit _______ is in the tens place. It has a value of ______________________.

g. The digit _______ is in the tenths place. It has a value of ______________________.

h. The digit _______ is in the hundredths place. It has a value of ______________________.

© 2015 Great Minds. eureka-math.org
G4-M6-TE-B5-1.3.1-01.2016

3. Write each decimal as an equivalent fraction. Then, write each number in expanded form, using both decimal and fraction notation. The first one has been done for you.

Decimal and Fraction Form	Expanded Form	
	Fraction Notation	Decimal Notation
$14.23 = 14\frac{23}{100}$	$(1 \times 10) + (4 \times 1) + (2 \times \frac{1}{10}) + (3 \times \frac{1}{100})$ $10 + 4 + \frac{2}{10} + \frac{3}{100}$	$(1 \times 10) + (4 \times 1) + (2 \times 0.1) + (3 \times 0.01)$ $10 + 4 + 0.2 + 0.03$
25.3 = _______		
39.07 = ______		
40.6 = _______		
208.90 = _____		
510.07 = _____		
900.09 = _____		

© 2015 Great Minds. eureka-math.org
G4-M6-TE-B5-1.3.1-01.2016

hundreds	tens	ones	.	tenths	hundredths

place value chart

© 2015 Great Minds. eureka-math.org
G4-M6-TE-B5-1.3.1-01.2016

Lesson 8

Objective: Use understanding of fraction equivalence to investigate decimal numbers on the place value chart expressed in different units.

Suggested Lesson Structure

■ Fluency Practice	(12 minutes)
■ Application Problem	(7 minutes)
■ Concept Development	(31 minutes)
■ Student Debrief	(10 minutes)
Total Time	**(60 minutes)**

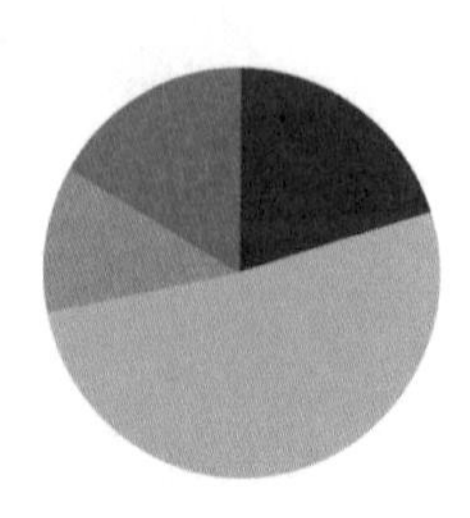

Fluency Practice (12 minutes)

- Sprint: Write Fractions and Decimals **4.NF.5** (9 minutes)
- Expanded Form **4.NF.5** (3 minutes)

Sprint: Write Fractions and Decimals (9 minutes)

Materials: (S) Write Fractions and Decimals Sprint

Note: This Sprint reviews Lessons 4–7.

Expanded Form (3 minutes)

Materials: (T/S) Personal white board

Note: This fluency activity reviews Lesson 7.

T: (Write $4\frac{17}{100}$.) Write 4 and 17 hundredths in expanded fraction form without multiplication.

S: (Write $4\frac{17}{100} = 4 + \frac{1}{10} + \frac{7}{100}$.)

T: Write 4 and 17 hundredths in expanded decimal form.

S: (Write 4.17 = 4 + 0.1 + 0.07.)

Repeat the process for $25\frac{64}{100}$.

T: (Write 5.93.) Write 5 and 93 hundredths in expanded decimal form.

S: (Write 5.93 = 5 + 0.9 + 0.03.)

© 2015 Great Minds. eureka-math.org
G4-M6-TE-B5-1.3.1-01.2016

T: Write 5 and 93 hundredths in expanded fraction form.

S: (Write $5\frac{93}{100} = 5 + \frac{9}{10} + \frac{3}{100}$.)

Application Problem (7 minutes)

Jashawn had 5 hundred dollar bills and 6 ten dollar bills in his wallet. Alva had 58 ten dollar bills under her mattress. James had 556 one dollar bills in his piggy bank. They decide to combine their money to buy a computer. Express the total amount of money they have using the following bills:

a. Hundreds, tens, and ones b. Tens and ones c. Ones

Jashawn 500 + 60 560
Alva 58 x 10 580
James + 556
$1,696

(a) 16 hundreds 9 tens 6 ones
(b) 169 tens 6 ones
(c) 1696 ones

Note: This Application Problem reviews expanded form and patterns of ten in the place value chart, as taught in Module 1. Reviewing patterns of ten and decomposition of familiar, larger place value units prepares students for today's exploration of decomposition and composition of smaller place value units.

Concept Development (31 minutes)

Materials: (T/S) Area model and place value chart (Template), personal white board

Problem 1: Represent numbers in unit form in terms of different units using the area model.

T: (Place the area model and place value chart template into personal white boards.) Show 2 ones 4 tenths shaded on the area model.

T: (Point to the first rectangle.) How many tenths are in 1?

S: 10 tenths.

T: Record 10 tenths below the first two rectangles. (Point to the third rectangle.) How many tenths are represented?

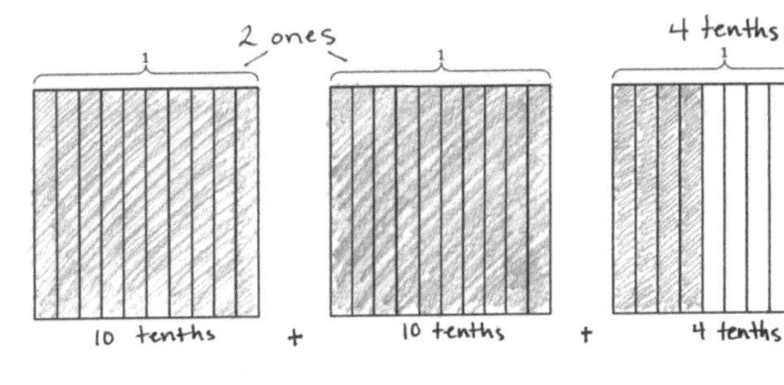

S: 4 tenths.

T: Record 4 tenths below this rectangle. (Write the addition symbol between the units.) What is 10 tenths plus 10 tenths plus 4 tenths?

S: 24 tenths.

© 2015 Great Minds. eureka-math.org
G4-M6-TE-B5-1.3.1-01.2016

T: (Write 2.4.) So, 2 and 4 tenths is equal to 24 tenths, true?

S: True.

T: Shade 2 ones 40 hundredths on the next set of area models.

T: Record an addition sentence in unit form that tells how many hundredths are shaded.

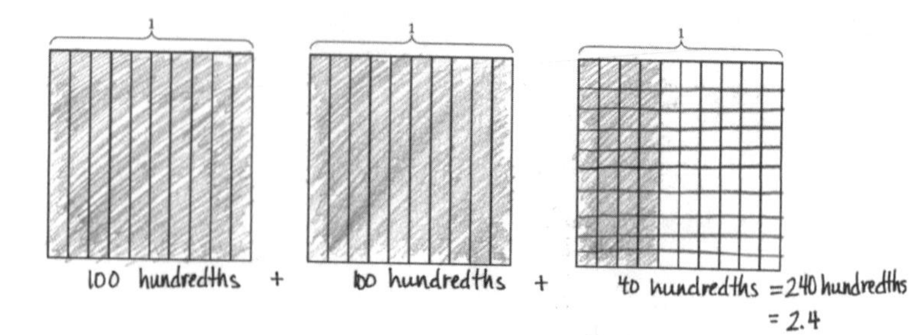

S: (Write 100 hundredths + 100 hundredths + 40 hundredths = 240 hundredths.)

T: What decimal number is 240 hundredths equal to?

S: 2.40. → 2.4.

T: How can it be equivalent to both?

S: 4 tenths is equal to 40 hundredths, so 0.4 equals 0.40.

Problem 2: Represent numbers in unit form in terms of different units using place value disks.

T: Represent 2 as tenths. How many tenths are in 2 ones?

S: $1 = \frac{10}{10}$, $2 = \frac{10}{10} + \frac{10}{10} = \frac{20}{10}$.

T: Say the equivalence.

S: 2 ones equals 20 tenths.

T: Show 2 ones 4 tenths on your place value chart using place value disks. Express the number in unit form as it is shown on the chart.

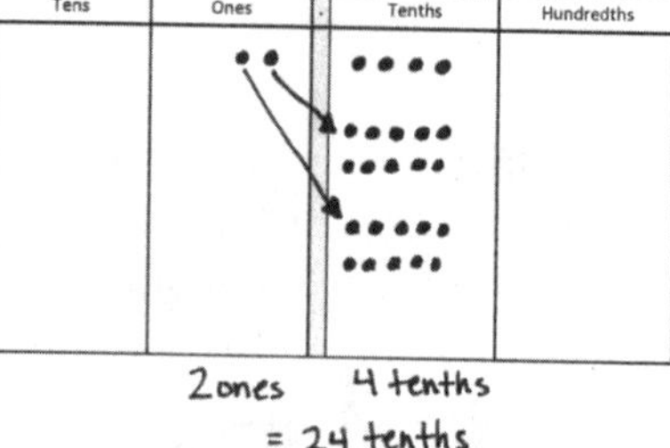

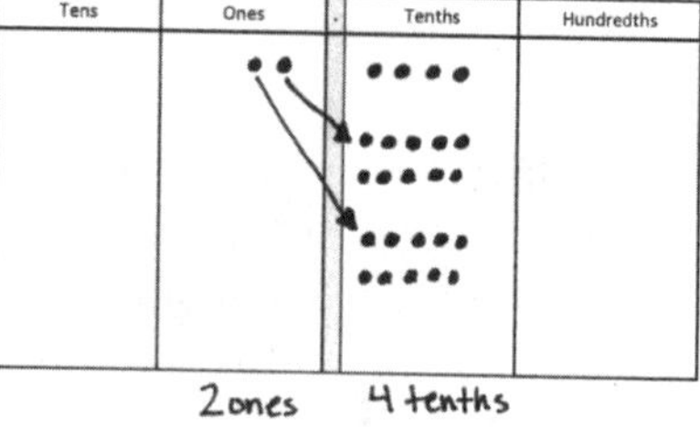

S: 2 ones 4 tenths.

T: Decompose the 2 ones, and express them as tenths.

S: 2 ones = $\frac{20}{10}$. There are 20 tenths + 4 tenths = 24 tenths.

$2\frac{4}{10} = \frac{24}{10} = 2.4$

$2\frac{40}{100} = \frac{240}{100} = 2.40$

MP.6

T: How can I express 24 tenths as hundredths?

S: You can decompose the tenths to hundredths and count the total number of hundredths. That's too many place value disks to draw!

T: You are right! Let's solve without drawing place value disks. 1 tenth equals how many hundredths?

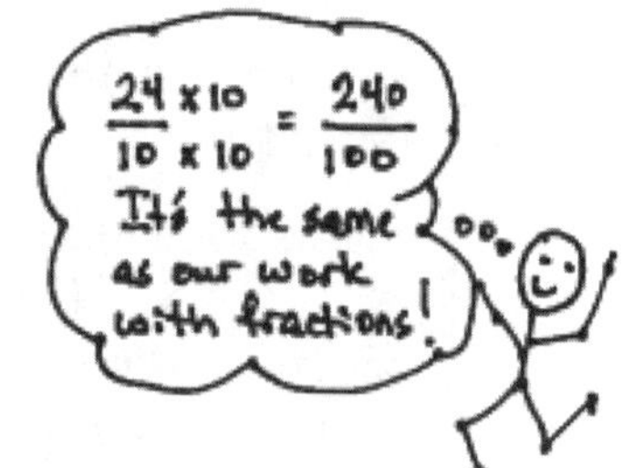

S: 1 tenth equals 10 hundredths.

T: 2 tenths is equivalent to how many hundredths?

S: 2 tenths equals 20 hundredths.

T: So, 24 tenths equals...? Discuss it with your partner.

S: 240 hundredths. There are 10 times as many hundredths as there are tenths. We showed that using area models. → We can multiply the numerator and denominator by the same number, just like with fractions.

© 2015 Great Minds. eureka-math.org
G4-M6-TE-B5-1.3.1-01.2016
EUREKA MATH

T: (Write $\frac{240}{100}$.) Write the equivalent decimal.

S: 2.40 or 2.4.

Repeat with 4.3.

Problem 3: Decompose mixed numbers to express as smaller units.

T: (Write 3.6.) Say this decimal.

S: 3 and 6 tenths.

T: How many tenths are in 3 ones?

S: 30 tenths.

T: How many tenths are in 3.6?

S: 36 tenths.

T: In fraction form and unit form, write how many tenths are equal to 3.6.

S: 3.6 = 36 tenths = $\frac{36}{10}$.

T: How many hundredths are in 3 ones?

S: 300 hundredths.

T: How many hundredths are in 6 tenths?

S: 60 hundredths.

T: How many hundredths are in 3.6?

S: 360 hundredths.

T: In fraction form and unit form, write how many hundredths are equal to 3.6.

S: 3.6 = 360 hundredths = $\frac{360}{100}$.

Repeat this process with 5.2 and 12.5.

Problem Set (10 minutes)

Students should do their personal best to complete the Problem Set within the allotted 10 minutes. For some classes, it may be appropriate to modify the assignment by specifying which problems they work on first. Some problems do not specify a method for solving. Students should solve these problems using the RDW approach used for Application Problems.

NOTES ON MULTIPLE MEANS OF ACTION AND EXPRESSION:

To scaffold the conversion of 24 tenths to 240 hundredths for students working below grade level, offer a few more steps. After verifying that 2 tenths equals 20 hundredths, ask, "5 tenths is equivalent to how many hundredths? (50.) 10 tenths is equivalent to how many hundredths? (100.) 20 tenths is equivalent to how many hundredths? (200.) So, 24 tenths equals...?"

3. Decompose the units to represent each number as tenths.

a. 1 = 10 tenths
b. 2 = 20 tenths
c. 1.7 = 17 tenths
d. 2.9 = 29 tenths
e. 10.7 = 107 tenths
f. 20.9 = 209 tenths

4. Decompose the units to represent each number as hundredths.

a. 1 = 100 hundredths
b. 2 = 200 hundredths
c. 1.7 = 170 hundredths
d. 2.9 = 290 hundredths
e. 10.7 = 1070 hundredths
f. 20.9 = 2090 hundredths

5. Complete the chart. The first one has been done for you.

Decimal	Mixed Number	Tenths	Hundredths
2.1	$2\frac{1}{10}$	21 tenths $\frac{21}{10}$	210 hundredths $\frac{210}{100}$
4.2	$4\frac{2}{10}$	42 tenths $\frac{42}{10}$	420 hundredths $\frac{420}{100}$
8.4	$8\frac{4}{10}$	84 tenths $\frac{84}{10}$	840 hundredths $\frac{840}{100}$
10.2	$10\frac{2}{10}$	102 tenths $\frac{102}{10}$	1020 hundredths $\frac{1020}{100}$
75.5	$75\frac{5}{10}$	755 tenths $\frac{755}{10}$	7550 hundredths $\frac{7550}{100}$

© 2015 Great Minds. eureka-math.org
G4-M6-TE-B5-1.3.1-01.2016

Student Debrief (10 minutes)

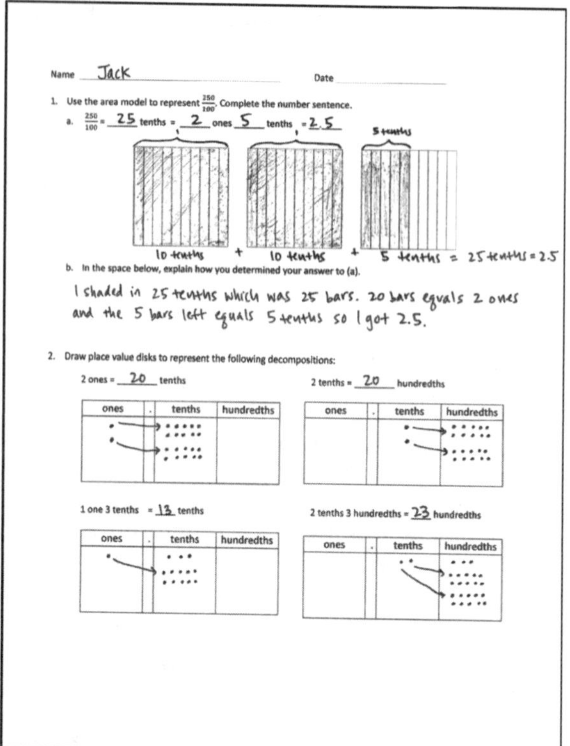

Name Jack Date

1. Use the area model to represent $\frac{250}{100}$. Complete the number sentence.

a. $\frac{250}{100}$ = 25 tenths = 2 ones 5 tenths = 2.5

5 tenths

10 tenths + 10 tenths + 5 tenths = 25 tenths = 2.5

b. In the space below, explain how you determined your answer to (a).

I shaded in 25 tenths which was 25 bars. 20 bars equals 2 ones and the 5 bars left equals 5 tenths so I got 2.5.

2. Draw place value disks to represent the following decompositions:

2 ones = 20 tenths

ones	.	tenths	hundredths

2 tenths = 20 hundredths

ones	.	tenths	hundredths

1 one 3 tenths = 13 tenths

ones	.	tenths	hundredths

2 tenths 3 hundredths = 23 hundredths

ones	.	tenths	hundredths

Lesson Objective: Use understanding of fraction equivalence to investigate decimal numbers on the place value chart expressed in different units.

The Student Debrief is intended to invite reflection and active processing of the total lesson experience.

Invite students to review their solutions for the Problem Set. They should check work by comparing answers with a partner before going over answers as a class. Look for misconceptions or misunderstandings that can be addressed in the Debrief. Guide students in a conversation to debrief the Problem Set and process the lesson.

Any combination of the questions below may be used to lead the discussion.

- Explain why the area model in Problem 1 is a good tool for representing the decimal fraction. How does it help to determine the equivalent decimal number?
- How did drawing the place value disks in Problem 2 help you to understand decomposing from one unit to another?
- How did solving Problem 3 help you to solve Problem 4?
- What strategies did you use when completing the chart in Problem 5? Did you complete one column at a time or one row at a time? Which columns were especially helpful in completing other columns?
- How is decomposing hundreds to tens or tens to ones similar to decomposing ones to tenths or tenths to hundredths?
- When decomposing numbers on the place value chart, each column to the right of another shows 10 times as many parts. Explain why this is so. Even though we have 10 times as many parts, we are really dividing. Explain.
- How did the Application Problem connect to today's lesson?

Exit Ticket (3 minutes)

After the Student Debrief, instruct students to complete the Exit Ticket. A review of their work will help with assessing students' understanding of the concepts that were presented in today's lesson and planning more effectively for future lessons. The questions may be read aloud to the students.

© 2015 Great Minds. eureka-math.org
G4-M6-TE-B5-1.3.1-01.2016

Number Correct: _______

A

Write Fractions and Decimals

1.	$\frac{3}{10} =$	.
2.	$\frac{3}{100} =$	.
3.	$\frac{23}{100} =$	.
4.	$1\frac{23}{100} =$	.
5.	$4\frac{23}{100} =$	.
6.	0.07 =	—
7.	1.07 =	—
8.	0.7 =	—
9.	1.7 =	—
10.	1.74 =	—
11.	$\frac{4}{100} =$	.
12.	0.6 =	—
13.	$\frac{7}{100} =$	.
14.	0.02 =	—
15.	$\frac{9}{100} =$	.
16.	$\frac{10}{100} =$	.
17.	$\frac{10}{100} + \frac{2}{100} =$	.
18.	$\frac{1}{10} + \frac{2}{100} =$	.
19.	$\frac{1}{10} + \frac{3}{100} =$	.
20.	$\frac{1}{10} + \frac{4}{100} =$	.
21.	$\frac{1}{10} + \frac{9}{100} =$	.
22.	$3 + \frac{1}{10} + \frac{9}{100} =$	.

23.	$2 + \frac{1}{10} + \frac{6}{100} =$	.
24.	2 + 0.1 + 0.06 =	.
25.	3 + 0.1 + 0.06 =	.
26.	3 + 0.1 + 0.04 =	.
27.	3 + 0.5 + 0.04 =	.
28.	2 + 0.3 + 0.08 =	.
29.	2 + 0.08 =	.
30.	1 + 0.3 =	.
31.	10 + 0.3 =	.
32.	1 + 0.4 + 0.06 =	.
33.	10 + 0.4 + 0.06 =	.
34.	30 + 0.7 + 0.02 =	.
35.	$2 + \frac{3}{10} + 0.05 =$	.
36.	$4 + 0.5 + \frac{3}{100} =$	.
37.	$4 + \frac{3}{100} + 0.5 =$	.
38.	$0.5 + \frac{3}{100} + 4 =$	.
39.	20 + 0.8 + 0.01 =	.
40.	$4 + \frac{9}{100} + \frac{2}{10} =$	.
41.	0.04 + 2 + 0.7 =	-
42.	$\frac{6}{10} + 8 + \frac{2}{100} =$	.
43.	$\frac{5}{100} + 8 + 0.9 =$	—
44.	$0.9 + 10 + \frac{4}{100} =$	.

© 2015 Great Minds. eureka-math.org
G4-M6-TE-B5-1.3.1-01.2016

B

Number Correct: ______

Improvement: ______

Write Fractions and Decimals

1.	$\frac{1}{10} =$	.
2.	$\frac{2}{10} =$	.
3.	$\frac{3}{10} =$	.
4.	$\frac{7}{10} =$	.
5.	$\frac{5}{10} =$	.
6.	$0.2 =$	—
7.	$0.3 =$	—
8.	$0.4 =$	—
9.	$0.8 =$	—
10.	$0.6 =$	—
11.	$\frac{4}{10} =$	.
12.	$0.9 =$	—
13.	$\frac{6}{10} =$	.
14.	$0.5 =$	—
15.	$\frac{9}{10} =$	.
16.	$\frac{10}{10} =$	.
17.	$\frac{11}{10} =$	.
18.	$\frac{12}{10} =$	.
19.	$\frac{17}{10} =$	.
20.	$\frac{27}{10} =$	.
21.	$\frac{47}{10} =$	.
22.	$\frac{34}{10} =$	.

23.	$2 + \frac{1}{10} + \frac{4}{100} =$	.
24.	$2 + 0.1 + 0.04 =$	.
25.	$3 + 0.1 + 0.04 =$	.
26.	$3 + 0.1 + 0.06 =$	.
27.	$3 + 0.5 + 0.06 =$	.
28.	$2 + 0.4 + 0.09 =$	.
29.	$2 + 0.06 =$	.
30.	$1 + 0.5 =$	.
31.	$10 + 0.5 =$	.
32.	$1 + 0.2 + 0.04 =$	.
33.	$10 + 0.2 + 0.04 =$	.
34.	$30 + 0.9 + 0.06 =$	.
35.	$2 + \frac{5}{10} + 0.07 =$	.
36.	$4 + 0.7 + \frac{5}{100} =$	.
37.	$4 + \frac{5}{100} + 0.7 =$	.
38.	$0.7 + \frac{5}{100} + 4 =$	.
39.	$20 + 0.6 + 0.01 =$	.
40.	$6 + \frac{7}{100} + \frac{4}{10} =$	.
41.	$0.06 + 2 + 0.9 =$	—
42.	$\frac{8}{10} + 6 + \frac{4}{100} =$	.
43.	$\frac{3}{100} + 8 + 0.7 =$	.
44.	$0.7 + 10 + \frac{6}{100} =$	—

© 2015 Great Minds. eureka-math.org
G4-M6-TE-B5-1.3.1-01.2016

Name ______________________________ Date ________________

1. Use the area model to represent $\frac{250}{100}$. Complete the number sentence.

   a. $\frac{250}{100}$ = ______ tenths = ______ ones ______ tenths = __.____

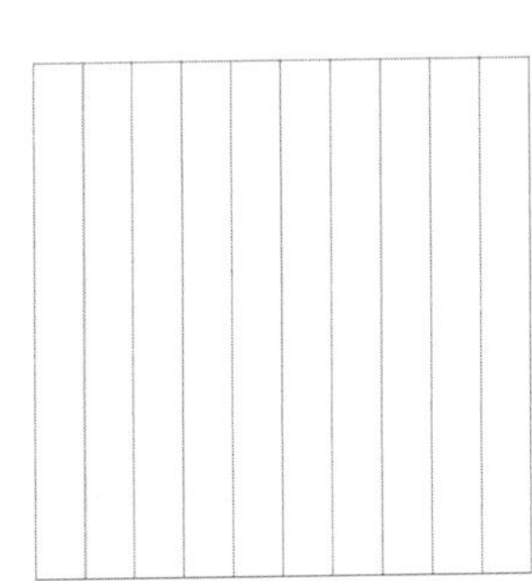
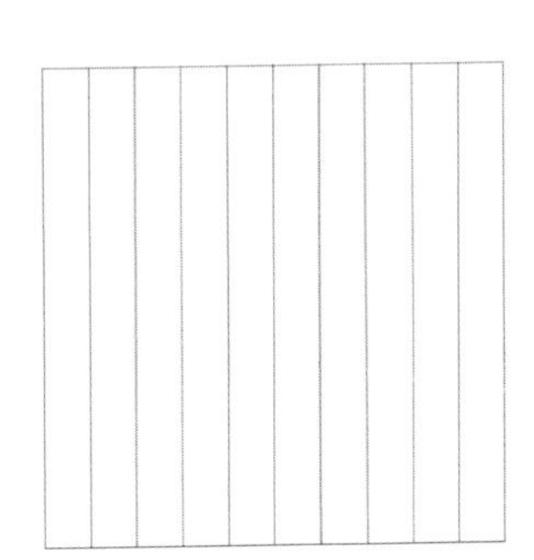
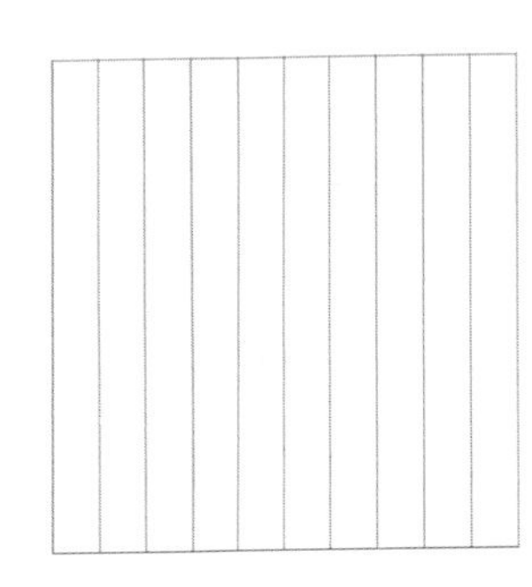

   b. In the space below, explain how you determined your answer to part (a).

2. Draw place value disks to represent the following decompositions:

2 ones = ________ tenths

ones	.	tenths	hundredths

2 tenths = ________ hundredths

ones	.	tenths	hundredths

1 one 3 tenths = ____ tenths

ones	.	tenths	hundredths

2 tenths 3 hundredths = ____ hundredths

ones	.	tenths	hundredths

© 2015 Great Minds. eureka-math.org
G4-M6-TE-B5-1.3.1-01.2016

3. Decompose the units to represent each number as tenths.

a. 1 = _____ tenths

b. 2 = _____ tenths

c. 1.7 = ______ tenths

d. 2.9 = ______ tenths

e. 10.7 = ______ tenths

f. 20.9 = ______ tenths

4. Decompose the units to represent each number as hundredths.

a. 1 = ______ hundredths

b. 2 = ______ hundredths

c. 1.7 = _______ hundredths

d. 2.9 = ______ hundredths

e. 10.7 = ______ hundredths

f. 20.9 = ______ hundredths

5. Complete the chart. The first one has been done for you.

Decimal	Mixed Number	Tenths	Hundredths
2.1	$2\frac{1}{10}$	21 tenths $\frac{21}{10}$	210 hundredths $\frac{210}{100}$
4.2			
8.4			
10.2			
75.5			

© 2015 Great Minds. eureka-math.org
G4-M6-TE-B5-1.3.1-01.2016
EUREKA MATH

Name ______________________________ Date ________________

1. a. Draw place value disks to represent the following decomposition:

   3 ones 2 tenths = ________ tenths

ones	.	tenths	hundredths

   b. 3 ones 2 tenths = ________ hundredths

2. Decompose the units.

   a. 2.6 = _____ tenths

   b. 6.1 = _____ hundredths

© 2015 Great Minds. eureka-math.org
G4-M6-TE-B5-1.3.1-01.2016

Name ______________________________ Date ______________

1. Use the area model to represent $\frac{220}{100}$. Complete the number sentence.

   a. $\frac{220}{100}$ = ______ tenths = ______ ones ______ tenths = __.____

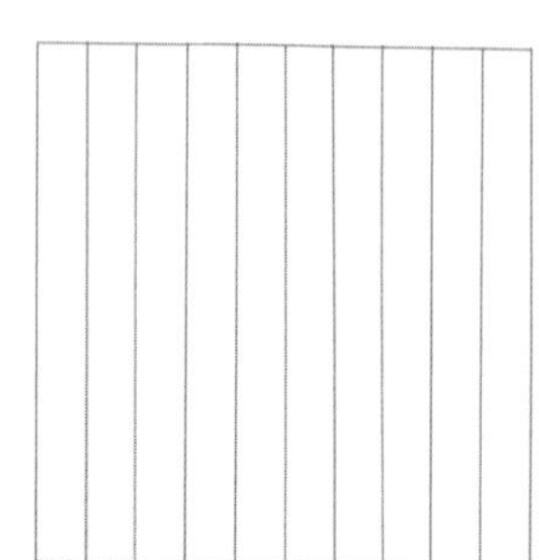
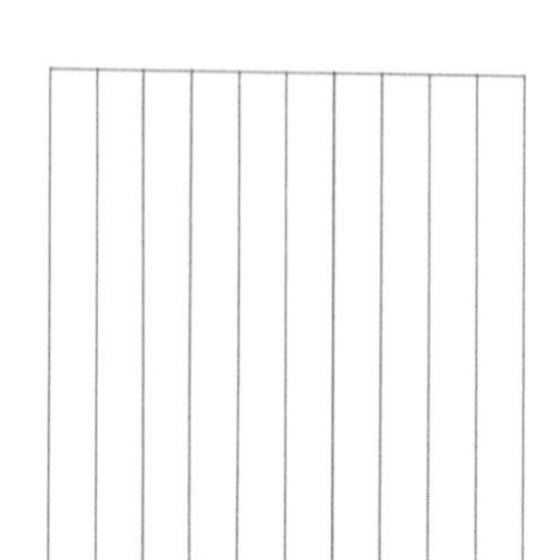
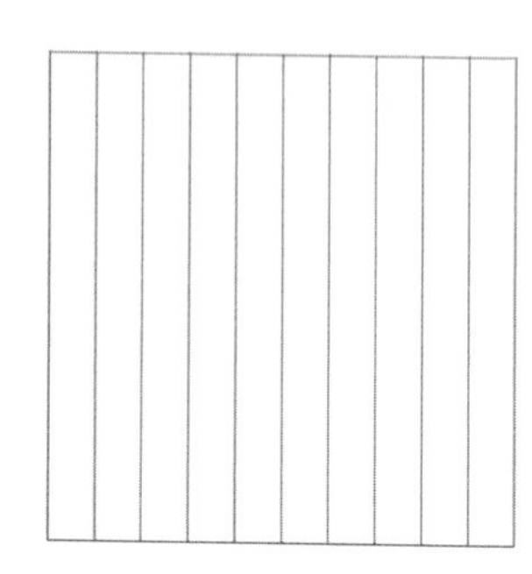

   b. In the space below, explain how you determined your answer to part (a).

2. Draw place value disks to represent the following decompositions:

3 ones = ________ tenths

ones	.	tenths	hundredths

3 tenths = ________ hundredths

ones	.	tenths	hundredths

2 ones 3 tenths = ____ tenths

ones	.	tenths	hundredths

3 tenths 3 hundredths = ____ hundredths

ones	.	tenths	hundredths

© 2015 Great Minds. eureka-math.org
G4-M6-TE-B5-1.3.1-01.2016

EUREKA MATH

3. Decompose the units to represent each number as tenths.

   a. 1 = _____ tenths
   b. 2 = _____ tenths
   c. 1.3 = _____ tenths
   d. 2.6 = _____ tenths
   e. 10.3 = _____ tenths
   f. 20.6 = _____ tenths

4. Decompose the units to represent each number as hundredths.

   a. 1 = _____ hundredths
   b. 2 = _____ hundredths
   c. 1.3 = _____ hundredths
   d. 2.6 = _____ hundredths
   e. 10.3 = _____ hundredths
   f. 20.6 = _____ hundredths

5. Complete the chart. The first one has been done for you.

Decimal	Mixed Number	Tenths	Hundredths
4.1	$4\frac{1}{10}$	41 tenths $\frac{41}{10}$	410 hundredths $\frac{410}{100}$
5.3			
9.7			
10.9			
68.5			

© 2015 Great Minds. eureka-math.org
G4-M6-TE-B5-1.3.1-01.2016

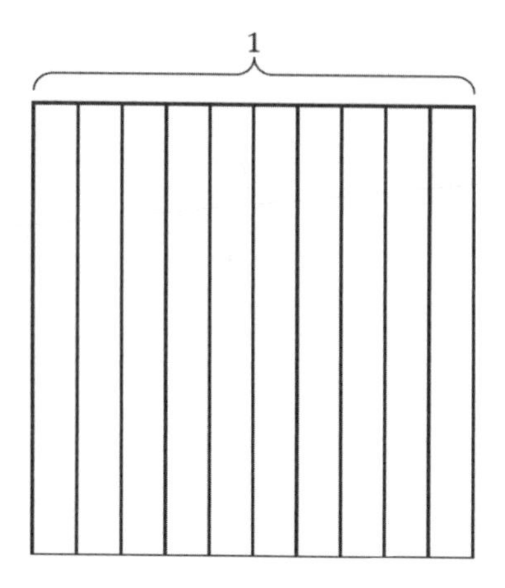

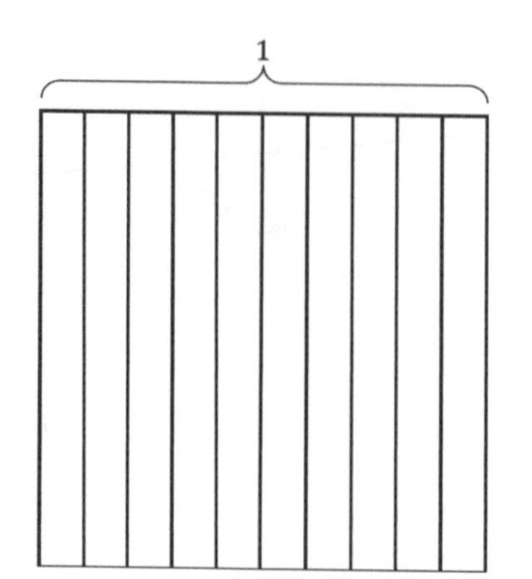

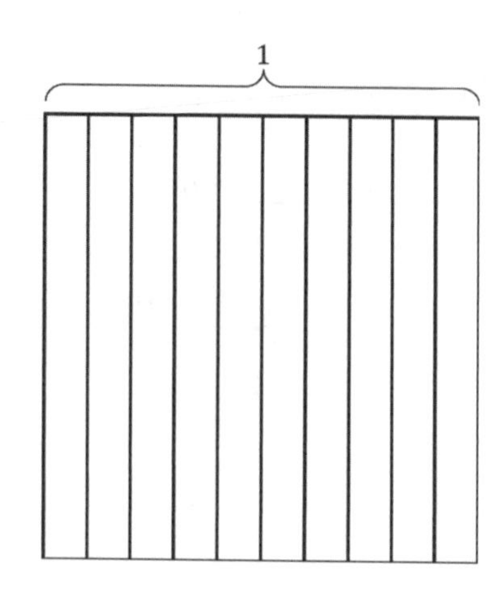

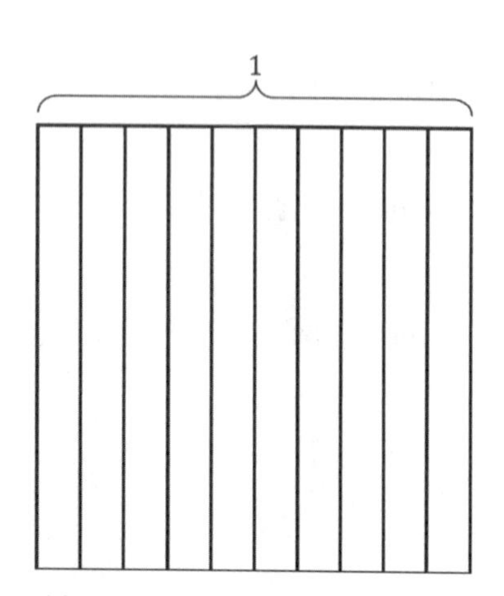

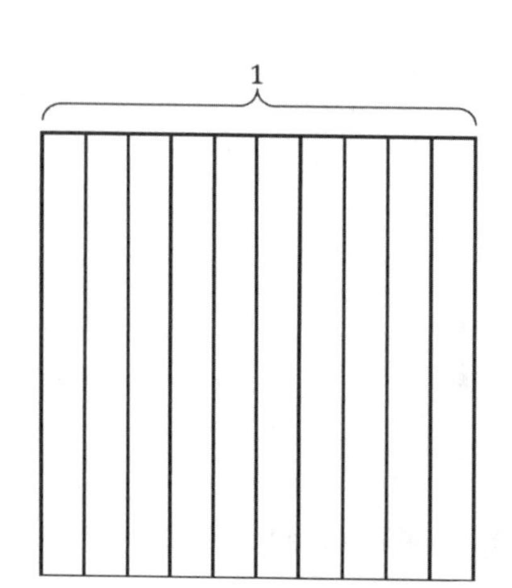

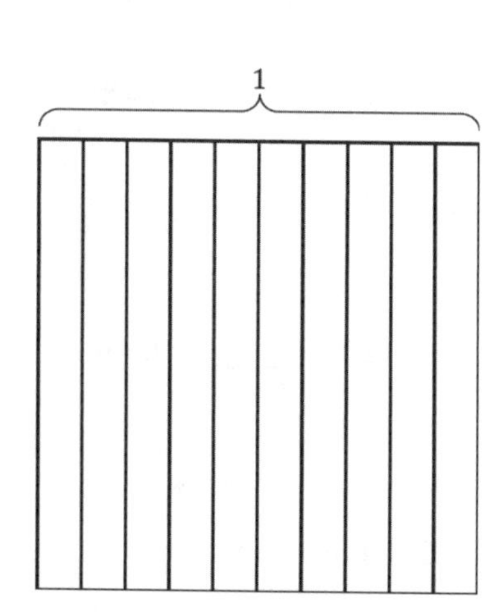

Tens	Ones	.	Tenths	Hundredths

area model and place value chart

© 2015 Great Minds. eureka-math.org
G4-M6-TE-B5-1.3.1-01.2016

Name ______________________________ Date ____________

1. Write the following fractions as equivalent decimals. Then, model each decimal with the given representation.

a. $\frac{2}{10}$ = ______

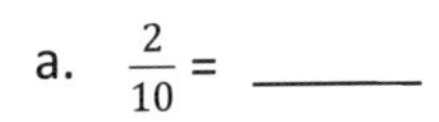

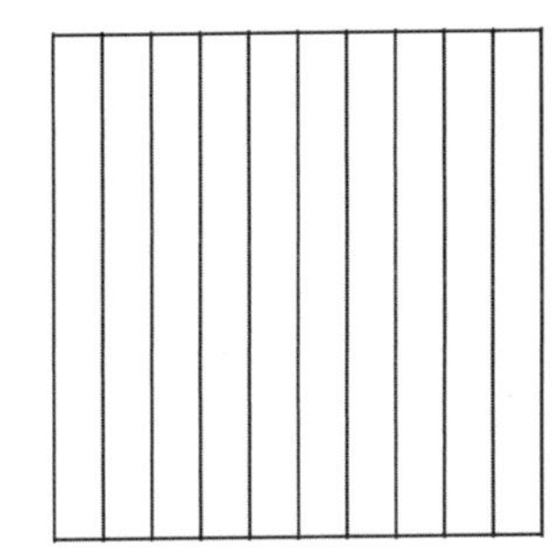

b. $\frac{3}{100}$ = ______

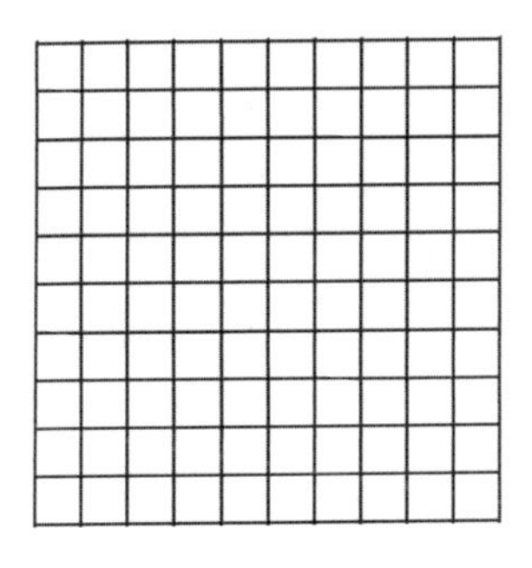

c. $\frac{4}{10}$ = ______

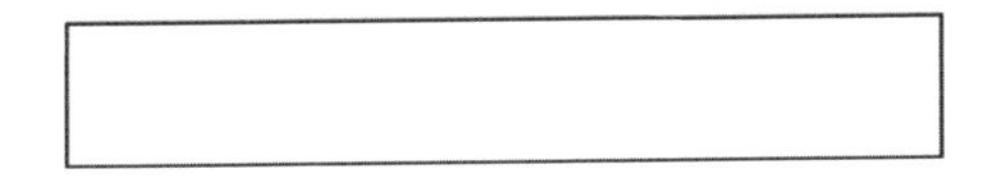

d. $\frac{46}{100}$ = ______

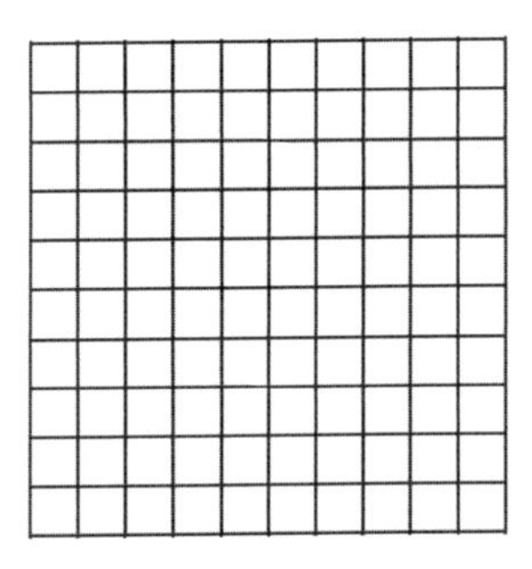

e. $7\frac{6}{10}$ = ______

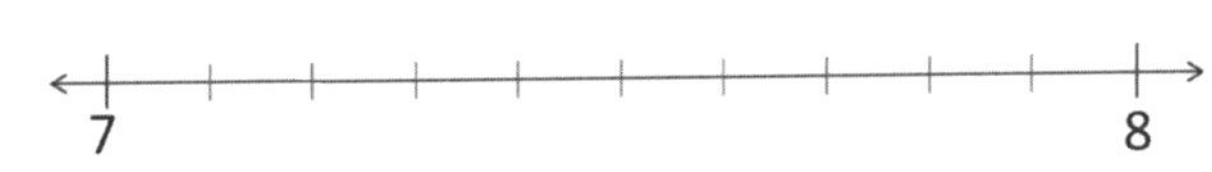

f. $3\frac{64}{100}$ = ______

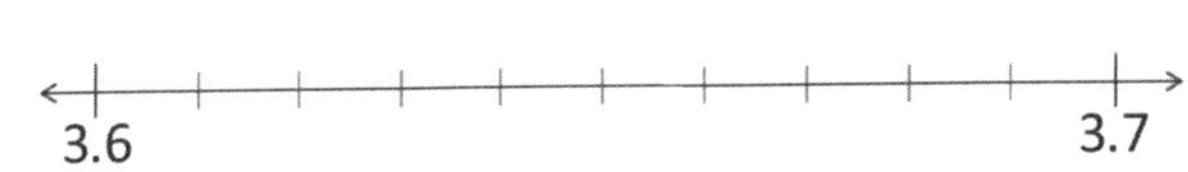

g. $4\frac{7}{10}$ = ______

ones	.	tenths

h. $5\frac{72}{100}$ = ______

ones	.	tenths	hundredths

© 2015 Great Minds. eureka-math.org
G4-M6-TE-B5-1.3.1-01.2016

2. Decompose tenths into hundredths using the areamodel. Express the equivalence of tenths and hundredths with fractions and with decimals.

   a. 3 tenths

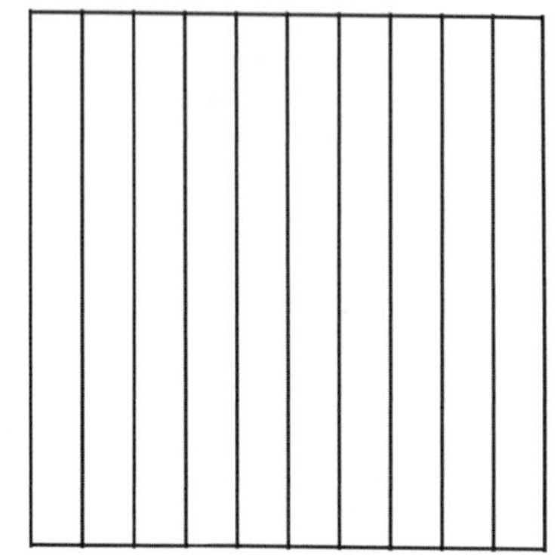

   b. 1 and 7 tenths

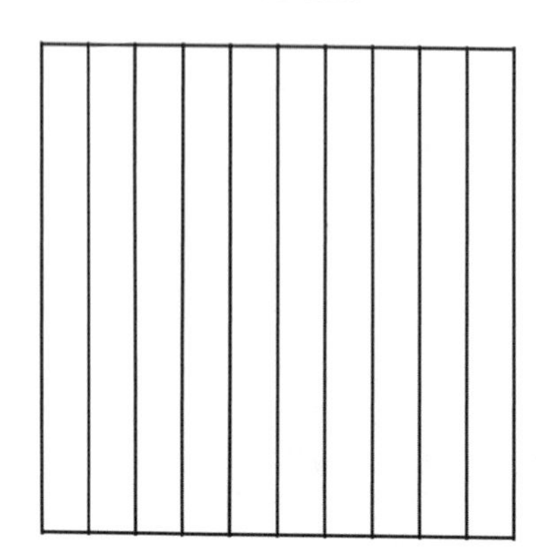

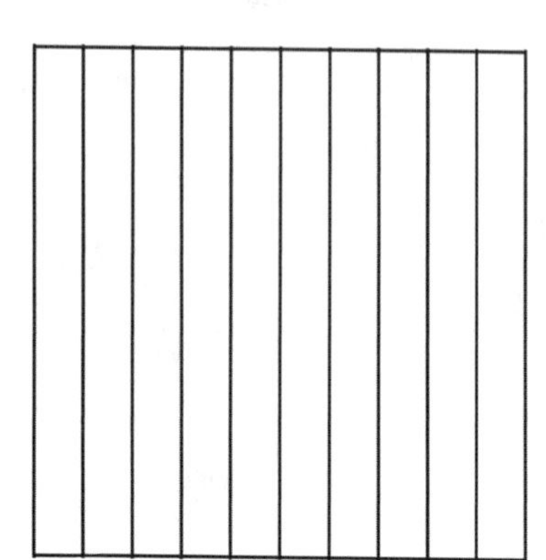

3. Use number bonds to complete parts (a) and (b) below:

   a. Decompose 3.24 by units.

   b. Compose 0.03, 0.5, and 2 as one decimal number.

4. Model the following equivalence on the place value chart using place value disks.

20 hundredths = 2 tenths

ones	.	tenths	hundredths

© 2015 Great Minds. eureka-math.org
G4-M6-TE-B5-1.3.1-01.2016

5. Complete the following chart.

	Unit Form	Fraction	Fraction Expanded Form	Decimal Expanded Form	Decimal
a.	1 tenth 6 hundredths				
b.		$2\frac{7}{10}$			
c.					6.34
d.				$(1 \times 10) + (6 \times 1) + (5 \times 0.01)$	
e.			$(2 \times 10) + (3 \times 1) + (7 \times \frac{1}{10}) + (8 + \frac{1}{100})$		

© 2015 Great Minds. eureka-math.org
G4-M6-TE-B5-1.3.1-01.2016

6. Maya puts groceries into bags. The items and their weights in kilograms are given below.

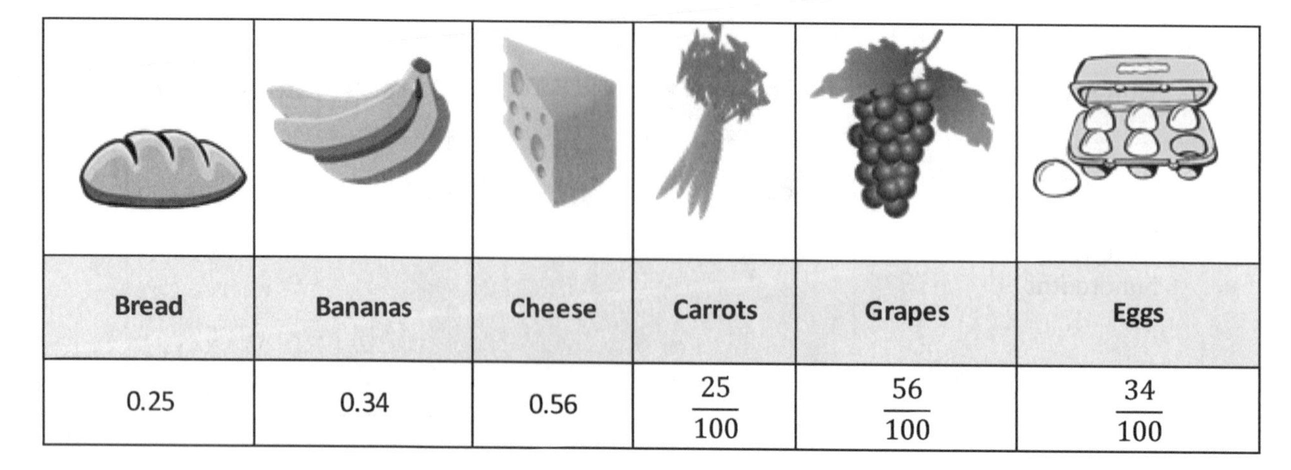

Bread	Bananas	Cheese	Carrots	Grapes	Eggs
0.25	0.34	0.56	$\frac{25}{100}$	$\frac{56}{100}$	$\frac{34}{100}$

a. Plot the weight in kilograms of each item on the number line below.

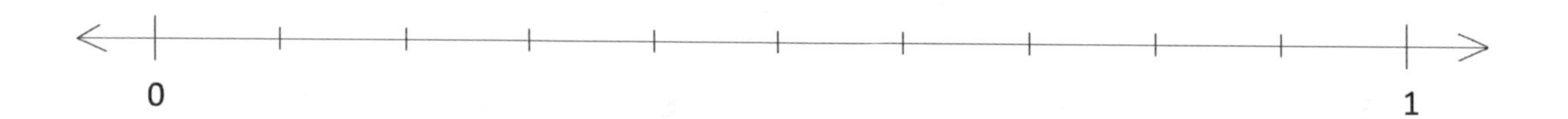

b. Write a number sentence using decimals to record the weight in kilograms of the bananas in expanded form.

c. Write a number sentence using fractions to record the weight in kilograms of the grapes in expanded form.

© 2015 Great Minds. eureka-math.org
G4-M6-TE-B5-1.3.1-01.2016

Maya packs the eggs and cheese into one of the bags. Together, these items weigh $\frac{90}{100}$ kilogram.

d. Use the area model to show that $\frac{90}{100}$ can be renamed as tenths.

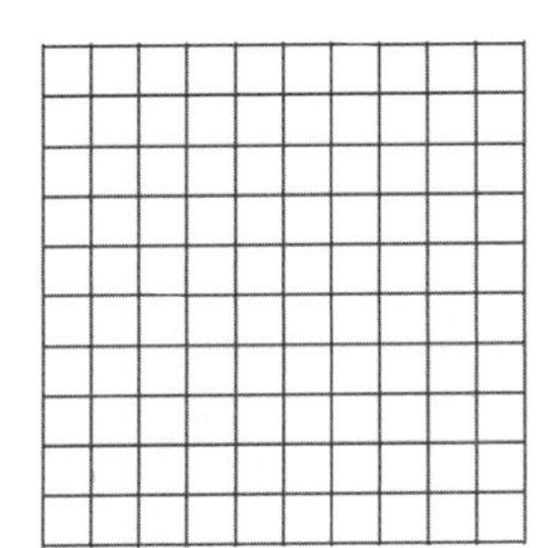 = 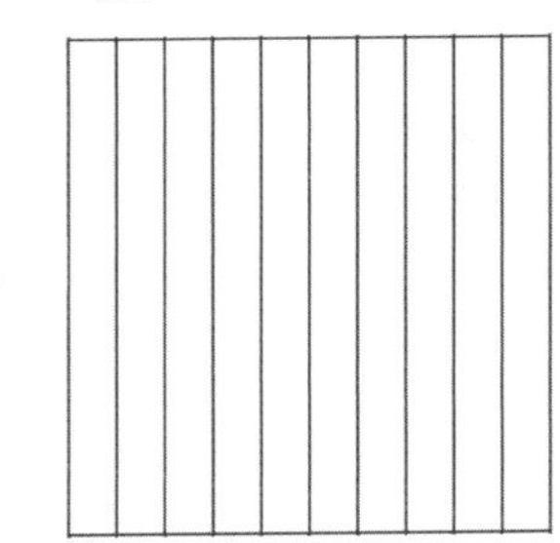

e. Use division to show how $\frac{90}{100}$ can be renamed as tenths.

Maya places the bread into the bag with the eggs and cheese. Together, all three items weigh 1 and 15 hundredths kilograms.

f. Use a model and words to explain how 1 and 15 hundredths can be written as a decimal and as a fraction.

Maya put the rest of the groceries in a second bag. The items in both bags weigh a total of $2\frac{30}{100}$ kilograms.

g. Using a model and words, explain how many tenths are in $2\frac{30}{100}$.

© 2015 Great Minds. eureka-math.org
G4-M6-TE-B5-1.3.1-01.2016

Mid-Module Assessment Task Standards Addressed	Topics A–B
Understand decimal notation for fractions, and compare decimal fractions.	
4.NF.5	Express a fraction with denominator 10 as an equivalent fraction with denominator 100, and use this technique to add two fractions with respective denominators 10 and 100. *For example, express 3/10 as 30/100, and add 3/10 + 4/100 = 34/100.* (Students who can generate equivalent fractions can develop strategies for adding fractions with unlike denominators in general. But addition and subtraction with unlike denominators in general is not a requirement at this grade.)
4.NF.6	Use decimal notation for fractions with denominators 10 or 100. *For example, rewrite 0.62 as 62/100; describe a length as 0.62 meters; locate 0.62 on a number line diagram.*

Evaluating Student Learning Outcomes

A Progression Toward Mastery is provided to describe steps that illuminate the gradually increasing understandings that students develop *on their way to proficiency.* In this chart, this progress is presented from left (Step 1) to right (Step 4). The learning goal for students is to achieve Step 4 mastery. These steps are meant to help teachers and students identify and celebrate what the students CAN do now and what they need to work on next.

© 2015 Great Minds. eureka-math.org
G4-M6-TE-B5-1.3.1-01.2016

A Progression Toward Mastery				
Assessment Task Item and Standards Assessed	**STEP 1 Little evidence of reasoning without a correct answer. (1 Point)**	**STEP 2 Evidence of some reasoning without a correct answer. (2 Points)**	**STEP 3 Evidence of some reasoning with a correct answer or evidence of solid reasoning with an incorrect answer. (3 Points)**	**STEP 4 Evidence of solid reasoning with a correct answer. (4 Points)**
1 **4.NF.6**	Student correctly completes three or fewer parts of the question with little to no modeling.	Student correctly solves at least four parts of the question, providing evidence of some reasoning.	Student correctly solves six or seven of the eight parts of the question. OR Student correctly answers all eight parts but incorrectly models on no more than two parts.	Student correctly writes the equivalent fractions and correctly models using the given representation: a. 0.2 b. 0.03 c. 0.4 d. 0.46 e. 7.6 f. 3.64 g. 4.7 h. 5.72
2 **4.NF.5** **4.NF.6**	Student is unable to correctly answer any of the parts.	Student answers one part correctly.	Student correctly represents the decomposition or correctly writes an equivalent equation in one of the questions. OR Student correctly writes equivalent statements for all parts but incorrectly decomposes in just one part.	Student correctly: ▪ Decomposes the models into hundredths, shading the correct amount. ▪ Expresses the equivalence using fractions and decimals: a. $\frac{3}{10} = \frac{30}{100}$ and 0.3 = 0.30. b. $1\frac{7}{10} = 1\frac{70}{100}$ and 1.7 = 1.70.
3 **4.NF.6**	Student is unable to correctly compose or decompose.	Student answers one part correctly.	Student decomposes 3.24 into just two bonds (3, 0.24) and answers part (b) correctly.	Student correctly: a. Decomposes 3.24 into number bonds: 3, 0.2, 0.04. b. Composes 2.53.

© 2015 Great Minds. eureka-math.org
G4-M6-TE-B5-1.3.1-01.2016

A Progression Toward Mastery				
4 **4.NF.5**	Student shows little understanding of the place value disks and equivalence.	Student models equivalence but does not use place value disks.	Student shows some understanding of the place value disks and supplements with a written explanation	Student correctly uses place value disks to show the equivalence of 20 hundredths and 2 tenths in the place value chart.
5 **4.NF.5** **4.NF.6**	Student correctly answers fewer than 10 of the expressions in the chart.	Student correctly answers 10 to 14 of the expressions in the chart.	Student correctly answers 15 to 19 of the expressions in the chart.	Student correctly answers each expression. (Note: Unit form may have more than one correct answer.) a. 1 tenth 6 hundredths; $\frac{16}{100}$; $(1 \times \frac{1}{10}) + (6 \times \frac{1}{100})$; $(1 \times 0.1) + (6 \times 0.01)$; 0.16. b. 2 ones 7 tenths; 2 $\frac{7}{10}$; $(2 \times 1) + (7 \times \frac{1}{10})$; $(2 \times 1) + (7 \times 0.1)$; 2.7. c. 6 ones 3 tenths 4 hundredths; $6\frac{34}{100}$; $(6 \times 1) + (3 \times \frac{1}{10}) + (4 \times \frac{1}{100})$; $(6 \times 1) + (3 \times 0.1) + (4 \times 0.01)$; 6.34. d. 1 ten 6 ones 5 hundredths; $16\frac{5}{100}$; $(1 \times 10) + (6 \times 1) + (5 \times \frac{1}{100})$; $(1 \times 10) + (6 \times 1) + (5 \times 0.01)$; 16.05. e. 2 tens 3 ones 7 tenths 8 hundredths; $23\frac{78}{100}$; $(2 \times 10) + (3 \times 1) + (7 \times \frac{1}{10}) + (8 \times \frac{1}{100})$; $(2 \times 10) + (3 \times 1) + (7 \times 0.1) + (8 \times 0.01)$; 23.78.

© 2015 Great Minds. eureka-math.org
G4-M6-TE-B5-1.3.1-01.2016

A Progression Toward Mastery

6 **4.NF.5** **4.NF.6**	Student correctly answers fewer than three problems.	Student correctly answers three or four of the seven problems, providing evidence of some reasoning.	Student correctly answers five or six of the seven problems. OR Student answers all parts correctly but without solid evidence or reasoning on fewer than two problems.	Student correctly: a. Plots each item on the number line. b. Responds 0.3 + 0.04 = 0.34 or (3 × 0.1) + (4 × 0.01) = 0.34. c. Responds $\frac{5}{10} + \frac{6}{100} = \frac{56}{100}$ or $(5 \times \frac{1}{10}) + (6 \times \frac{1}{100}) = \frac{56}{100}$. d. Represents $\frac{90}{100} = \frac{9}{10}$ in the area models. e. Responds $\frac{90}{100} = \frac{90 \div 10}{100 \div 10} = \frac{9}{10}$. f. Models and explains that 1 and 15 hundredths equals $1\frac{15}{100}$ and 1.15. g. Models and explains that there are 23 tenths in $2\frac{30}{100}$.

© 2015 Great Minds. eureka-math.org
G4-M6-TE-B5-1.3.1-01.2016

Name Jack Date ____________

1. Write the following fractions as equivalent decimals. Then, model each decimal with the given representation.

a. $\frac{2}{10}$ = 0.2

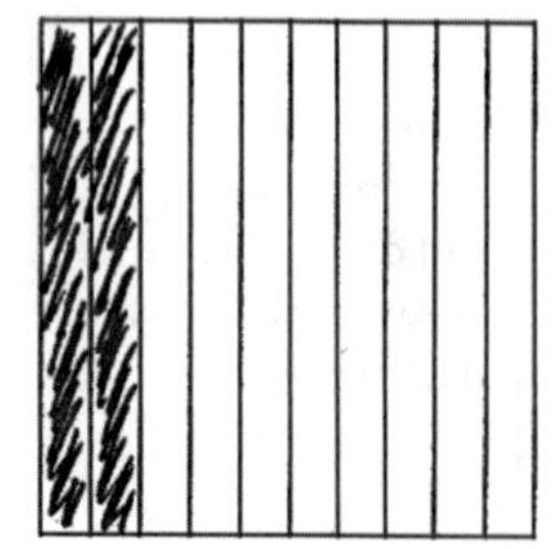

b. $\frac{3}{100}$ = 0.03

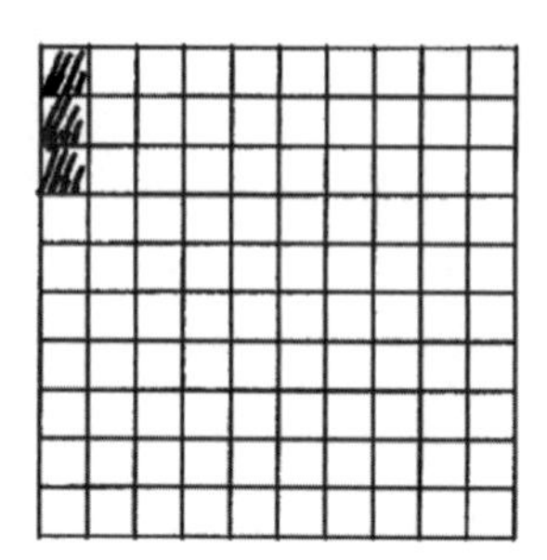

c. $\frac{4}{10}$ = 0.4

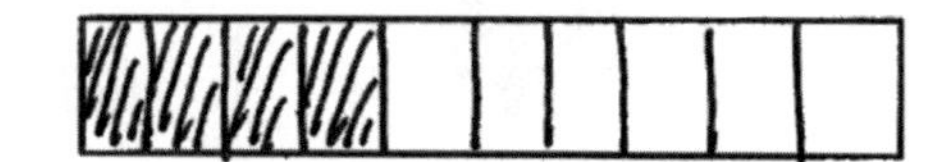

d. $\frac{46}{100}$ = 0.46

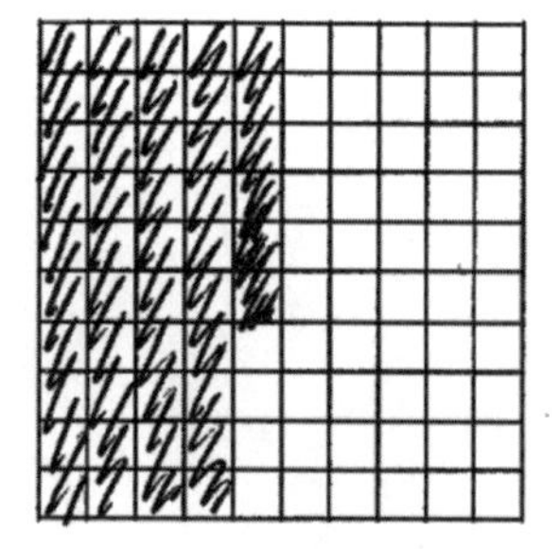

e. $7\frac{6}{10}$ = 7.6

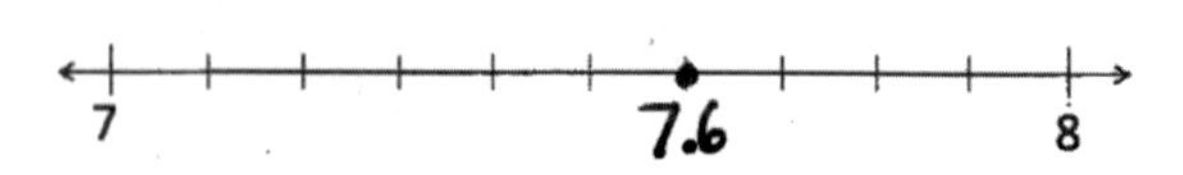

f. $3\frac{64}{100}$ = 3.64

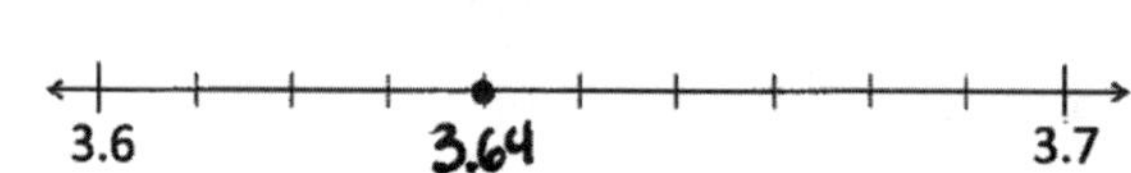

g. $4\frac{7}{10}$ = 4.7

ones	.	tenths
• • • •		• • • • • • •

h. $5\frac{72}{100}$ = 5.72

ones	.	tenths	hundredths
• • • • •		• • • • • • •	• •

© 2015 Great Minds. eureka-math.org
G4-M6-TE-B5-1.3.1-01.2016

2. Decompose tenths into hundredths using the area model. Express the equivalence of tenths and hundredths with fractions and with decimals.

   a. 3 tenths

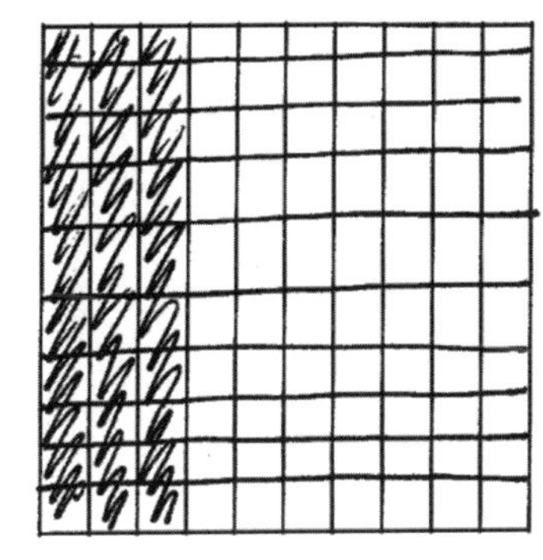

$\frac{3}{10} = \frac{30}{100}$

$0.3 = 0.30$

   b. 1 and 7 tenths

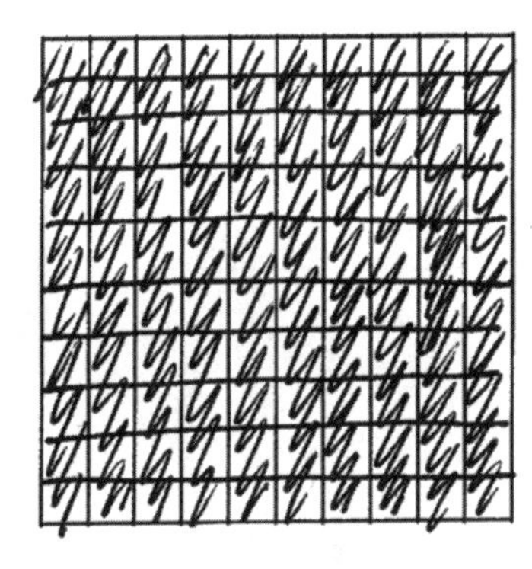

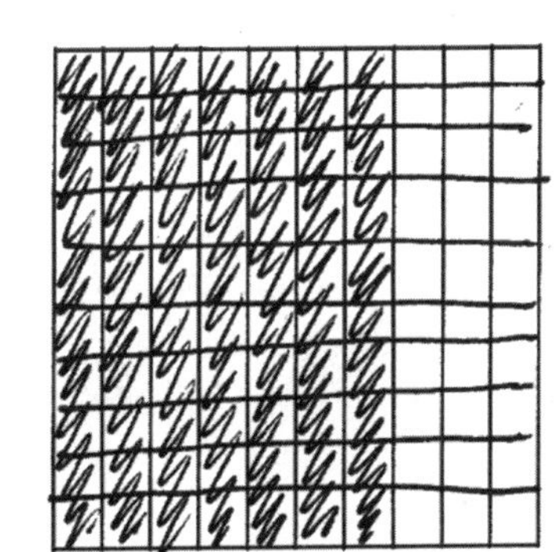

$1\frac{7}{10} = 1\frac{70}{100}$

$1.7 = 1.70$

3. Use number bonds to complete Parts (a) and (b) below:

   a. Decompose 3.24 by units.

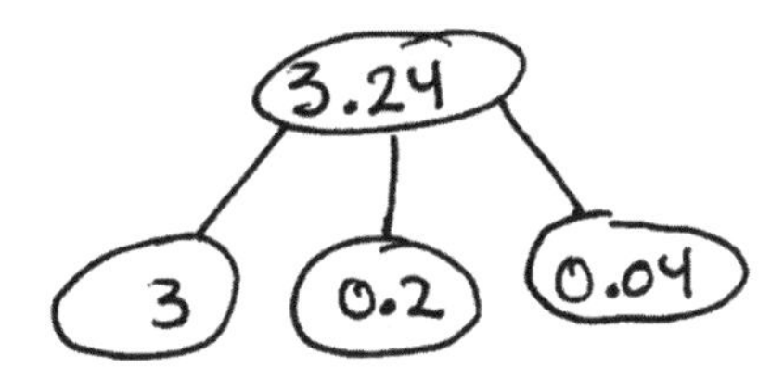

   b. Compose 0.03, 0.5, and 2 as one decimal number.

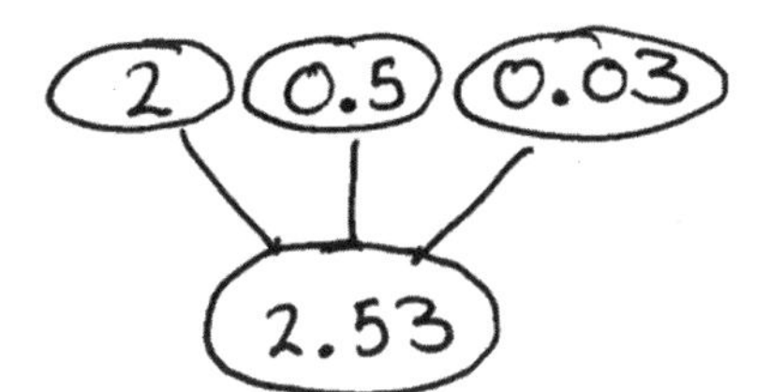

© 2015 Great Minds. eureka-math.org
G4-M6-TE-B5-1.3.1-01.2016

4. Model the following equivalence on the place value chart using place value disks.

20 hundredths = 2 tenths

ones	.	tenths	hundredths
		• ← • ←	(10 disks circled) (10 disks circled)

5. Complete the following chart.

	Unit Form	Fraction	Fraction Expanded Form	Decimal Expanded Form	Decimal
a.	1 tenth 6 hundredths	$\frac{16}{100}$	$(1 \times \frac{1}{10}) + (6 \times \frac{1}{100})$	$(1 \times 0.1) + (6 \times 0.01)$	0.16
b.	2 ones 7 tenths	$2\frac{7}{10}$	$(2 \times 1) + (7 \times \frac{1}{10})$	$(2 \times 1) + (7 \times 0.1)$	2.7
c.	6 ones 3 tenths 4 hundredths	$6\frac{34}{100}$	$(6 \times 1) + (3 \times \frac{1}{10}) + (4 \times \frac{1}{100})$	$(6 \times 1) + (3 \times 0.1) + (4 \times 0.01)$	6.34
d.	1 ten 6 ones 5 hundredths	$16\frac{5}{100}$	$(1 \times 10) + (6 \times 1) + (5 \times \frac{1}{100})$	$(1 \times 10) + (6 \times 1) + (5 \times 0.01)$	16.05
e.	2 tens 3 ones 7 tenths 8 hundredths	$23\frac{78}{100}$	$(2 \times 10) + (3 \times 1) + (7 \times \frac{1}{10}) + (8 \times \frac{1}{100})$	$(2 \times 10) + (3 \times 1) + (7 \times 0.1) + (8 \times 0.01)$	23.78

© 2015 Great Minds. eureka-math.org
G4-M6-TE-B5-1.3.1-01.2016

6. Maya puts groceries into bags. The items and their weights in kilograms are given below.

		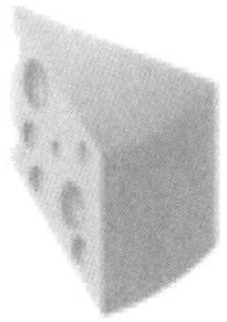			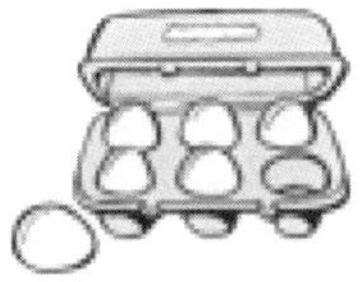
Bread	Bananas	Cheese	Carrots	Grapes	Eggs
0.25	0.34	0.56	$\frac{25}{100}$	$\frac{56}{100}$	$\frac{34}{100}$

a. Plot the weight in kilograms of each item on the number line below.

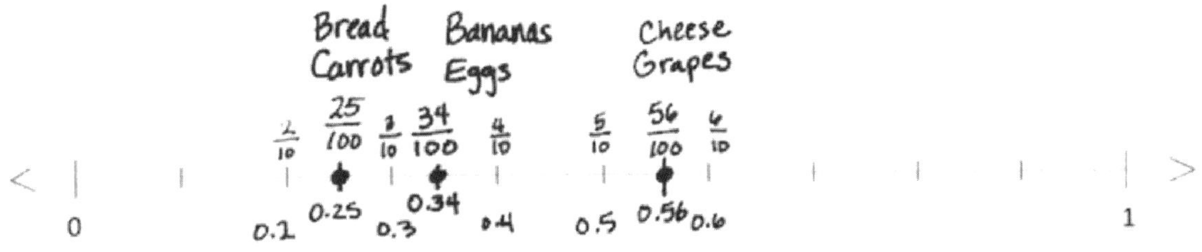

b. Write a number sentence using decimals to record the weight in kilograms of the bananas in expanded form.

$$0.34 = 0.3 + 0.04$$

c. Write a number sentence using fractions to record the weight in kilograms of the grapes in expanded form.

$$\frac{56}{100} = \frac{5}{10} + \frac{6}{100}$$

© 2015 Great Minds. eureka-math.org
G4-M6-TE-B5-1.3.1-01.2016

Maya packs the eggs and cheese into one of the bags. Together, these items weigh $\frac{90}{100}$ kilogram.

d. Use the area model to show that $\frac{90}{100}$ can be renamed as tenths.

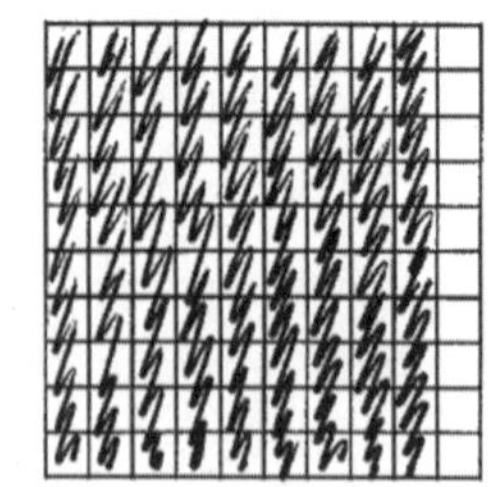 = 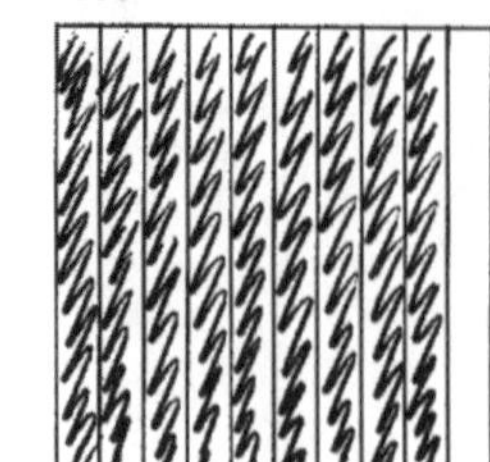

e. Use division to show how $\frac{90}{100}$ can be renamed as tenths.

$$\frac{90}{100} = \frac{90 \div 10}{100 \div 10} = \frac{9}{10}$$

Maya places the bread into the bag with the eggs and cheese. Together, all three items weigh 1 and 15 hundredths kilograms.

f. Use a model and words to explain how 1 and 15 hundredths can be written as a decimal and as a fraction.

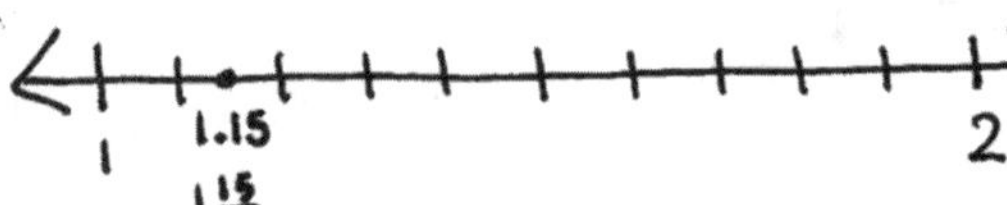

$1\frac{15}{100}$

1 and 15 hundredths is written as a fraction as $1\frac{15}{100}$ since there is one whole and fifteen hundredths. Written as a decimal, it is 1.15 since there is one whole and fifteen hundredths.

1	0.1	0.01
1	1	5

Maya put the rest of the groceries in a second bag. The items in both bags weigh a total of $2\frac{30}{100}$ kilograms.

g. Using a model and words, explain how many tenths are in $2\frac{30}{100}$.

  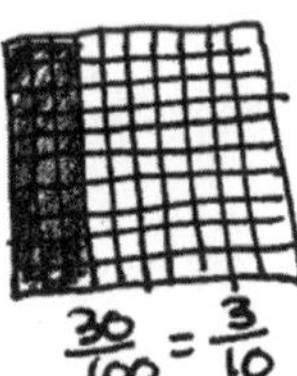

$1 = \frac{10}{10}$ $1 = \frac{10}{10}$ $\frac{30}{100} = \frac{3}{10}$

$$\frac{10}{10} + \frac{10}{10} + \frac{3}{10} = \frac{23}{10}$$

There are 10 tenths in each whole, so $2 = \frac{10}{10} + \frac{10}{10} = \frac{20}{10}$. $\frac{30}{100} = \frac{3}{10}$ since $\frac{30 \div 10}{100 \div 10} = \frac{3}{10}$. $\rightarrow \frac{20}{10} + \frac{3}{10} = \frac{23}{10}$

There are 23 tenths in $2\frac{30}{100}$.

© 2015 Great Minds. eureka-math.org
G4-M6-TE-B5-1.3.1-01.2016

Topic C

Decimal Comparison

4.NF.7, 4.MD.1, 4.MD.2

Focus Standard:		4.NF.7	Compare two decimals to hundredths by reasoning about their size. Recognize that comparisons are valid only when the two decimals refer to the same whole. Record the results of comparisons with the symbols >, =, or <, and justify the conclusions, e.g., by using a visual model.
Instructional Days:		3	
Coherence	**-Links from:**	G3–M5	Fractions as Numbers on the Number Line
	-Links to:	G5–M1	Place Value and Decimal Fractions

The focus of Topic C is comparison of decimal numbers. In Lesson 9, students compare pairs of decimal numbers representing lengths, masses, or volumes by recording them on the place value chart and reasoning about which measurement is longer than (shorter than, heavier than, lighter than, more than, or less than) the other. Comparing decimals in the context of measurement supports their justifications of their conclusions and begins their work with comparison at a more concrete level.

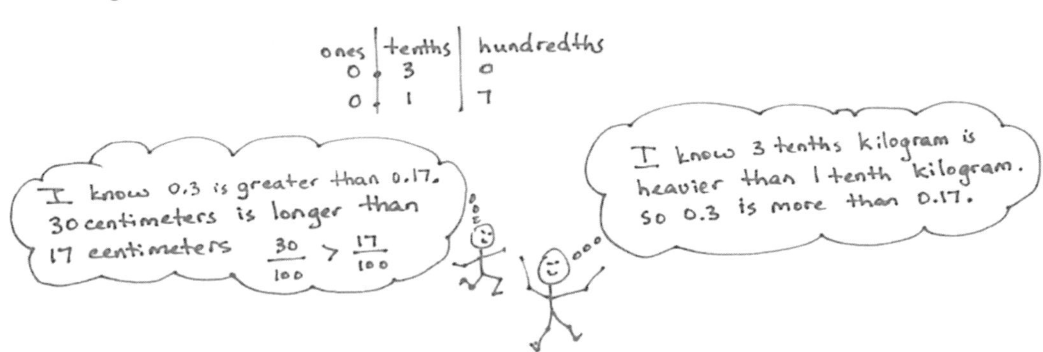

Students move on to more abstract representations in Lesson 10, using area models and the number line to justify their comparison of decimal numbers (**4.NF.7**). They record their observations with the <, >, and = symbols. In both Lessons 9 and 10, the intensive work at the concrete and pictorial levels eradicates the common misconception that occurs, for example, in the comparison of 7 tenths and 27 hundredths, where students believe that 0.7 is less than 0.27 simply because it resembles the comparison of 7 ones and 27 ones. This reinforces the idea that, in any comparison, one must consider the *size of the units.*

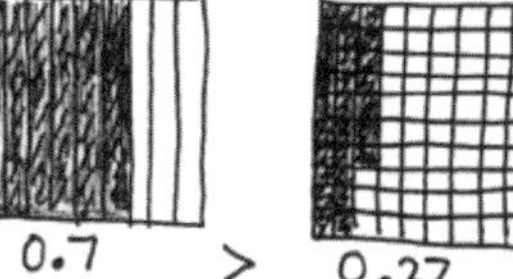

© 2015 Great Minds. eureka-math.org
G4-M6-TE-B5-1.3.1-01.2016

Finally, in Lesson 11, students use their understanding of different ways of expressing equivalent values to arrange a set of decimal fractions in unit, fraction, and decimal form from greatest to least or least to greatest.

A Teaching Sequence Toward Mastery of Decimal Comparison	
Objective 1:	**Use the place value chart and metric measurement to compare decimals and answer comparison questions.** **(Lesson 9)**
Objective 2:	**Use area models and the number line to compare decimal numbers, and record comparisons using <, >, and =.** **(Lesson 10)**
Objective 3:	**Compare and order mixed numbers in various forms.** **(Lesson 11)**

© 2015 Great Minds. eureka-math.org
G4-M6-TE-B5-1.3.1-01.2016

Lesson 9

Objective: Use the place value chart and metric measurement to compare decimals and answer comparison questions.

Suggested Lesson Structure

■ Fluency Practice	(10 minutes)
■ Application Problem	(5 minutes)
■ Concept Development	(35 minutes)
■ Student Debrief	(10 minutes)
Total Time	**(60 minutes)**

Fluency Practice (10 minutes)

- Decompose Larger Units **4.NF.5** (3 minutes)
- Decimal Fraction Equivalence **4.NF.5** (5 minutes)
- Rename the Decimal **4.NF.5** (2 minutes)

Decompose Larger Units (3 minutes)

Materials: (S) Personal white board, place value chart (Lesson 7 Template)

Note: This fluency activity reviews Lesson 8.

T: (Write 1.) Say the number in unit form.
S: 1 one.
T: Draw 1 one on your place value chart.
S: (Draw 1 one disk.)
T: (Write 1 one = ___ tenths.) Rename 1 one for tenths.
S: (Cross out the one disk, and draw 10 tenth disks.)

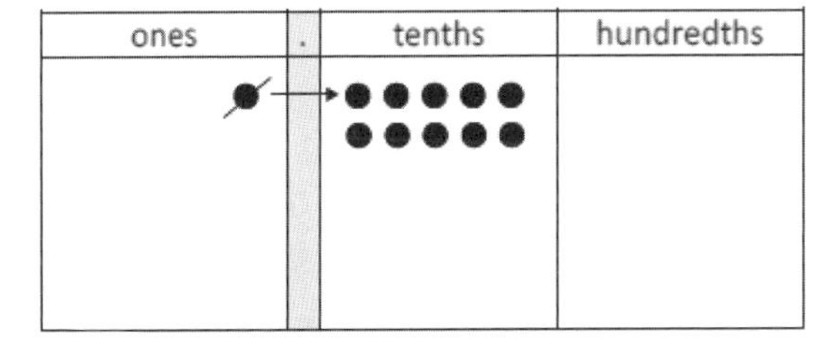

1 one = 10 tenths

Continue this process using the following possible sequence:

- Rename 1 one 2 tenths for tenths.
- Rename 1 tenth for hundredths.
- Rename 1 tenth 2 hundredths for hundredths.
- Rename 2 ones 3 tenths for tenths (leads into the next fluency activity).

© 2015 Great Minds. eureka-math.org
G4-M6-TE-B5-1.3.1-01.2016

Decimal Fraction Equivalence (5 minutes)

Materials: (S) Personal white board, place value chart (Lesson 7 Template)

Note: This fluency activity reviews Lesson 8. For 4 ones 23 hundredths, 1 ten 7 tenths, and 3 tens 4 ones 12 hundredths, have the students express their answers in tenths and hundredths.

T: (Write 2 ones and 3 tenths.) Write the number in digits on your place value chart.

S: (Write the digit 2 in the ones place and the digit 3 in the tenths place.)

T: (Write 2.3 = ___ $\frac{}{}$.) Write the number as a mixed number.

S: (Write $2.3 = 2\frac{3}{10}$.)

T: (Write $2.3 = 2\frac{3}{10} = \frac{}{10}$.) Write the number as a fraction greater than 1.

S: (Write $2.3 = 2\frac{3}{10} = \frac{23}{10}$.)

ones	.	tenths	hundredths
2	.	3	

$$2.3 = 2\frac{3}{10} = \frac{23}{10}$$

Continue this process for the following possible sequence: 4 ones 23 hundredths, 1 ten 7 tenths, and 3 tens 4 ones 12 hundredths.

Rename the Decimal (2 minutes)

Materials: (S) Personal white board

Note: This fluency activity reviews Lesson 8.

T: (Write 3.1.) Write the decimal as a mixed number.

S: (Write $3\frac{1}{10}$.)

T: (Write $3.1 = 3\frac{1}{10} = \frac{}{10}$.) Complete the number sentence.

S: (Write $3.1 = 3\frac{1}{10} = \frac{31}{10}$.)

T: (Write $3.1 = 3\frac{1}{10} = \frac{31}{10} = \frac{}{100}$.) Complete the number sentence.

S: (Write $3.1 = 3\frac{1}{10} = \frac{31}{10} = \frac{310}{100}$.)

Continue this process for the following possible sequence: 9.8, 10.4, and 64.3.

© 2015 Great Minds. eureka-math.org
G4-M6-TE-B5-1.3.1-01.2016

Application Problem (5 minutes)

Kelly's dog weighs 14 kilograms 24 grams. Mary's dog weighs 14 kilograms 205 grams. Hae Jung's dog weighs 4,720 grams.

a. Order the weight of the dogs in grams from least to greatest.

b. How much more does the heaviest dog weigh than the lightest dog?

K: 14 Kg 24g

M: 14 kg 205g

HJ: 4,720g

a) $4{,}720g < 14{,}024g < 14{,}205g$

b)

$$\begin{array}{r} 14{,}205\text{ g} \\ -\ 4{,}720\text{ g} \\ \hline 9{,}485\text{ g} \end{array}$$

Mary's dog weighs 9,485g more than Hae Jung's dog.

Note: This Application Problem reviews decomposition of a number with mixed units. Students need to convert the weight of Kelly's dog to 14,024 grams. The weight of Mary's dog may help them avoid the common error of 1,424 grams because of its inclusion of 205 grams.

Concept Development (35 minutes)

Materials: (T) 2 meter sticks, 2 rolls of different color masking tape (e.g., yellow and blue), metric scale, 4 graduated cylinders, bags of rice, water, food coloring, document camera (S) Personal white board, measurement record (Template)

Materials Note:

- Prepare 2 meter sticks by taping colored masking tape onto the edge of each meter stick to the following lengths: 0.67 m (yellow tape), 0.59 m (blue tape). Do not cover the hash marks or the numbers on the meter sticks.
- Prepare and label 4 bags of rice weighing 0.10 kg (Bag A), 0.65 kg (Bag B), 0.7 kg (Bag C), and 0.46 kg (Bag D).

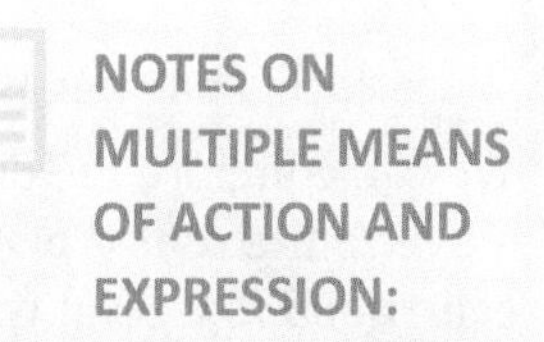

NOTES ON MULTIPLE MEANS OF ACTION AND EXPRESSION:

If a document camera, overhead projector, interactive white board, or other means of magnifying the image of the meter stick is not available, consider having students use pre-marked meter sticks at their desks. Certain hardware and home furnishings stores and websites offer meter sticks or tape for free. A meter tape template is also available in Grade 2 Module 2 Lesson 6.

- Prepare and label four graduated cylinders with water measuring 0.3 liter (Cylinder A), 0.15 liter (Cylinder B), 0.29 liter (Cylinder C), and 0.09 liter (Cylinder D). Use food coloring to help students read the measurements.

© 2015 Great Minds. eureka-math.org
G4-M6-TE-B5-1.3.1-01.2016

Problem 1: Compare pairs of decimal numbers representing length.

T: (Hold up the meter stick with the yellow tape that measures 0.67 m, and then place it under the document camera.) Express the length of this yellow tape as a fraction of a meter.

S: $\frac{67}{100}$ meter.

T: On the measurement record, shade the tape diagram to represent the length of the yellow tape on the meter stick. Write the length of the tape in decimal form.

T: (Hold up the meter stick with blue tape that measures 0.59 m, and then project the portion of the meter stick that shows the length of the blue tape under the document camera.) Express the length of this blue tape as a fraction of a meter.

S: $\frac{59}{100}$ meter.

T: On the measurement record, shade the tape diagram to represent the length of the blue tape on the meter stick. Write the length of the tape in decimal form. Record both lengths in a place value chart. (Allow students time to complete the task.)

T: Use the words *longer than* or *shorter than* to compare these two lengths of tape.

S: 0.67 meter is longer than 0.59 meter. → 0.59 meter is shorter than 0.67 meter.
→ 67 centimeters is longer than 59 centimeters, so I know 0.67 meter is longer than 0.59 meter.

0.67

0.59

T: Share with a partner. How can the place value chart help you compare these numbers?

S: We can compare the digits in the largest place first. Both measures have 0 in the ones place, so we move to the tenths place. The first tape has 6 tenths. That's greater than 5 tenths. → You don't even need to look at the hundredths place. Once you see that 6 tenths is greater than 5 tenths, you know that the first tape is longer.

ones	●	tenths	hundredths
0	.	6	7
0	.	5	9

Remove enough tape from each meter stick to create the following lengths: 0.4 m and 0.34 m. Repeat the above process.

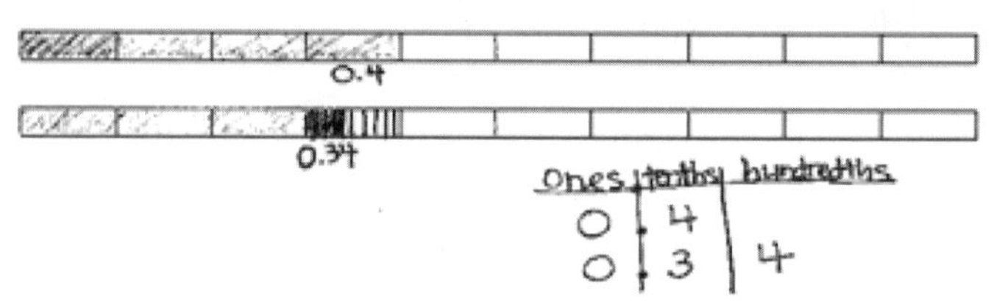

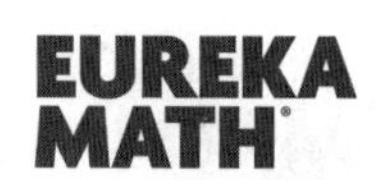

© 2015 Great Minds. eureka-math.org
G4-M6-TE-B5-1.3.1-01.2016

Problem 2: Compare pairs of decimal numbers representing mass.

T: (Place Rice Bag A on the scale.) What is the mass of this bag of rice?

S: Zero point one kilogram. → $\frac{1}{10}$ kilogram. → $\frac{10}{100}$ kilogram (see image below).

T: Record the mass in the table on the measurement record.

Repeat this process for the remaining bags.

T: (Leave Bag D, weighing 0.46 kg, on the scale.) Which bags are heavier than Bag D? How do you know?

S: Bags B and C were heavier than Bag D. → Bag B was 0.65 kg, and Bag C was 0.7 kg. Those numbers are both larger than 0.46 kg, so the bags are heavier. → I looked at my chart, from left to right. In the tenths column, I could see that Bag A was lighter. It had only 1 tenth. Bags B and C were heavier than D because they both had more tenths.

T: Let's look at Bags B and C. Make a statement comparing their mass.

S: 0.65 kilogram is lighter than 0.7 kilogram. → 0.7 kilogram is heavier than 0.65 kilogram.

T: How do you know?

S: I could just see that the bag was fuller and feel that the bag has more mass. → At first, I thought 65 hundredths was more because it looks like you are comparing 65 and 7, and 65 is greater than 7. But then we saw that it was 7 tenths, which is more than 6 tenths. → I realized that 7 tenths is 70 hundredths, and that is greater than 65 hundredths.

T: With your partner, make another statement to compare the bags. You can compare just two items, or you can compare more than two items.

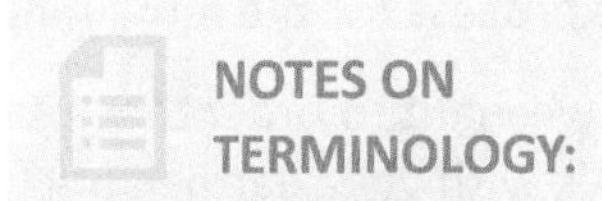

Mass is a fundamental measure of the amount of matter in an object. While weight is a measurement that depends upon the force of gravity (one would weigh less on the moon than one does on Earth), mass does not depend upon the force of gravity. Both words are used here, but it is not important for students to recognize the distinction in mathematics at this time.

Mass of Rice Bags (kilograms)

Rice Bag	ones	.	tenths	hundredths
A	0	.	1	0
B	0	.	6	5
C	0	.	7	
D	0	.	4	6

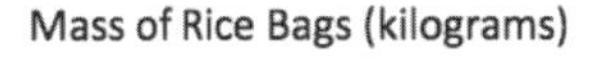

S: (Responses will vary.)

T: Based on these comparisons, what is the mass of the bags in order from heaviest to lightest?

S: 0.7 kg, 0.65 kg, 0.46 kg, 0.1 kg.

T: (Select a student volunteer.) Arrange the bags from heaviest to lightest. Looking at the bags, does it *appear* that we have properly ordered the bags from heaviest to lightest? Do they match the order we determined?

S: Yes.

© 2015 Great Minds. eureka-math.org
G4-M6-TE-B5-1.3.1-01.2016

Problem 3: Compare pairs of decimal numbers representing volume.

T: (Place all four graduated cylinders in front of the class.) Express the volume of the liquid in tenths or hundredths liter. (Use the document camera to project the side of Cylinder A so students can see the liter measurements. If this is not possible, select a student to read the volume aloud.)

S: $\frac{3}{10}$ liter. → $\frac{30}{100}$ liter.

T: Record this volume in the table on the measurement record.

Repeat the process for the remaining water samples.

T: If we want to order these samples from least volume to greatest volume, what would the order be? Talk with your partner, and record your thinking on the measurement record. (Circulate to encourage use of the place value chart as students compare the measurements.)

S: (Complete the task.)

S: 0.09 liter, 0.15 liter, 0.29 liter, 0.3 liter.

T: How did you determine the order?

S: The place value chart made it easy to compare the decimals. → We compared the digits in the largest place first. That was the tenths. → In 0.3, there are 3 tenths. That is more than the others. 0.29 comes next, followed by 0.15 and 0.09.

Volume of Liquid (liters)

Cylinder	ones	.	tenths	hundredths
A	0	.	3	
B	0	.	1	5
C	0	.	2	9
D	0	.	0	9

0.09 L, 0.15 L, 0.29 L, 0.3 L

T: (Select a student volunteer to order cylinders from least volume to greatest volume.) Let's look at the cylinders. Do they appear to match the order we determined?

S: Yes!

Problem Set (10 minutes)

Students should do their personal best to complete the Problem Set within the allotted 10 minutes. For some classes, it may be appropriate to modify the assignment by specifying which problems they work on first. Some problems do not specify a method for solving. Students should solve these problems using the RDW approach used for Application Problems.

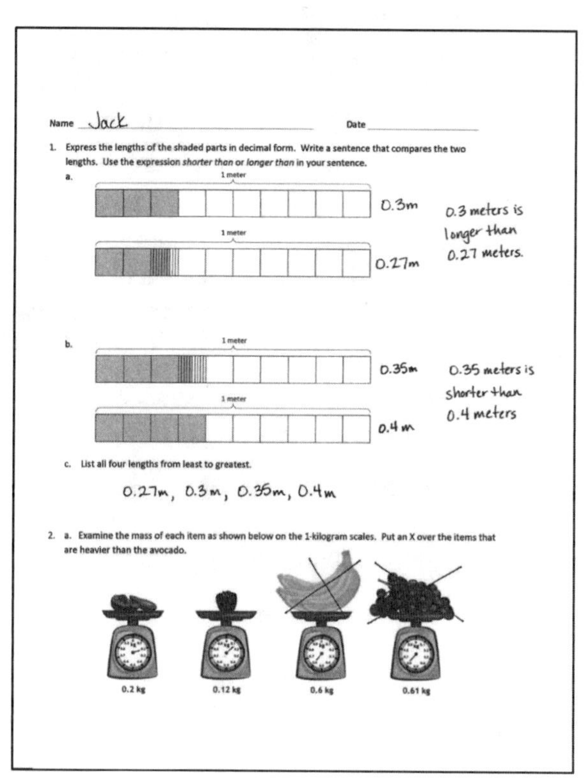

Name Jack Date

1. Express the lengths of the shaded parts in decimal form. Write a sentence that compares the two lengths. Use the expression *shorter than* or *longer than* in your sentence.

a. 1 meter — 0.3m; 1 meter — 0.27m. 0.3 meters is longer than 0.27 meters.

b. 1 meter — 0.35m; 1 meter — 0.4m. 0.35 meters is shorter than 0.4 meters

c. List all four lengths from least to greatest.

0.27m, 0.3m, 0.35m, 0.4m

2. a. Examine the mass of each item as shown below on the 1-kilogram scales. Put an X over the items that are heavier than the avocado.

0.2 kg 0.12 kg 0.6 kg 0.61 kg

Student Debrief (10 minutes)

Lesson Objective: Use the place value chart and metric measurement to compare decimals and answer comparison questions.

The Student Debrief is intended to invite reflection and active processing of the total lesson experience.

© 2015 Great Minds. eureka-math.org
G4-M6-TE-B5-1.3.1-01.2016

Invite students to review their solutions for the Problem Set. They should check work by comparing answers with a partner before going over answers as a class. Look for misconceptions or misunderstandings that can be addressed in the Debrief. Guide students in a conversation to debrief the Problem Set and process the lesson.

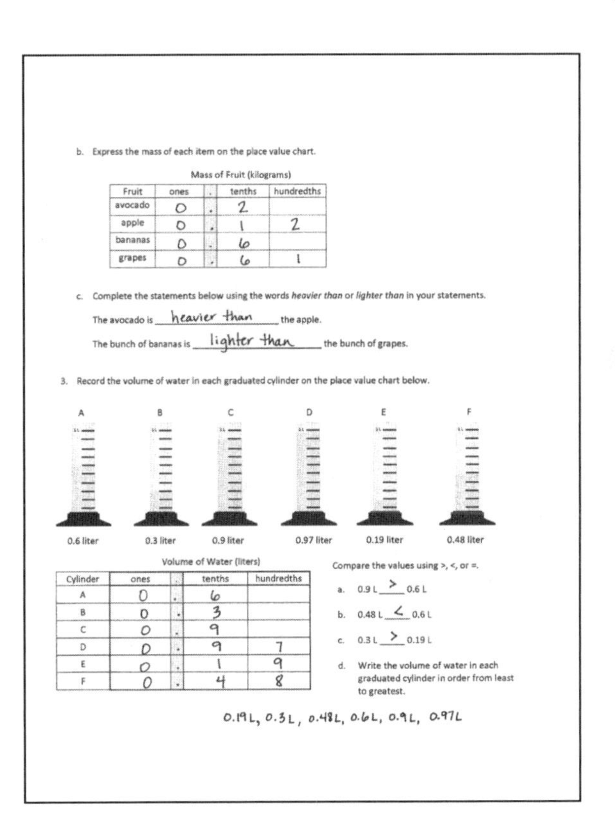

b. Express the mass of each item on the place value chart.

Mass of Fruit (kilograms)

Fruit	ones	.	tenths	hundredths
avocado	0	.	2	
apple	0	.	1	2
bananas	0	.	6	
grapes	0	.	6	1

c. Complete the statements below using the words *heavier than* or *lighter than* in your statements.

The avocado is heavier than the apple.

The bunch of bananas is lighter than the bunch of grapes.

3. Record the volume of water in each graduated cylinder on the place value chart below.

Volume of Water (liters)

Cylinder	ones	.	tenths	hundredths
A	0	.	6	
B	0	.	3	
C	0	.	9	
D	0	.	9	7
E	0	.	1	9
F	0	.	4	8

Compare the values using >, <, or =.

a. 0.9 L > 0.6 L

b. 0.48 L < 0.6 L

c. 0.3 L > 0.19 L

d. Write the volume of water in each graduated cylinder in order from least to greatest.

0.19L, 0.3L, 0.48L, 0.6L, 0.9L, 0.97L

Any combination of the questions below may be used to lead the discussion.

- How do the tape diagrams in Problem 1 support your statements? Make a statement comparing a length from part (a) to a length from part (b).
- Share one of your statements for Problem 2(c). Explain your reasoning.
- How did the place value chart help to compare and order the different measurements in Problem 3?
- How is comparing decimal measurements of length, mass, and volume similar? How is it different?
- How did the Application Problem connect to today's lesson?

Exit Ticket (3 minutes)

After the Student Debrief, instruct students to complete the Exit Ticket. A review of their work will help with assessing students' understanding of the concepts that were presented in today's lesson and planning more effectively for future lessons. The questions may be read aloud to the students.

© 2015 Great Minds. eureka-math.org
G4-M6-TE-B5-1.3.1-01.2016

Name ______________________________ Date ______________

1. Express the lengths of the shaded parts in decimal form. Write a sentence that compares the two lengths. Use the expression *shorter than* or *longer than* in your sentence.

a.

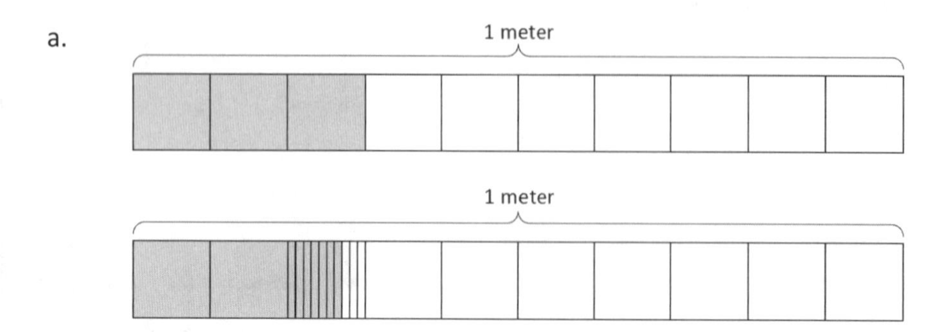

b.

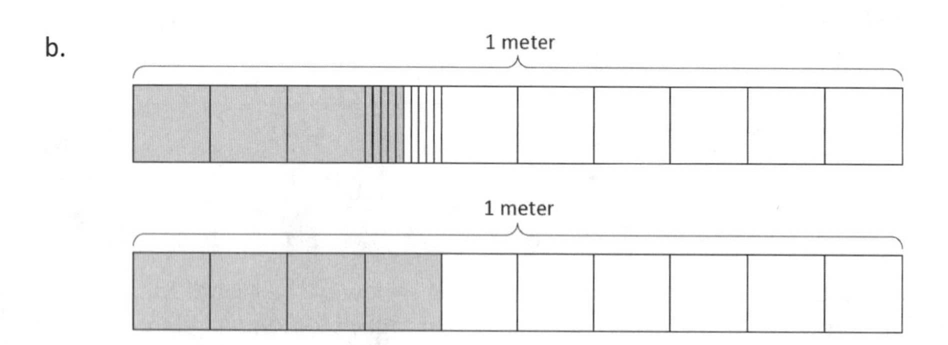

c. List all four lengths from least to greatest.

2. a. Examine the mass of each item as shown below on the 1-kilogram scales. Put an X over the items that are heavier than the avocado.

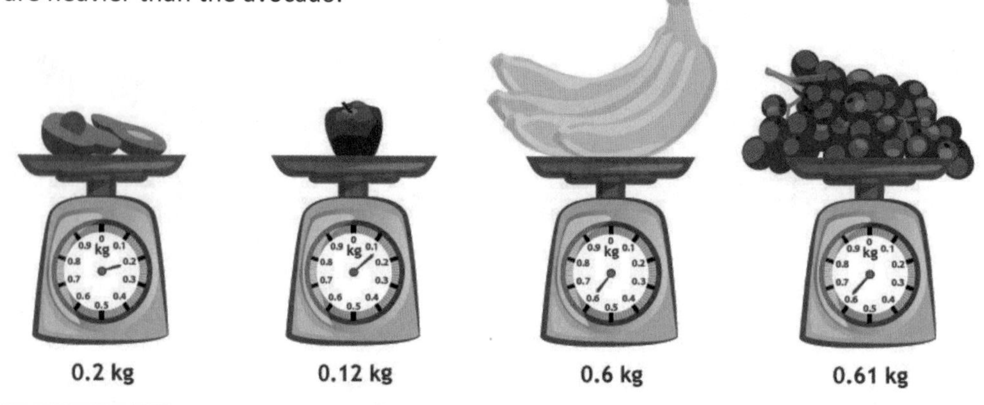

© 2015 Great Minds. eureka-math.org
G4-M6-TE-B5-1.3.1-01.2016

b. Express the mass of each item on the place value chart.

Mass of Fruit (kilograms)

Fruit	ones	.	tenths	hundredths
avocado				
apple				
bananas				
grapes				

c. Complete the statements below using the words *heavier than* or *lighter than* in your statements.

The avocado is ________________ the apple.

The bunch of bananas is ________________ the bunch of grapes.

3. Record the volume of water in each graduated cylinder on the place value chart below.

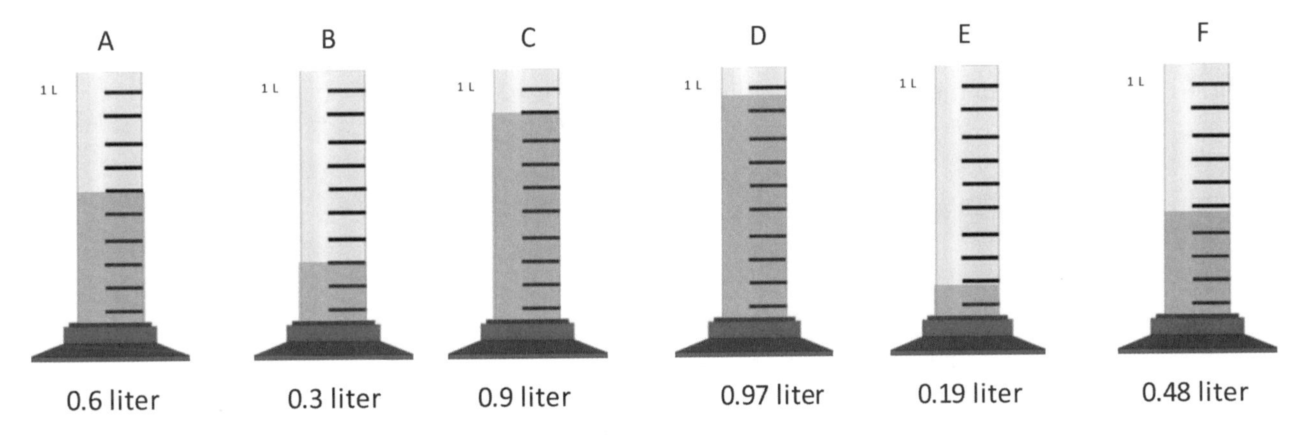

Volume of Water (liters)

Cylinder	ones	.	tenths	hundredths
A				
B				
C				
D				
E				
F				

Compare the values using >, <, or =.

a. 0.9 L _____ 0.6 L

b. 0.48 L _____ 0.6 L

c. 0.3 L _____ 0.19 L

d. Write the volume of water in each graduated cylinder in order from least to greatest.

© 2015 Great Minds. eureka-math.org
G4-M6-TE-B5-1.3.1-01.2016

Name ______________________________ Date ______________

1. a. Doug measures the lengths of three strings and shades tape diagrams to represent the length of each string as show below. Express, in decimal form, the length of each string.

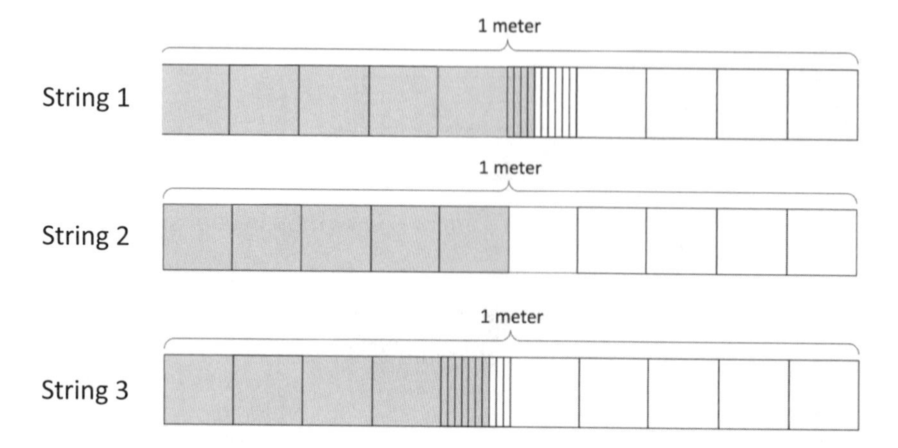

b. List the lengths of the strings in order from greatest to least.

2. Compare the values below using >, <, or =.

a. 0.8 kg _____ 0.6 kg

b. 0.36 kg _____ 0.5 kg

c. 0.4 kg _____ 0.47 kg

© 2015 Great Minds. eureka-math.org
G4-M6-TE-B5-1.3.1-01.2016
EUREKA MATH

Name _______________________________ Date _______________

1. Express the lengths of the shaded parts in decimal form. Write a sentence that compares the two lengths. Use the expression *shorter than* or *longer than* in your sentence.

a.

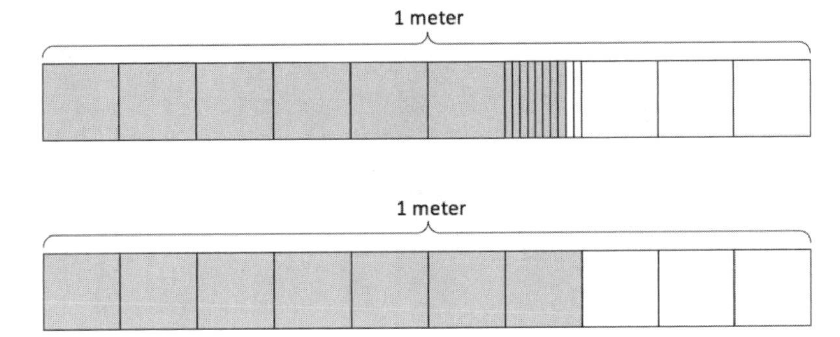

b.

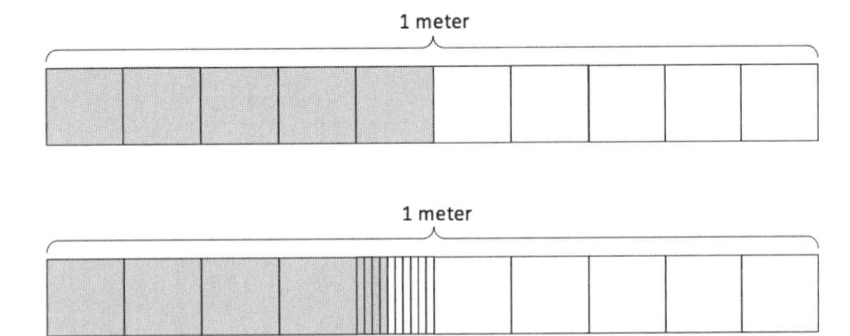

c. List all four lengths from least to greatest.

© 2015 Great Minds. eureka-math.org
G4-M6-TE-B5-1.3.1-01.2016

2. a. Examine the mass of each item as shown below on the 1-kilogram scales. Put an X over the items that are heavier than the volleyball

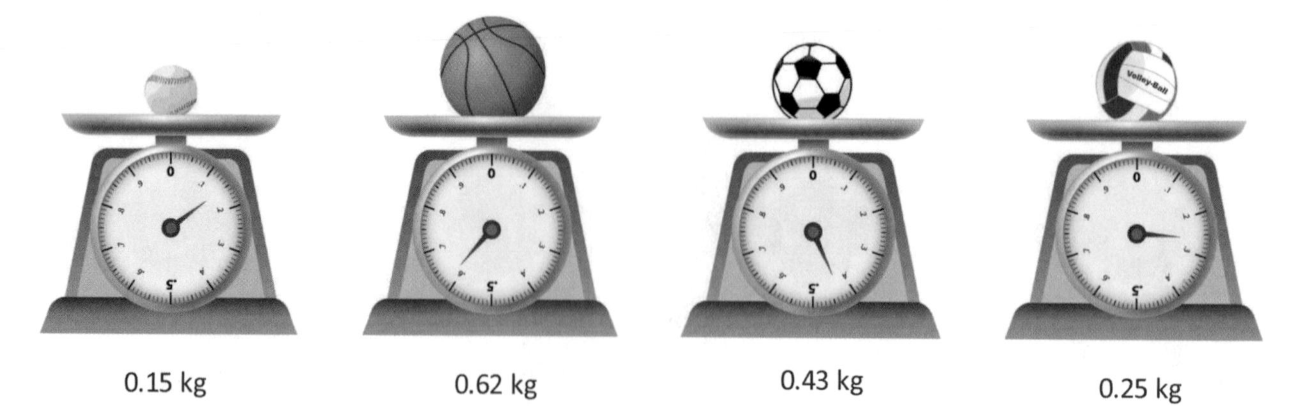

0.15 kg 0.62 kg 0.43 kg 0.25 kg

b. Express the mass of each item on the place value chart.

Mass of Sport Balls (kilograms)

Sport Balls	ones	.	tenths	hundredths
baseball				
volleyball				
basketball				
soccer ball				

c. Complete the statements below using the words *heavier than* or *lighter than* in your statements.

The soccer ball is ________________ the baseball.

The volleyball is ______________________ the basketball.

© 2015 Great Minds. eureka-math.org
G4-M6-TE-B5-1.3.1-01.2016

3. Record the volume of water in each graduated cylinder on the place value chart below.

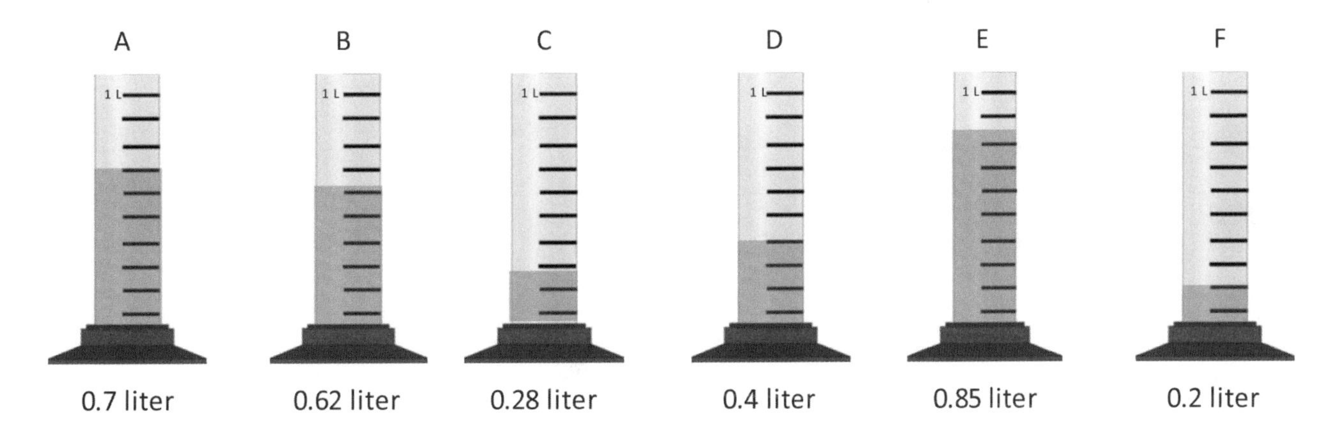

Volume of Water(liters)

Cylinder	ones	.	tenths	hundredths
A				
B				
C				
D				
E				
F				

Compare the values using >, <, or =.

a. 0.4 L _____ 0.2 L

b. 0.62 L _____ 0.7 L

c. 0.2 L _____ 0.28 L

d. Write the volume of water in each graduated cylinder in order from least to greatest.

© 2015 Great Minds. eureka-math.org
G4-M6-TE-B5-1.3.1-01.2016

Mass of Rice Bags (kilograms)

Rice Bag	ones	.	tenths	hundredths
A				
B				
C				
D				

Volume of Liquid (liters)

Cylinder	ones	.	tenths	hundredths
A				
B				
C				
D				

measurement record

© 2015 Great Minds. eureka-math.org
G4-M6-TE-B5-1.3.1-01.2016

Lesson 10

Objective: Use area models and the number line to compare decimal numbers, and record comparisons using <, >, and =.

Suggested Lesson Structure

■ Fluency Practice	(10 minutes)
■ Application Problem	(5 minutes)
■ Concept Development	(35 minutes)
■ Student Debrief	(10 minutes)
Total Time	**(60 minutes)**

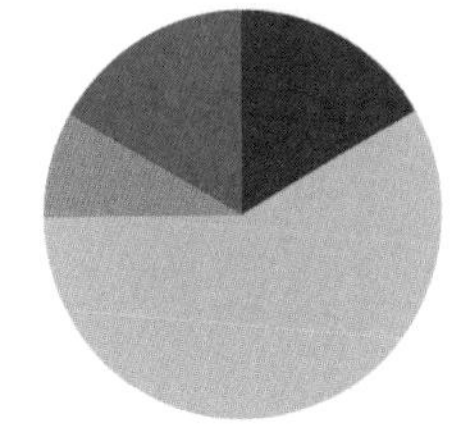

Fluency Practice (10 minutes)

- Decompose Larger Units **4.NF.5** (3 minutes)
- Decimal Fraction Equivalence **4.NF.5** (5 minutes)
- Rename the Decimal **4.NF.5** (2 minutes)

Decompose Larger Units (3 minutes)

Materials: (S) Personal white board, place value chart (Lesson 7 Template)

Note: This fluency activity reviews Lesson 8.

T: (Write 2.) Say the number in unit form.

S: 2 ones.

T: Draw 2 ones on your place value chart.

S: (Draw 2 ones disks.)

T: (Write 2 ones = __ tenths.) Regroup 2 ones for tenths.

S: (Cross out the ones disks, and draw 20 tenths disks. Write 2 ones = 20 tenths.)

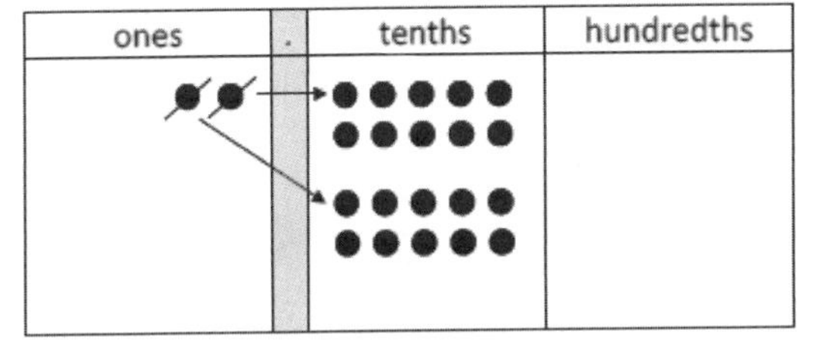

2 ones = 20 tenths

Continue with the following possible sequence:

- Regroup 2 ones 5 tenths for tenths.
- Regroup 2 tenths for hundredths.
- Regroup 2 tenths 4 hundredths for hundredths.

© 2015 Great Minds. eureka-math.org
G4-M6-TE-B5-1.3.1-01.2016

Decimal Fraction Equivalence (5 minutes)

Materials: (S) Personal white board, place value chart (Lesson 7 Template)

Note: This fluency activity reviews Lesson 8.

T: (Write 5 ones 7 tenths.) Write the number in digits on your place value chart.

S: (Write the digit 5 in the ones place and the digit 7 in the tenths place.)

ones	.	tenths	hundredths
5	.	7	

$$5.7 = 5\frac{7}{10} = \frac{57}{10}$$

T: (Write 5.7 = __ —.) Write the number as a mixed number.

S: (Write $5.7 = 5\frac{7}{10}$.)

T: (Write $5.7 = 5\frac{7}{10} = \frac{\ }{10}$.) Write the number as a fraction greater than 1.

S: (Write $5.7 = 5\frac{7}{10} = \frac{57}{10}$.)

T: Read this number as written on the chart.

S: 5 and 7 tenths.

T: Express the answer as ones and hundredths.

S: 5 and 70 hundredths.

Continue with the following possible sequence: 3 ones 8 tenths, 1 ten 9 tenths, and 2 tens 3 ones 3 tenths.

Rename the Decimal (2 minutes)

Materials: (S) Personal white board

Note: This fluency activity reviews Lesson 8.

T: (Write 5.2.) Write the decimal as a mixed number.

S: (Write $5\frac{2}{10}$.)

T: (Write $5.2 = 5\frac{2}{10} = \frac{\ }{10}$.) Complete the number sentence.

S: (Write $5.2 = 5\frac{2}{10} = \frac{52}{10}$.)

T: (Write $5.2 = 5\frac{2}{10} = \frac{52}{10} = \frac{\ }{100}$.) Complete the number sentence.

S: (Write $5.2 = 5\frac{2}{10} = \frac{52}{10} = \frac{520}{100}$.)

Continue with the following possible sequence: 9.6, 10.6, and 78.9.

© 2015 Great Minds. eureka-math.org
G4-M6-TE-B5-1.3.1-01.2016
EUREKA MATH

Application Problem (5 minutes)

In science class, Emily's 1-liter beaker contains 0.3 liter of water. Ali's beaker contains 0.8 liter of water, and Katie's beaker contains 0.63 liter of water. Who can pour all of her water into Emily's beaker without going over 1 liter, Ali or Katie?

E [0.3L]
A [0.8 L]
K [0.63L]

0.3 —(+0.7)→ 1

0.8 > 0.7
0.63 < 0.7

Emily's beaker can only fit 0.7L water more. 0.8L is greater than 0.7L so it would spill. Katie's water will fit because 0.63 < 0.7.

Note: This Application Problem reviews comparison of metric measurements from Lesson 9. Students contextualize and compare volumes of water with measurements of tenths and hundredths. Students may try to use addition and subtraction, but encourage them to use what they know about completing the whole and benchmark numbers.

Concept Development (35 minutes)

Materials: (T/S) Personal white board, comparing with area models (Template), number line (Lesson 6 Template 2)

Problem 1: Compare pairs of decimal numbers using an area model. Record the comparison using <, >, and =.

MP.6

T: (Write 0.15 on the board. Distribute the comparing with area models template.) Shade the first area model to represent this decimal.

T: (Write 0.51 on the board.) In the second area model, represent this decimal number.

T: What statements using the phrases *greater than* and *less than* can we make to compare these decimals?

S: 0.51 is greater than 0.15. → 0.15 is less than 0.51.

T: How does the area model help you compare 0.15 and 0.51?

S: The shaded part of 0.51 covers a lot more area than the shaded part for 0.15. → I only shaded 1 full column and 1 half of a column to represent 0.15, but I shaded 5 full columns plus another small part of the next column for 0.51, so 0.51 is greater than 0.15. → I have 15 hundredths shaded on the first area model, but I have 51 hundredths shaded on the second area model.

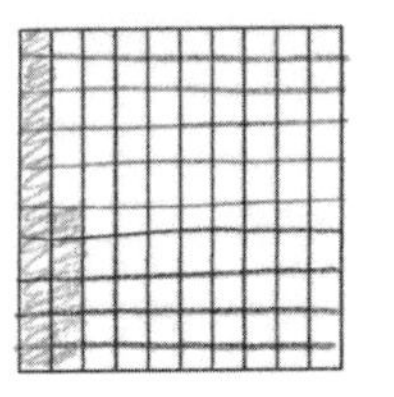
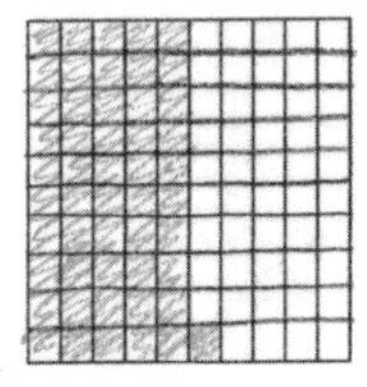

0.15 < 0.51
0.51 > 0.15

T: (Write <, >, and = on the board.) Use the appropriate comparison symbol to write both statements on comparing with area models.

S: (Write 0.51 > 0.15. 0.15 < 0.51.)

© 2015 Great Minds. eureka-math.org
G4-M6-TE-B5-1.3.1-01.2016

Repeat the process using the following sequence:

- 0.37 and 0.3
- 0.27 and 0.7
- 0.7 and 0.70
- 0.06 and 0.6

Problem 2: Compare decimal numbers on a number line. Record the comparison using <, >, and =.

T: (Distribute the number line template.) Look at the first number line. Label the endpoints as 4 and 3 tenths and 4 and 6 tenths.

T: Label the other tenths that can be labeled on this number line.

S: (Label 4.4 and 4.5.)

T: (Write 4.50 and 4.38 on the board.) Plot and label these two points on the number line.

T: How did you locate the points?

S: I went to 4.5. Since there are no hundredths, you just stop there. → 4.5 is the same as 4.50. → To locate 4.38, I started at 4.3. Then, I went 8 hundredths more to get to 4.38. → I knew 4.38 was 2 hundredths less than 4.4, so I went to 4.4 and counted back 2 hundredths.

T: What statements can we make to compare these decimals?

S: 4.5 is greater than 4.38. → 4.38 is less than 4.5.

T: (Write <, >, and = on the board.) Use the appropriate comparison symbol to write both statements.

S: (Write 4.5 > 4.38. 4.38 < 4.5.)

T: 4.38 has three digits. 4.5 only has two digits. At a quick glance, it appears that 4.38 would have a greater value. Talk with your partner. Why does 4.5 have a greater value even though it has fewer digits?

S: 4.5 has more tenths than 4.38. Tenths are larger than hundredths. → Make the tenths into hundredths. 4 and 5 tenths renamed is 4 and 50 hundredths. Now, it's obvious that it is greater. → Four point five is four point five zero. Now, it has three digits, too. → 4.5 is halfway between 4 and 5, and 4.38 is part of the way between 4 and 4.5, so 4.38 is less than 4.5.

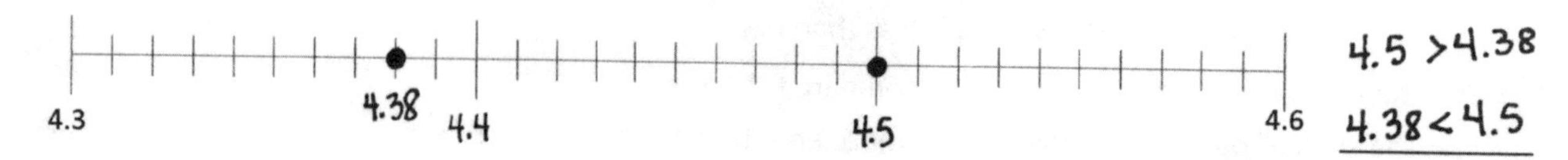

Repeat the process with the number line using the sequence below. Have students label the blank number line to best match each number pair. Ask students to consider what the endpoints should be in order to represent both numbers on the same number line.

- 6.37 ____ 6.3
- 2.68 ____ 2.8
- 10.1 ____ 10.10
- 10.2 ____ 10.02

© 2015 Great Minds. eureka-math.org
G4-M6-TE-B5-1.3.1-01.2016

Problem 3: Compare decimal numbers using <, >, and =.

Project the sequence below, and ask students to compare using <, >, and =. With each pair of numbers, ask students to share their reasoning with a partner. They may use the area model, a number line, a place value chart, or other reasonable strategies.

- 6.24 ____ 5.24
- 13.24 ____ 13.42
- 0.48 ____ 2.1
- 2.17 ____ 2.7
- 3.3 ____ 3.30
- 7.9 ____ 7.09
- 8.02 ____ $8\frac{2}{10}$
- 5.3 ____ 5 ones and 3 hundredths
- 5.2 ____ 52 tenths
- 4 ones and 6 tenths ____ 4 ones and 60 hundredths
- 0.25 ____ $\frac{25}{10}$
- $\frac{237}{100}$ ____ 2.73
- 4 tenths ____ 45 hundredths
- 2.31 ____ 23 tenths and 5 hundredths

The sequence above engages students with practice that addresses common misconceptions and becomes increasingly more complex. For instance, the sequence opens with two examples that have the same number of digits and simply requires students to attend to the value of each place. In the next four examples, the pairs being compared have differing numbers of digits. Students come to understand that the value of the number is not dependent on the number of digits. The sequence of the examples then goes on to numbers written in different forms. Students may choose to model the numbers, convert into common units, or rewrite in the same form.

Problem Set (10 minutes)

Students should do their personal best to complete the Problem Set within the allotted 10 minutes. For some classes, it may be appropriate to modify the assignment by specifying which problems they work on first. Some problems do not specify a method for solving. Students should solve these problems using the RDW approach used for Application Problems.

© 2015 Great Minds. eureka-math.org
G4-M6-TE-B5-1.3.1-01.2016

Student Debrief (10 minutes)

Lesson Objective: Use area models and the number line to compare decimal numbers, and record comparisons using <, >, and =.

The Student Debrief is intended to invite reflection and active processing of the total lesson experience.

Invite students to review their solutions for the Problem Set. They should check work by comparing answers with a partner before going over answers as a class. Look for misconceptions or misunderstandings that can be addressed in the Debrief. Guide students in a conversation to debrief the Problem Set and process the lesson.

Any combination of the questions below may be used to lead the discussion.

- Compare your area model for Problem 1(d) with your partner's area model. Explain why it was possible to shade both models without decomposing one to hundredths.
- Find an example on your Problem Set where a decimal number with only three digits has a greater value than a decimal number with four digits. Explain why this is so.
- During our lesson, we saw that 0.27 is less than 0.7. Explain why this is so. How can looking at the numbers quickly instead of considering the size of the unit lead to mistakes when comparing? How can we rename 0.7 to compare it easily to 0.27? Which model helped you compare numbers most easily? Was it easier to represent particular problems with certain types of models?
- How did the Application Problem connect to today's lesson?

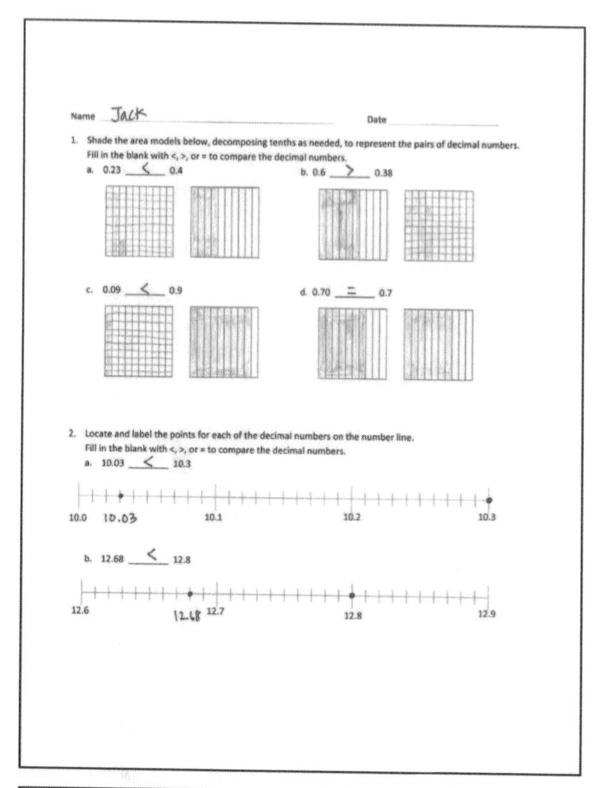
Name Jack Date

1. Shade the area models below, decomposing tenths as needed, to represent the pairs of decimal numbers. Fill in the blank with <, >, or = to compare the decimal numbers.

a. 0.23 < 0.4 b. 0.6 > 0.38

c. 0.09 < 0.9 d. 0.70 = 0.7

2. Locate and label the points for each of the decimal numbers on the number line. Fill in the blank with <, >, or = to compare the decimal numbers.

a. 10.03 < 10.3

10.0 10.03 10.1 10.2 10.3

b. 12.68 < 12.8

12.6 12.68 12.7 12.8 12.9

3. Use the symbols <, >, or = to compare.

a. 3.42 < 3.75 b. 4.21 > 4.12

c. 2.15 < 3.15 d. 4.04 < 6.02

e. 12.7 = 12.70 f. 1.9 > 1.21

4. Use the symbols <, >, or = to compare. Use pictures as needed to solve.

a. 23 tenths = 2.3 b. 1.04 < 1 one and 4 tenths
1.4

c. 6.07 < $6\frac{7}{10}$
6.7

d. 0.45 < $\frac{45}{10}$
4.5

e. $\frac{127}{100}$ < 1.72
1.27

f. 6 tenths < 66 hundredths
.6 .66

Exit Ticket (3 minutes)

After the Student Debrief, instruct students to complete the Exit Ticket. A review of their work will help with assessing students' understanding of the concepts that were presented in today's lesson and planning more effectively for future lessons. The questions may be read aloud to the students.

© 2015 Great Minds. eureka-math.org
G4-M6-TE-B5-1.3.1-01.2016
EUREKA MATH

Name ______________________________ Date ______________

1. Shade the area models below, decomposing tenths as needed, to represent the pairs of decimal numbers. Fill in the blank with <, >, or = to compare the decimal numbers.

a. 0.23 ________ 0.4

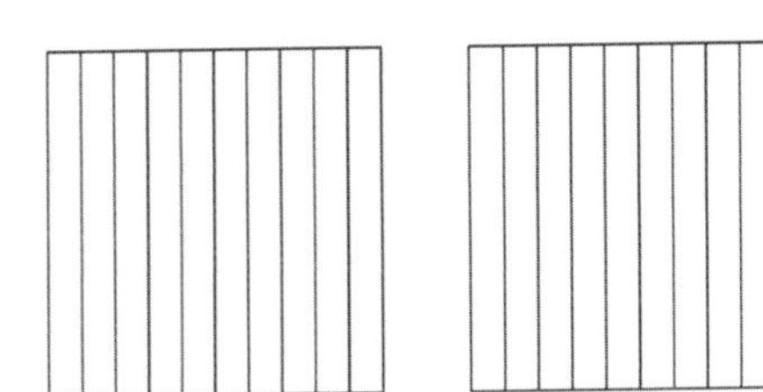

b. 0.6 ________ 0.38

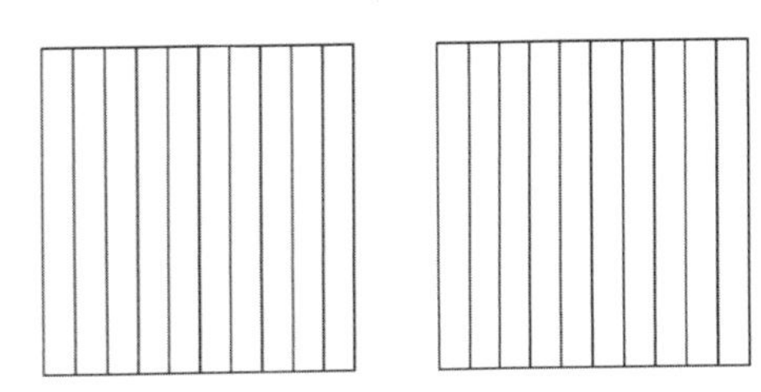

c. 0.09 ________ 0.9

d. 0.70 ________ 0.7

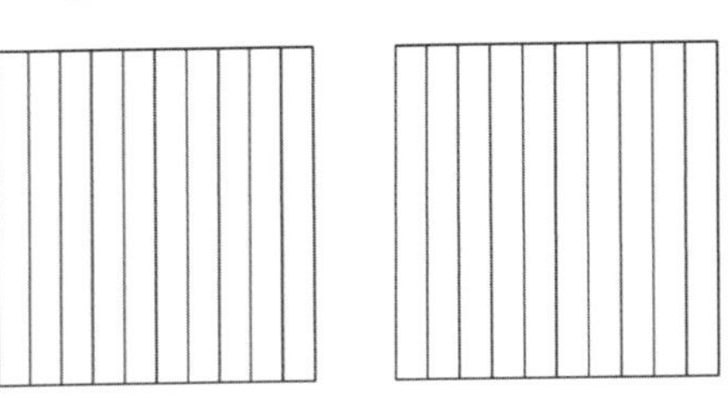

2. Locate and label the points for each of the decimal numbers on the number line. Fill in the blank with <, >, or = to compare the decimal numbers.

a. 10.03 ________ 10.3

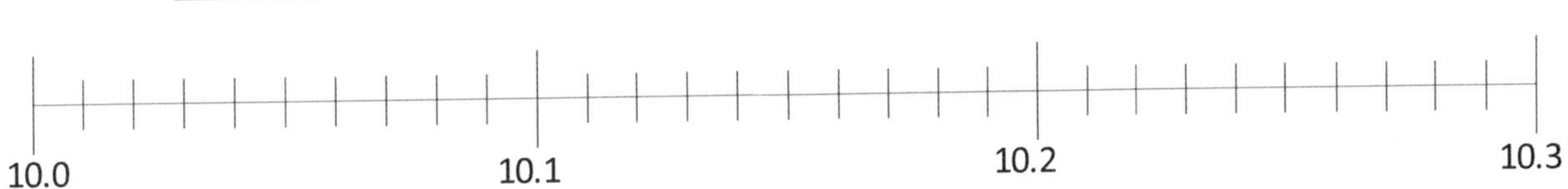

b. 12.68 ________ 12.8

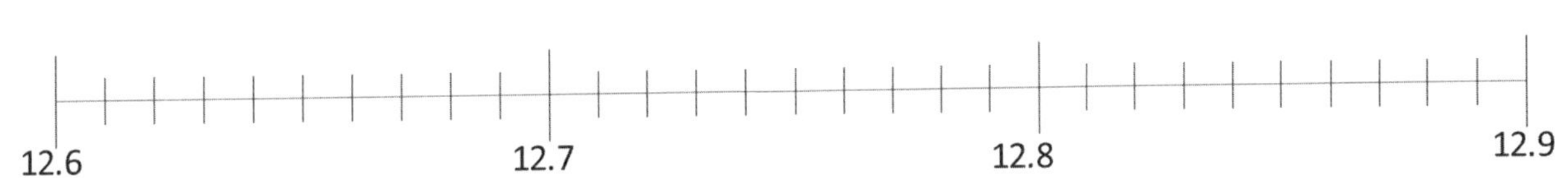

© 2015 Great Minds. eureka-math.org
G4-M6-TE-B5-1.3.1-01.2016

3. Use the symbols <, >, or = to compare.

 a. 3.42 ________ 3.75

 b. 4.21 ________ 4.12

 c. 2.15 ________ 3.15

 d. 4.04 ________ 6.02

 e. 12.7 ________ 12.70

 f. 1.9 ________ 1.21

4. Use the symbols <, >, or = to compare. Use pictures as needed to solve.

 a. 23 tenths ________ 2.3

 b. 1.04 ________ 1 one and 4 tenths

 c. 6.07 ________ $6\frac{7}{10}$

 d. 0.45 ________ $\frac{45}{10}$

 e. $\frac{127}{100}$ ________ 1.72

 f. 6 tenths ________ 66 hundredths

© 2015 Great Minds. eureka-math.org
G4-M6-TE-B5-1.3.1-01.2016

Name ______________________________ Date ________________

1. Ryan says that 0.6 is less than 0.60 because it has fewer digits. Jessie says that 0.6 is greater than 0.60. Who is right? Why? Use the area models below to help explain your answer.

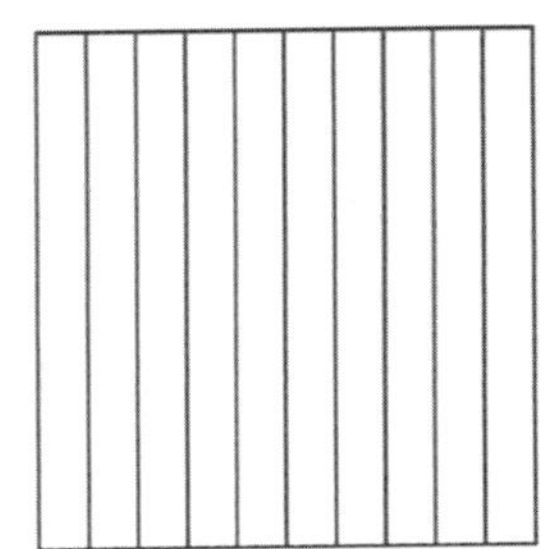

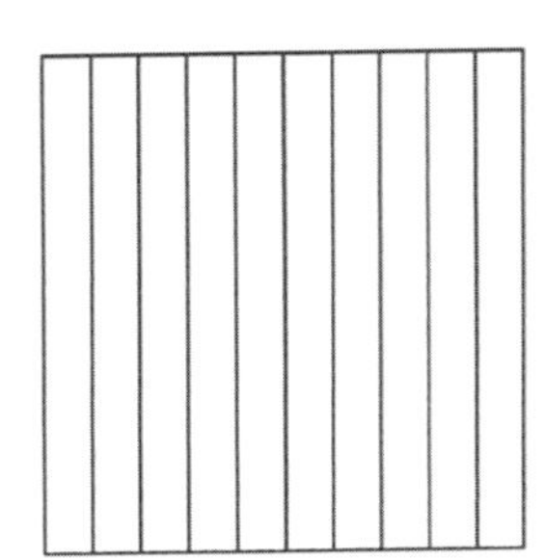

2. Use the symbols <, >, or = to compare.

   a. 3.9 ________ 3.09

   b. 2.4 ________ 2 ones and 4 hundredths

   c. 7.84 ________ 78 tenths and 4 hundredths

© 2015 Great Minds. eureka-math.org
G4-M6-TE-B5-1.3.1-01.2016

Name ______________________________ Date ______________

1. Shade the parts of the area models below, decomposing tenths as needed, to represent the pairs of decimal numbers. Fill in the blank with <, >, or = to compare the decimal numbers.

   a. 0.19 ________ 0.3

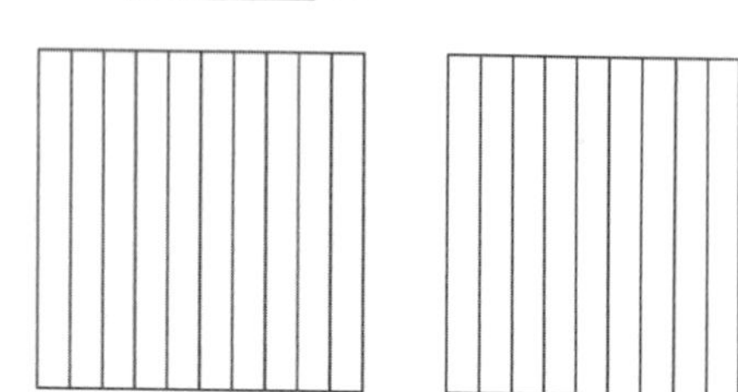

   b. 0.6 ________ 0.06

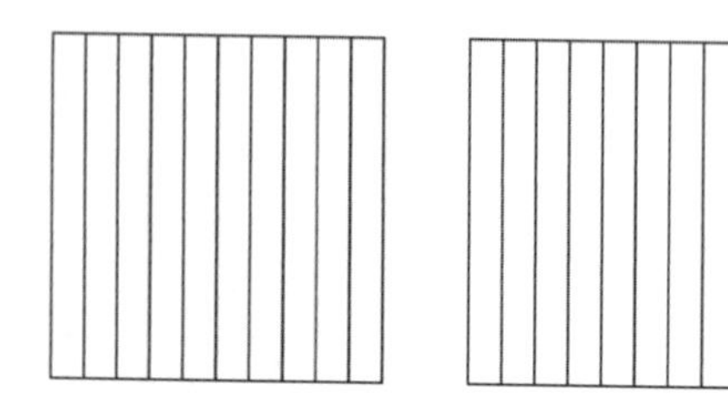

   c. 1.8 ________ 1.53

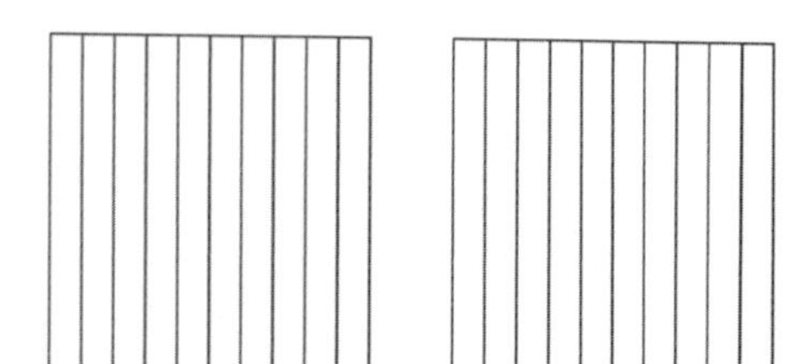

   d. 0.38 ________ 0.7

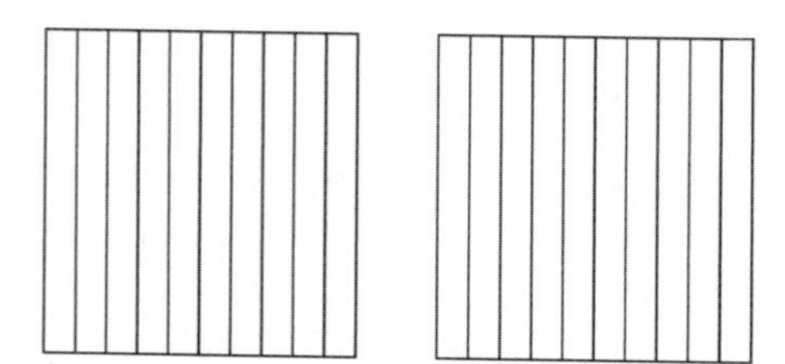

2. Locate and label the points for each of the decimal numbers on the number line. Fill in the blank with <, >, or = to compare the decimal numbers.

   a. 7.2 ________ 7.02

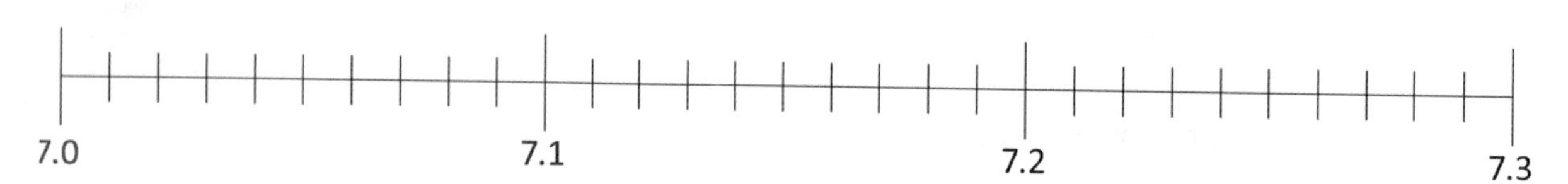

   b. 18.19 ________ 18.3

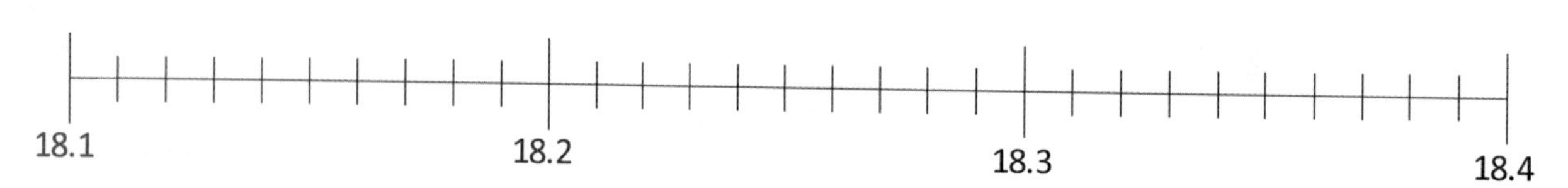

© 2015 Great Minds. eureka-math.org
G4-M6-TE-B5-1.3.1-01.2016

EUREKA MATH

3. Use the symbols <, >, or = to compare.

a. 2.68 ________ 2.54

b. 6.37 ________ 6.73

c. 9.28 ________ 7.28

d. 3.02 ________ 3.2

e. 13.1 ________ 13.10

f. 5.8 ________ 5.92

4. Use the symbols <, >, or = to compare. Use pictures as needed to solve.

a. 57 tenths ________ 5.7

b. 6.2 ________ 6 ones and 2 hundredths

c. 33 tenths ________ 33 hundredths

d. 8.39 ________ $8\frac{39}{10}$

e. $\frac{236}{100}$ ________ 2.36

f. 3 tenths ________ 22 hundredths

© 2015 Great Minds. eureka-math.org
G4-M6-TE-B5-1.3.1-01.2016

comparing with area models

© 2015 Great Minds. eureka-math.org
G4-M6-TE-B5-1.3.1-01.2016

Lesson 11

Objective: Compare and order mixed numbers in various forms.

Suggested Lesson Structure

- Fluency Practice (10 minutes)
- Application Problem (5 minutes)
- Concept Development (35 minutes)
- Student Debrief (10 minutes)

Total Time **(60 minutes)**

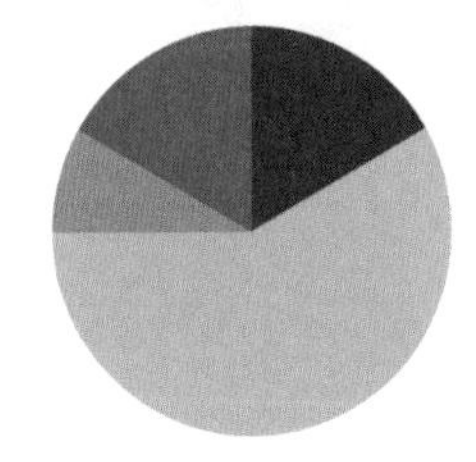

Fluency Practice (10 minutes)

- Expanded Form **4.NBT.2** (3 minutes)
- Rename the Decimal **4.NF.5** (4 minutes)
- Compare Decimal Numbers **4.NF.7** (3 minutes)

Expanded Form (3 minutes)

Materials: (S) Personal white board

Note: This fluency activity reviews Lesson 7.

T: (Write $6\frac{13}{100}$.) Write 6 and 13 hundredths in expanded fraction form without multiplication.

S: (Write $6\frac{13}{100} = 6 + \frac{1}{10} + \frac{3}{100}$.)

T: Write 6 and 13 hundredths in expanded decimal form.

S: (Write 6.13 = 6 + 0.1 + 0.03.)

Repeat the process for $54\frac{73}{100}$.

T: (Write 8.53.) Write 8 and 53 hundredths in expanded decimal form.

S: (Write 8.53 = 8 + 0.5 + 0.03.)

T: Write 8 and 53 hundredths in expanded fraction form.

S: (Write $8\frac{53}{100} = 8 + \frac{5}{10} + \frac{3}{100}$.)

© 2015 Great Minds. eureka-math.org
G4-M6-TE-B5-1.3.1-01.2016

Rename the Decimal (4 minutes)

Materials: (S) Personal white board

Note: This fluency activity reviews Lesson 8.

T: (Write 9.4.) Write the decimal as a mixed number.

S: (Write $9\frac{4}{10}$.)

T: (Write $9.4 = 9\frac{4}{10} = \frac{\quad}{10}$.) Complete the number sentence.

S: (Write $9.4 = 9\frac{4}{10} = \frac{94}{10}$.)

T: (Write $9.4 = 9\frac{4}{10} = \frac{94}{10} = \frac{\quad}{100}$.) Complete the number sentence.

S: (Write $9.4 = 9\frac{4}{10} = \frac{94}{10} = \frac{940}{100}$.)

Continue with the following possible sequence: 12.3, 4.27, and 53.8.

NOTES ON MULTIPLE MEANS OF REPRESENTATION:

The Compare Decimal Numbers fluency activity gives students working below grade level and others useful practice using the less than (<) and greater than (>) symbols, which are easily confused. Mnemonic devices such as imagining the < symbol to be an alligator mouth that eats the larger amount can be effective. To enhance the practice, ask students to read the comparison statements aloud.

Compare Decimal Numbers (3 minutes)

Materials: (S) Personal white board

Note: This fluency activity reviews Lesson 10.

T: (Write 2.5 ___ 2.50.) Complete the number sentence, filling in a greater than, less than, or equal sign.

S: (Write 2.5 = 2.50.)

Continue with the following possible sequence: 6.74 ___ 6.7, 4.16 ___ 4.61, 3.89 ___ 3.9, 8.64 ___ 8.46, 10.04 ___ 10.4, and 13.28 ___ 13.8.

Application Problem (5 minutes)

While sewing, Kikanza cut 3 strips of colored fabric: a yellow 2.8-foot strip, an orange 2.08-foot strip, and a red 2.25-foot strip.

She put the shortest strip away in a drawer and placed the other 2 strips side by side on a table. Draw a tape diagram comparing the lengths of the strips on the table. Which measurement is longer?

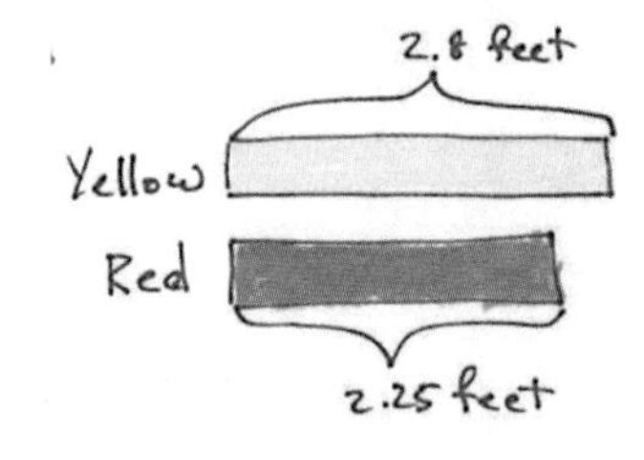

2.8 feet is longer than 2.25 feet.

Note: Students apply their comparison skills from Lesson 10 by not including the orange strip in the drawing, recognizing it is the shortest. This also introduces students to a part–whole tape diagram with decimals without calculations.

© 2015 Great Minds. eureka-math.org
G4-M6-TE-B5-1.3.1-01.2016

Concept Development (35 minutes)

Materials: (T) Number line (Lesson 6 Template 2) (S) Number line (Lesson 6 Template 2), decimal number flash cards (Template) (1 set per group), personal white board

Note: The onset of Problem 1 asks students to work in small groups. Each group needs one set of flash cards. The recommended group size is three students.

Problem 1: Arrange mixed numbers, fractions, and decimals on a number line.

T: (Distribute 1 set of decimal number flash cards to each group.) In your small groups, work together to arrange your decimal number flash cards in order from least to greatest.

Allow three to five minutes for students to work. Students may renumber the cards if they wish. Do not correct their ordering yet, but do ask students to provide reasoning for their ordering choices.

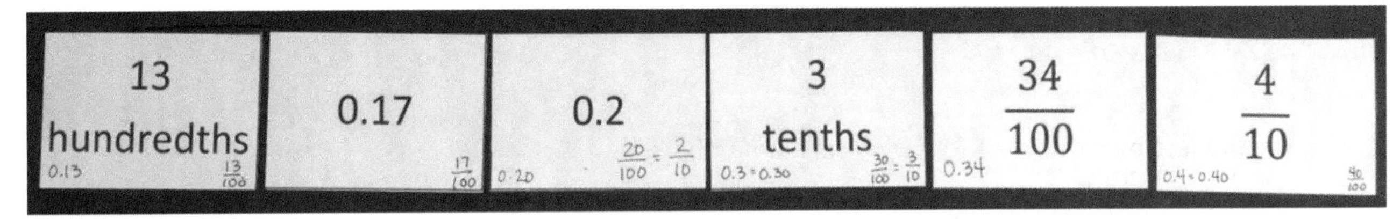

T: We want to plot all of these numbers on the number line. (Distribute the number line template. Project the first number line on the number line template.)

T: What is the smallest number in this set?

S: 13 hundredths.

T: What is the greatest number in this set?

S: 4 tenths.

T: Talk with your group to determine what the most appropriate endpoints are.

S: (Determine the endpoints.)

T: Turn to another group, and compare your endpoints. Discuss how you chose your endpoints.

S: Our endpoints are 1 tenth and 4 tenths since the smallest number in this set is 13 hundredths. We started at the tenth that comes before 13 hundredths.

T: Work with your group to plot and label each number from the set on the number line.

S: (Work with the group to complete the task.)

T: Did your group discover an ordering mistake when it came time to plot the numbers? Explain how you found the mistake.

T: (Project three number lines, completed by students, similar to the ones shown on the following page.) Did these groups represent the numbers using the same form that you did?

S: No, we changed some of the numbers into decimal form so they are all in the same form. → We wrote all the numbers in fraction form. → We left some of them the way they were given to us.

T: Does the form change the order of the numbers?

S: No. No matter which form we used, the numbers are in the same position on the number line.

© 2015 Great Minds. eureka-math.org
G4-M6-TE-B5-1.3.1-01.2016

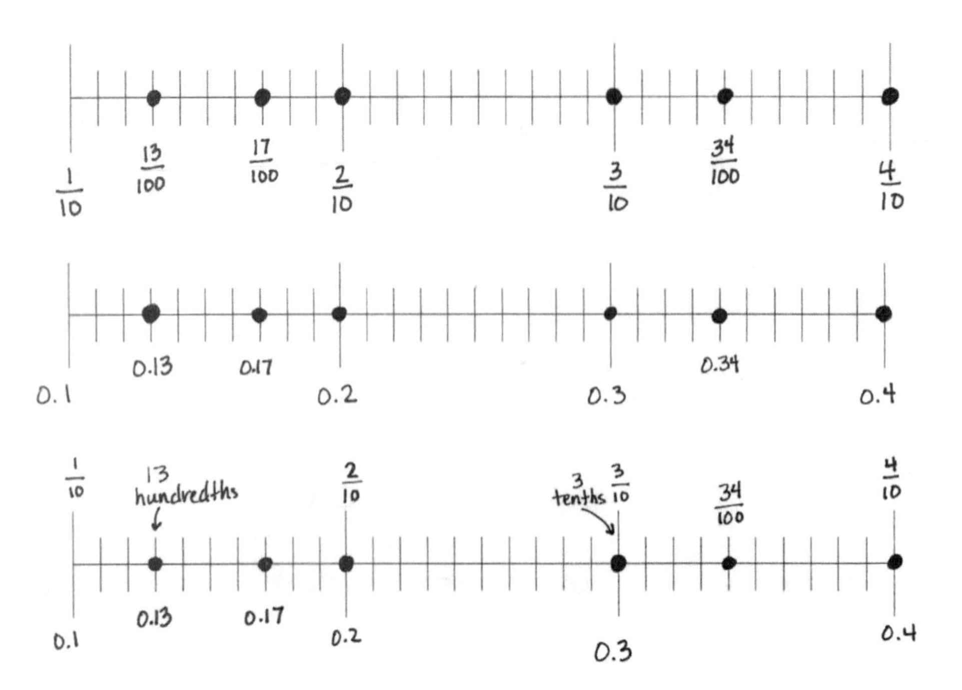

Repeat the process by writing the following sets of numbers:

- $7.92, 8.1, 7\frac{86}{100}, \frac{79}{10}, \frac{802}{100}$
- $9\frac{5}{10}, 9.41, \frac{968}{100}, \frac{96}{10}, 9.7, 9.63$

T: Look at your number line. How are your numbers arranged? In what order are they?

S: The numbers go from least to greatest. → The smallest numbers come first. When ever you read numbers on a number line, they always go in order, with the smallest numbers on the left and larger numbers on the right.

Problem 2: Arrange mixed numbers, fractions, and decimals in order from greatest to least.

T: (Write $\frac{18}{10}$, 1.08, $\frac{18}{100}$, $1\frac{81}{100}$, $\frac{190}{100}$, 1.82.)

T: Instead of using the number line to order the numbers from least to greatest, work with your group to arrange the numbers in order from *greatest to least* using decimal form. Use the > symbol between the numbers as you list them from greatest to least on your personal white board.

S: (Work with the group to complete the task.)

T: List the numbers in order from greatest to least. (Accept numbers in any correct form.)

S: $1.9 > 1.82 > 1.81 > 1.8 > 1.08 > 0.18$.

T: How did you decide on the order of the numbers?

S: We changed all of the numbers to decimal form or fraction form because it's easier for us to compare in the same form. → We renamed every number to hundredths. → We left the numbers in tenths and hundredths and used place value to compare: first the ones, then the tenths, and then the hundredths. → We compared the decimals or fractions first. Then, we found where the mixed numbers would go.

© 2015 Great Minds. eureka-math.org
G4-M6-TE-B5-1.3.1-01.2016

Repeat the process with the following sets of numbers:

- $14\frac{5}{10}$, 15.5, $\frac{154}{100}$, 15.05, $14\frac{40}{100}$
- $8\frac{61}{100}$, $8\frac{6}{10}$, $8\frac{1}{10}$, $\frac{816}{100}$, 86, 8.01

Problem 3: Compare and order mixed numbers in the context of a word problem.

MP.4

T: (Project the following word problem.) During a triple jump contest, Hae Jung jumped 8.76 meters. Marianne jumped $8\frac{7}{10}$ meters. Beth jumped $\frac{880}{100}$ meters. Lily jumped 8.07 meters. In what place did each student rank?

T: Use what you know to answer this question on your personal white board and demonstrate your reasoning. (Allow students time to work.)

T: In what place did each student rank?

S: Beth came in first. Hae Jung came in second. Marianne placed third. Lily placed fourth.

T: How did you solve this problem?

S: I changed all of the numbers to decimal form. → I changed all the numbers to fractions. I used hundredths so that they were all the same unit. → I changed everything to a mixed number so I could compare the ones first. I realized I had one fraction with tenths, so I made that 70 hundredths so it would be easier to compare.

Extension: Give six blank flash cards or index cards to each group. Ask the groups to record decimal numbers using various forms for another group to order. Pair up groups, trade cards, and then have the groups check the work of their partnered group.

Problem Set (10 minutes)

Students should do their personal best to complete the Problem Set within the allotted 10 minutes. For some classes, it may be appropriate to modify the assignment by specifying which problems they work on first. Some problems do not specify a method for solving. Students should solve these problems using the RDW approach used for Application Problems.

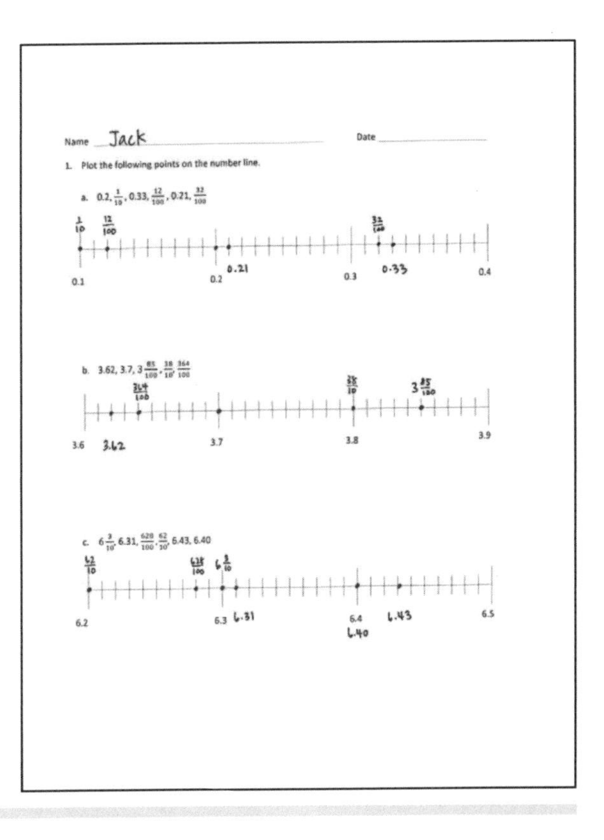

Student Debrief (10 minutes)

Lesson Objective: Compare and order mixed numbers in various forms.

The Student Debrief is intended to invite reflection and active processing of the total lesson experience.

© 2015 Great Minds. eureka-math.org
G4-M6-TE-B5-1.3.1-01.2016

Invite students to review their solutions for the Problem Set. They should check work by comparing answers with a partner before going over answers as a class. Look for misconceptions or misunderstandings that can be addressed in the Debrief. Guide students in a conversation to debrief the Problem Set and process the lesson.

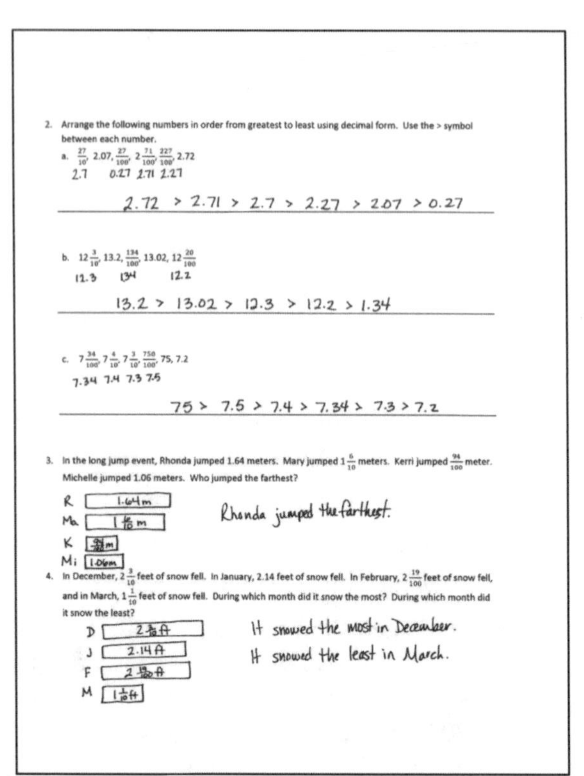
2. Arrange the following numbers in order from greatest to least using decimal form. Use the > symbol between each number.

a. $\frac{27}{10}$, 2.07, $\frac{27}{100}$, $2\frac{71}{100}$, $\frac{227}{100}$, 2.72

2.7 0.27 2.71 2.27

2.72 > 2.71 > 2.7 > 2.27 > 2.07 > 0.27

b. $12\frac{3}{10}$, 13.2, $\frac{134}{100}$, 13.02, $12\frac{20}{100}$

12.3 134 12.2

13.2 > 13.02 > 12.3 > 12.2 > 1.34

c. $7\frac{34}{100}$, $7\frac{4}{10}$, $7\frac{3}{10}$, $\frac{750}{100}$, 75, 7.2

7.34 7.4 7.3 7.5

75 > 7.5 > 7.4 > 7.34 > 7.3 > 7.2

3. In the long jump event, Rhonda jumped 1.64 meters. Mary jumped $1\frac{6}{10}$ meters. Kerri jumped $\frac{94}{100}$ meter. Michelle jumped 1.06 meters. Who jumped the farthest?

R 1.64 m
Ma $1\frac{6}{10}$ m
K $\frac{94}{100}$ m
Mi 1.06 m

Rhonda jumped the farthest.

4. In December, $2\frac{3}{10}$ feet of snow fell. In January, 2.14 feet of snow fell. In February, $2\frac{19}{100}$ feet of snow fell, and in March, $1\frac{1}{10}$ feet of snow fell. During which month did it snow the most? During which month did it snow the least?

D $2\frac{3}{10}$ ft
J 2.14 ft
F $2\frac{19}{100}$ ft
M $1\frac{1}{10}$ ft

It snowed the most in December.
It snowed the least in March.

Any combination of the questions below may be used to lead the discussion.

- In Problem 1(a), which numbers were the easiest for you to plot? Why?
- How did the number line help you to order—or to check the order of—the numbers from least to greatest? Do you think it could be useful to use the number line to order numbers from greatest to least like in Problem 2? Why or why not?
- How could a place value chart help you solve Problem 2(a)? Create an example to share with the class. What other models or tools have we used this year that might help you with Problem 2?
- In Problem 2(b), which numbers did you start ordering first? How did ordering some numbers help you with the remaining numbers? Use specific numbers to explain your process.
- In Problems 3 and 4, how did you make it easier to compare the various numbers? Explain your reasoning.

Exit Ticket (3 minutes)

After the Student Debrief, instruct students to complete the Exit Ticket. A review of their work will help with assessing students' understanding of the concepts that were presented in today's lesson and planning more effectively for future lessons. The questions may be read aloud to the students.

© 2015 Great Minds. eureka-math.org
G4-M6-TE-B5-1.3.1-01.2016

Name ______________________________ Date ________________

1. Plot the following points on the number line.

a. $0.2, \frac{1}{10}, 0.33, \frac{12}{100}, 0.21, \frac{32}{100}$

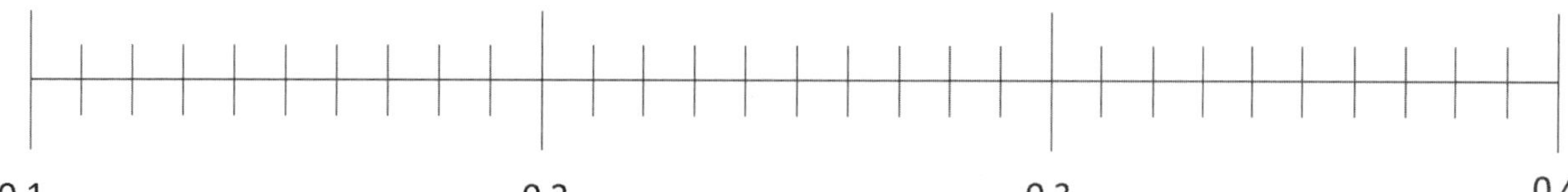

b. $3.62, 3.7, 3\frac{85}{100}, \frac{38}{10}, \frac{364}{100}$

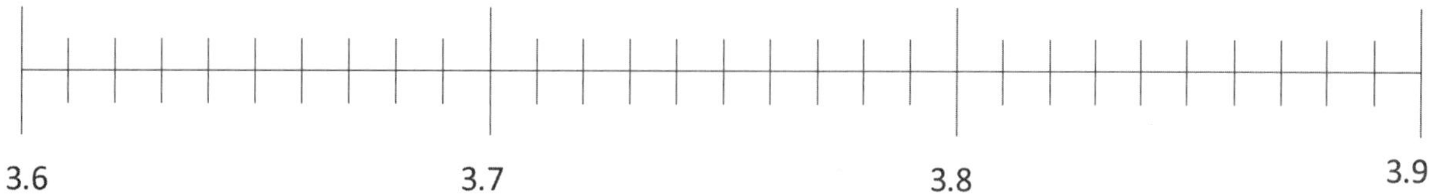

c. $6\frac{3}{10}, 6.31, \frac{628}{100}, \frac{62}{10}, 6.43, 6.40$

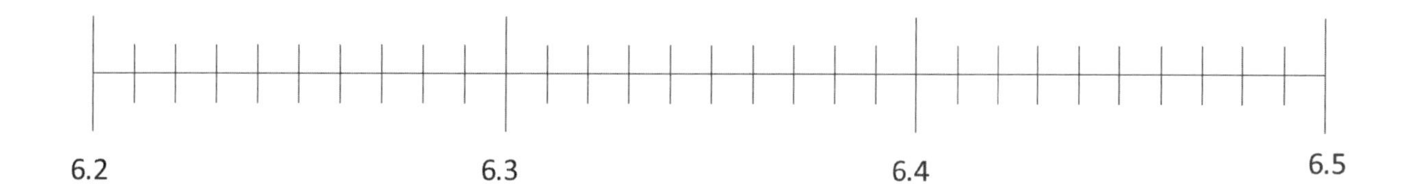

© 2015 Great Minds. eureka-math.org
G4-M6-TE-B5-1.3.1-01.2016

2. Arrange the following numbers in order from greatest to least using decimal form. Use the > symbol between each number.

a. $\frac{27}{10}$, 2.07, $\frac{27}{100}$, $2\frac{71}{100}$, $\frac{227}{100}$, 2.72

____

b. $12\frac{3}{10}$, 13.2, $\frac{134}{100}$, 13.02, $12\frac{20}{100}$

____

c. $7\frac{34}{100}$, $7\frac{4}{10}$, $7\frac{3}{10}$, $\frac{750}{100}$, 75, 7.2

____

3. In the long jump event, Rhonda jumped 1.64 meters. Mary jumped $1\frac{6}{10}$ meters. Kerri jumped $\frac{94}{100}$ meter. Michelle jumped 1.06 meters. Who jumped the farthest?

4. In December, $2\frac{3}{10}$ feet of snow fell. In January, 2.14 feet of snow fell. In February, $2\frac{19}{100}$ feet of snow fell, and in March, $1\frac{1}{10}$ feet of snow fell. During which month did it snow the most? During which month did it snow the least?

EUREKA MATH

© 2015 Great Minds. eureka-math.org
G4-M6-TE-B5-1.3.1-01.2016

Name ______________________________ Date ______________

1. Plot the following points on the number line using decimal form.

   1 one and 1 tenth, $\frac{13}{10}$, 1 one and 20 hundredths, $\frac{129}{100}$, 1.11, $\frac{102}{100}$

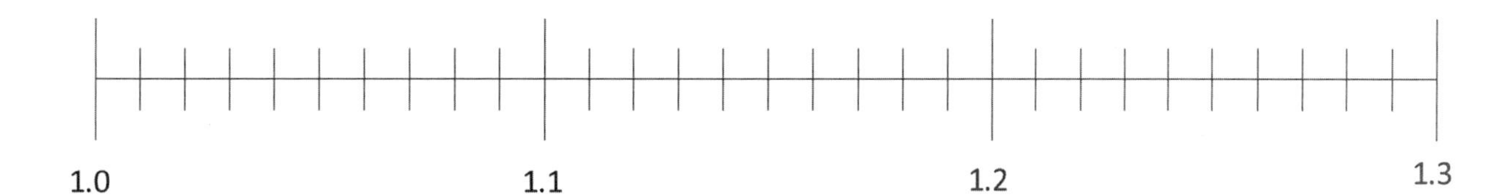

2. Arrange the following numbers in order from greatest to least using decimal form. Use the > symbol between each number.

   5.6, $\frac{605}{100}$, 6.15, $6\frac{56}{100}$, $\frac{516}{100}$, 6 ones and 5 tenths

   ____

© 2015 Great Minds. eureka-math.org
G4-M6-TE-B5-1.3.1-01.2016

Name ______________________________ Date ________________

1. Plot the following points on the number line using decimal form.

   a. 0.6, $\frac{5}{10}$, 0.76, $\frac{79}{100}$, 0.53, $\frac{67}{100}$

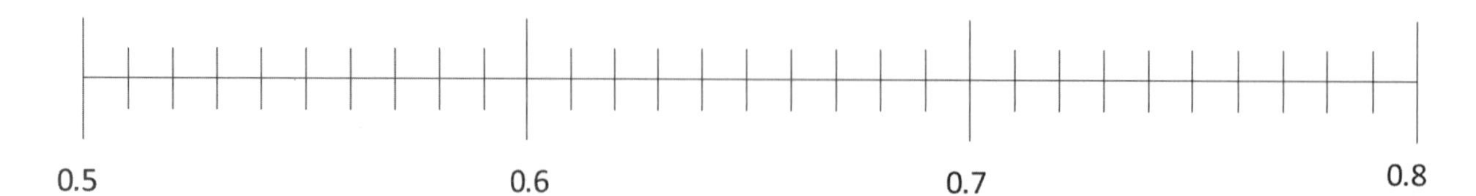

   b. 8 ones and 15 hundredths, $\frac{832}{100}$, $8\frac{27}{100}$, $\frac{82}{10}$, 8.1

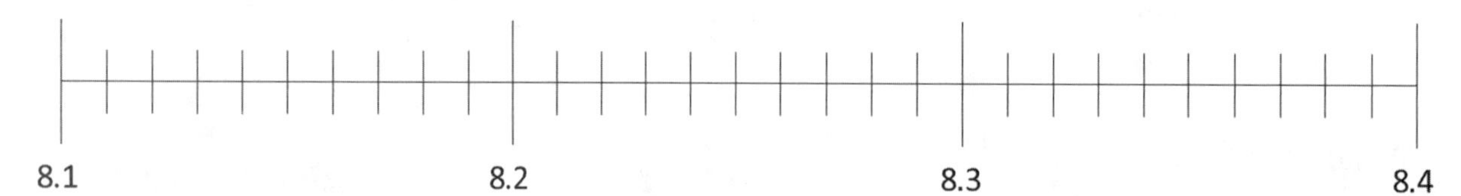

   c. $13\frac{12}{100}$, $\frac{130}{10}$, 13 ones and 3 tenths, 13.21, $13\frac{3}{100}$

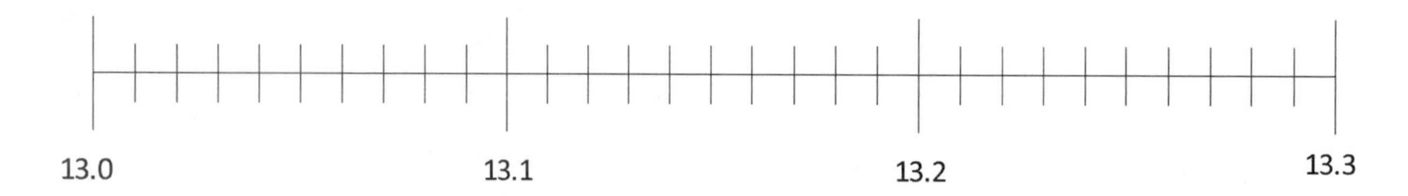

© 2015 Great Minds. eureka-math.org
G4-M6-TE-B5-1.3.1-01.2016

2. Arrange the following numbers in order from greatest to least using decimal form. Use the > symbol between each number.

   a. 4.03, 4 ones and 33 hundredths, $\frac{34}{100}$, $4\frac{43}{100}$, $\frac{430}{100}$, 4.31

   ____

   b. $17\frac{5}{10}$, 17.55, $\frac{157}{10}$, 17 ones and 5 hundredths, 15.71, $15\frac{75}{100}$

   ____

   c. 8 ones and 19 hundredths, $9\frac{8}{10}$, 81, $\frac{809}{100}$, 8.9, $8\frac{1}{10}$

   ____

3. In a paper airplane contest, Matt's airplane flew 9.14 meters. Jenna's airplane flew $9\frac{4}{10}$ meters. Ben's airplane flew $\frac{904}{100}$ meters. Leah's airplane flew 9.1 meters. Whose airplane flew the farthest?

4. Becky drank $1\frac{41}{100}$ liters of water on Monday, 1.14 liters on Tuesday, 1.04 liters on Wednesday, $\frac{11}{10}$ liters on Thursday, and $1\frac{40}{100}$ liters on Friday. Which day did Becky drink the most? Which day did Becky drink the least?

© 2015 Great Minds. eureka-math.org
G4-M6-TE-B5-1.3.1-01.2016

3 tenths	0.2
0.17	$\frac{34}{100}$
13 hundredths	$\frac{4}{10}$

decimal number flash cards

© 2015 Great Minds. eureka-math.org
G4-M6-TE-B5-1.3.1-01.2016

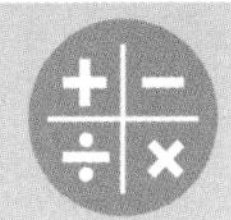

Topic D
Addition with Tenths and Hundredths

4.NF.5, 4.NF.6, 4.NF.3c, 4.MD.1

Focus Standards:	4.NF.5	Express a fraction with denominator 10 as an equivalent fraction with denominator 100, and use this technique to add two fractions with respective denominators 10 and 100. *For example, express 3/10 as 30/100, and add 3/10 + 4/100 = 34/100.* (Students who can generate equivalent fractions can develop strategies for adding fractions with unlike denominators in general. But addition and subtraction with unlike denominators in general is not a requirement at this grade.)
	4.NF.6	Use decimal notation for fractions with denominators 10 or 100. *For example, rewrite 0.62 as 62/100; describe a length as 0.62 meters; locate 0.62 on a number line diagram.*
Instructional Days:	3	
Coherence -Links from:	G3–M5	Fractions as Numbers on the Number Line
-Links to:	G5–M2	Multi-Digit Whole Number and Decimal Fraction Operations

Topic D brings together students' work with addition of fractions and their work with decimals. In Lesson 12, students begin at the pictorial level, decomposing tenths using the area model and place value chart to add tenths and hundredths. They progress to using multiplication to generate equivalent fractions and express the sum in fraction form as a decimal, as pictured below.

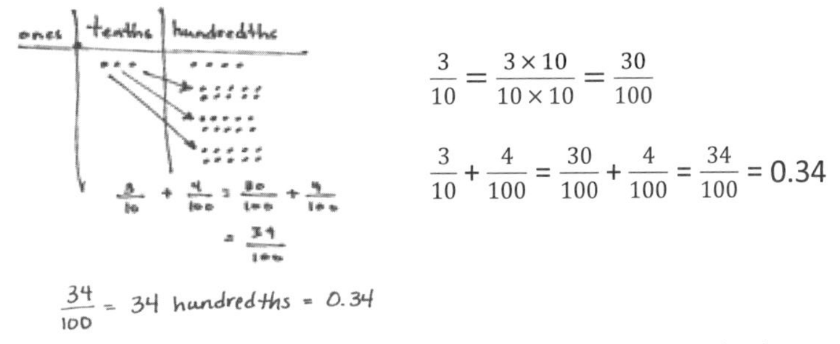

Students next apply what they know about fraction addition to use multiple strategies to solve sums of tenths and hundredths with totals greater than 1 (see the two examples pictured below), again expressing the solution in decimal form.

$\frac{9}{10} + \frac{64}{100} = \frac{90}{100} + \frac{64}{100} = 1\frac{54}{100} = 1.54$ (with $\frac{64}{100}$ decomposed into $\frac{10}{100}$ and $\frac{54}{100}$)

$\frac{9}{10} + \frac{64}{100} = \frac{90}{100} + \frac{64}{100} = \frac{154}{100} = 1\frac{54}{100} = 1.54$ (with $\frac{154}{100}$ decomposed into $\frac{100}{100}$ and $\frac{54}{100}$)

© 2015 Great Minds. eureka-math.org
G4-M6-TE-B5-1.3.1-01.2016

In Lesson 13, students add ones, tenths, and hundredths in decimal form by converting the addends to mixed numbers in fraction form, creating like denominators, and applying their understanding of the addition of mixed numbers. Once the decimal fractions are added (**4.NF.5**), the number sentence is written in decimal notation (**4.NF.6**).

$$5.6 + 4.53 = 5\tfrac{6}{10} + 4\tfrac{53}{100} = 5\tfrac{60}{100} + 4\tfrac{53}{100} = 9\tfrac{60}{100} + \tfrac{53}{100} = 9\tfrac{113}{100} = 10\tfrac{13}{100}$$

$$5.6 + 4.53 = 10.13$$

$$5.6 + 4.53 = 5\tfrac{6}{10} + 4\tfrac{53}{100} = 9 + 1 + \tfrac{13}{100} = 10\tfrac{13}{100}$$

$$5.6 + 4.53 = 10.13$$

$$5.6 + 4.53 = 5\tfrac{60}{100} + 4\tfrac{53}{100} = 10\tfrac{13}{100}$$

$$5.6 + 4.53 = 10.13$$

The addition of decimals is a Grade 5 standard. By converting addends in decimal form to fraction form, Grade 4 students strengthen their understanding both of fraction and decimal equivalence and of fraction addition.

In Lesson 14, students apply this work to solve measurement word problems involving addition. They convert decimals to fraction form, solve the problem, and write their statement using the decimal form of the solution as pictured below.

*An apple orchard sold 140.5 kilograms of apple*s in the morning. The orchard sold 15.85 kilograms more apples in the afternoon than in the morning. How *many total kilograms of apples were sold that day?*

M: 140.5 kg
A: 140.5 kg | 15.85 kg
?

Solution A

$$140\tfrac{5}{10} + 15\tfrac{85}{100} = 155\tfrac{50}{100} + \tfrac{85}{100} = 155\tfrac{135}{100} = 156\tfrac{35}{100}$$

$$140\tfrac{5}{10} + 156\tfrac{35}{100} = 296\tfrac{50}{100} + \tfrac{35}{100} = 296\tfrac{85}{100}$$

The apple orchard sold 296.85 kilograms of apples.

Solution B

$$\left(2 \times 140\tfrac{5}{10}\right) + 15.85 = 280\tfrac{10}{10} + 15\tfrac{85}{100} = 296\tfrac{85}{100}$$

The apple orchard sold 296.85 kilograms that day.

© 2015 Great Minds. eureka-math.org
G4-M6-TE-B5-1.3.1-01.2016

A Teaching Sequence Toward Mastery of Addition with Tenths and Hundredths

Objective 1: **Apply understanding of fraction equivalence to add tenths and hundredths.**
(Lesson 12)

Objective 2: **Add decimal numbers by converting to fraction form.**
(Lesson 13)

Objective 3: **Solve word problems involving the addition of measurements in decimal form.**
(Lesson 14)

© 2015 Great Minds. eureka-math.org
G4-M6-TE-B5-1.3.1-01.2016

Lesson 12

Objective: Apply understanding of fraction equivalence to add tenths and hundredths.

Suggested Lesson Structure

■ Fluency Practice	(12 minutes)
■ Application Problem	(5 minutes)
■ Concept Development	(33 minutes)
■ Student Debrief	(10 minutes)
Total Time	**(60 minutes)**

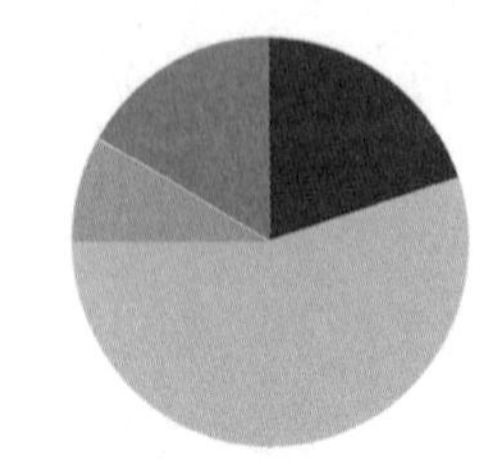

Fluency Practice (12 minutes)

- Add and Subtract **4.NBT.4** (3 minutes)
- Compare Decimal Numbers **4.NF.7** (4 minutes)
- Order Decimal Numbers **4.NF.7** (5 minutes)

Add and Subtract (3 minutes)

Materials: (S) Personal white board

Note: This fluency activity reviews adding and subtracting using the standard algorithm.

T: (Write 473 thousands 379 ones + 473 thousands 379 ones.) On your personal white board, write this addition sentence in standard form.

S: (Write 473,379 + 473,379.)

T: Add using the standard algorithm.

S: (Write 473,379 + 473,379 = 946,758 using the standard algorithm.)

Continue the process for 384,917 + 384,917.

T: (Write 700 thousand 1 ten.) On your board, write this number in standard form.

S: (Write 700,010.)

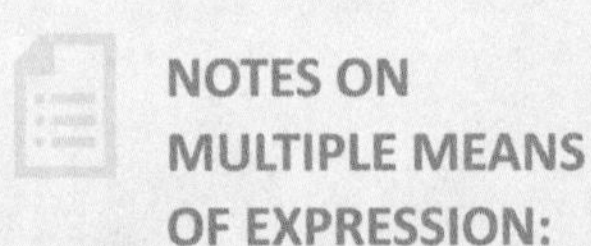

NOTES ON MULTIPLE MEANS OF EXPRESSION:

Challenge students working above grade level and others to apply efficient alternative strategies learned since Grade 1 to solve the Add and Subtract fluency activity. For example, students can avoid renaming to solve 700,010 – 199,856 by subtracting 11 from both the minuend and the subtrahend (i.e., 699,999 – 199,845) or by adding 144 to both the minuend and subtrahend (i.e., 700,154 – 200,000). Prompt students to explore and explain why the difference is the same using all three methods.

© 2015 Great Minds. eureka-math.org
G4-M6-TE-B5-1.3.1-01.2016

T: (Write 199 thousands 856 ones.) Subtract this number from 700,010 using the standard algorithm.

S: (Write 700,010 – 199,856 = 500,154 using the standard algorithm.)

Continue the process for 900,080 – 288,099.

Compare Decimal Numbers (4 minutes)

Materials: (S) Personal white board

Note: This fluency activity reviews Lesson 10.

T: (Write 3.20 __ 3.2.) Complete the number sentence, filling in a greater than, less than, or equal sign.

S: (Write 3.20 = 3.2.)

Continue with the following possible sequence: 7.8 __ 7.85, 5.72 __ 5.27, 2.9 __ 2.89, 6.24 __ 6.42, 10.8 __ 10.08, and 14.39 __ 14.9.

Order Decimal Numbers (5 minutes)

Materials: (S) Personal white board

Note: This fluency activity reviews Lesson 11.

T: (Write 0.3, $\frac{1}{10}$, and 0.44.) Arrange the numbers in order from least to greatest.

S: (Write $\frac{1}{10}$, 0.3, and 0.44.)

Continue with the following possible sequence:

- $\frac{13}{10}$, $\frac{43}{100}$, $\frac{1}{100}$, 0.54, 0.1, 0.55, 0.66
- $\frac{93}{10}$, 3 ones and 9 hundredths, $\frac{39}{100}$, 30 and 9 tenths, $\frac{390}{100}$, 3.93

Application Problem (5 minutes)

On Monday, $1\frac{7}{8}$ inches of rain fell. On Tuesday, it rained $\frac{1}{4}$ inch. What was the total rainfall for the two days?

Note: This Application Problem builds from Module 5 work where students learned to add fractions with related units (wherein one denominator is a factor of the other) and mixed numbers. Review of this lesson leads to today's Concept Development where students convert tenths to hundredths before adding decimal numbers.

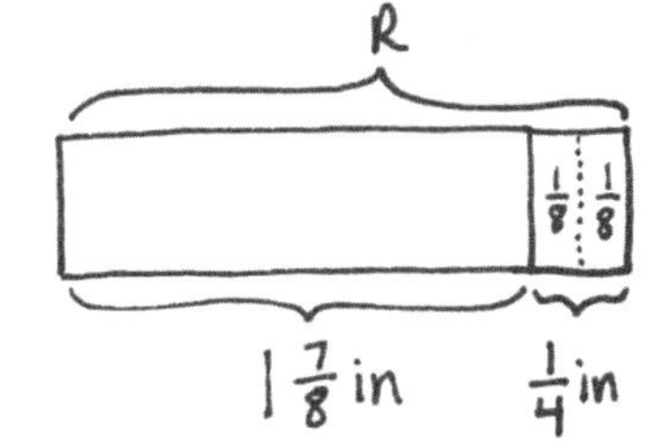

$R = 1\frac{7}{8}$ in $+ \frac{1}{4}$ in ($\frac{1}{4}$ split into $\frac{1}{8}$, $\frac{1}{8}$)

$\frac{1}{4} = \frac{1 \times 2}{4 \times 2} = \frac{2}{8}$

$R = 2$ in $+ \frac{1}{8}$ in

$R = 2\frac{1}{8}$ in

The total rainfall for the 2 days was $2\frac{1}{8}$ inches.

© 2015 Great Minds. eureka-math.org
G4-M6-TE-B5-1.3.1-01.2016

Concept Development (33 minutes)

Materials: (T) Area model and place value chart (Template) (S) Personal white board, area model and place value chart (Template)

Problem 1: Add tenths and hundredths written in unit form using pictorial models.

T: What is 3 girls + 2 girls?

S: 5 girls.

T: What is 3 girls + 2 students?

S: We can't add girls and students. The units don't match.

T: True. But, let's say the girls are students. Tell me the new number sentence, renaming to make like units.

S: 3 students + 2 students = 5 students.

T: What is 3 fourths + 2 fourths?

S: 5 fourths.

T: What is 3 fourths + 1 half? How can you solve? Discuss with your partner.

S: We have to make like units. → We have to rename a half as fourths. → We can convert halves to fourths: $\frac{1}{2} = \frac{2}{4}$. Then, we can add, $\frac{3}{4} + \frac{2}{4} = \frac{5}{4}$.

T: Is this true? (Write $\frac{3}{4} + \frac{1}{2} = \frac{3}{4} + \frac{2}{4}$.)

S: Yes!

T: 3 tenths + 4 tenths is...?

S: 7 tenths.

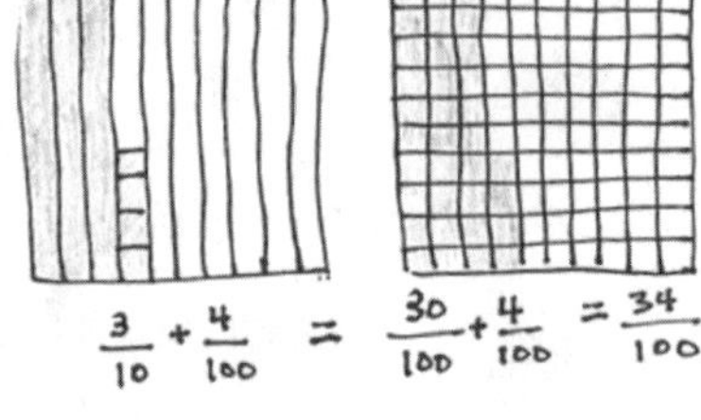

T: 3 tenths + 4 hundredths is...? How can you solve? Discuss with a partner.

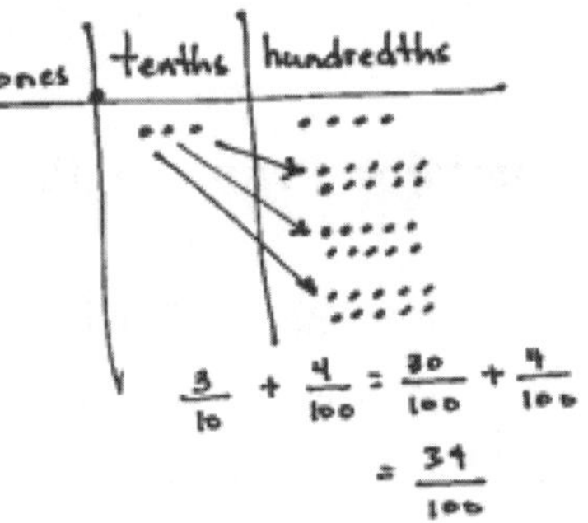

S: We have to make like units. → We have to rename 3 tenths as 30 hundredths. → We can decompose tenths to hundredths. → We can convert tenths to hundredths: $\frac{3}{10} = \frac{30}{100}$. Then, we can add, $\frac{30}{100} + \frac{4}{100} = \frac{34}{100}$.

T: Is this true? (Write 3 tenths + 4 hundredths = 30 hundredths + 4 hundredths.)

S: Yes!

T: Model the addition using an area model or place value chart. Show the conversion of tenths to hundredths. Discuss with your partner.

S: I drew the area model showing 3 tenths and 4 hundredths. Then, I decomposed the area into hundredths to make like units. That meant that I had 30 hundredths and 4 hundredths to have a total of 34 hundredths. → On the place value chart, I drew 3 tenths and 4 hundredths and then decomposed each tenth into 10 hundredths. That gave me a total of 34 hundredths.

Repeat the process for 2 tenths + 17 hundredths and 36 hundredths + 6 tenths.

© 2015 Great Minds. eureka-math.org
G4-M6-TE-B5-1.3.1-01.2016

Problem 2: Add tenths and hundredths by converting using multiplication. Express the sum as a decimal.

T: (Write $\frac{3}{10} + \frac{13}{100}$.) Are we ready to add?

S: No.

T: Discuss with a partner. How can we solve using multiplication to make like units?

S: Multiply both the numerator and denominator of 3 tenths by 10 so that we have like units—hundredths. → Convert 3 tenths to hundredths. $\frac{3}{10} = \frac{3 \times 10}{10 \times 10} = \frac{30}{100}$. $\frac{30}{100} + \frac{13}{100} = \frac{43}{100}$.

T: Write $\frac{43}{100}$ as a decimal.

S: 0.43.

T: Is this true? (Write $\frac{3}{10} + \frac{13}{100} = \frac{30}{100} + \frac{13}{100} = \frac{43}{100} = 0.43$.)

S: Yes.

Repeat the process with $\frac{2}{10} + \frac{36}{100}$ and $\frac{40}{100} + \frac{6}{10}$.

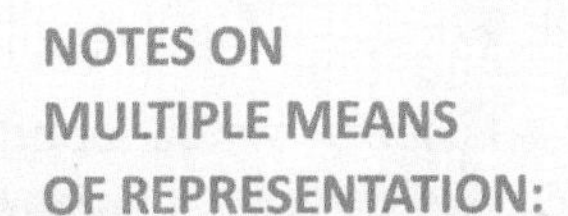

NOTES ON MULTIPLE MEANS OF REPRESENTATION:

After the initial use of multiplication to convert tenths to hundredths, many students may be able to do the conversion mentally. Encourage this shortcut because it is empowering. This is an important application of students' work with equivalence from Module 5, which leads to addition and subtraction of fractions with unlike denominators in Grade 5.

If some students still struggle with the conversion, directly link the multiplication to the area model and place value chart.

Problem 3: Add tenths and hundredths with sums greater than 1. Express the sum as a decimal.

T: (Write $\frac{6}{10} + \frac{57}{100}$.) Read the expression.

S: 6 tenths + 57 hundredths.

MP.6

T: Solve, and then explain your solution to your partner. (Two solution strategies are pictured below.)

$$\frac{6}{10} + \frac{57}{100} = \frac{60}{100} + \frac{57}{100} = 1\frac{17}{100} = 1.17$$

$\frac{10}{100}$ $\frac{50}{100}$ $\frac{50}{100}$ $\frac{7}{100}$

$$\frac{6}{10} + \frac{57}{100} = \frac{60}{100} + \frac{57}{100} = \frac{117}{100} = 1\frac{17}{100} = 1.17$$

$\frac{100}{100}$ $\frac{17}{100}$

S: I changed 6 tenths to 60 hundredths and then made 1 by adding 50 hundredths, which I took out of each addend. That meant 10 hundredths and 7 hundredths were left to be added. The sum is $1\frac{17}{100}$. → I just added 60 hundredths and 57 hundredths to get 117 hundredths and then decomposed to get 100 hundredths and 17 hundredths. → I converted 6 tenths to 60 hundredths and then took out 40 hundredths from 57 hundredths to make 1 and added on the leftover 17 hundredths.

T: Write your answer as a decimal.

S: 1.17.

© 2015 Great Minds. eureka-math.org
G4-M6-TE-B5-1.3.1-01.2016

T: (Write $\frac{9}{10} + \frac{64}{100}$.)

T: Solve, and then share your solution strategy with a partner.

S: I used a number bond to decompose 64 hundredths into 10 hundredths and 54 hundredths to make 1.
→ I added to get 154 hundredths and decomposed the sum into 100 hundredths and 54 hundredths, or 1 and 54 hundredths.

T: Write your answer as a decimal.

S: 1.54.

$$\frac{9}{10} + \frac{64}{100} = \frac{90}{100} + \frac{64}{100} = 1\frac{54}{100} = 1.54$$

(number bond: $\frac{64}{100}$ → $\frac{10}{100}$ and $\frac{54}{100}$)

$$\frac{9}{10} + \frac{64}{100} = \frac{90}{100} + \frac{64}{100} = \frac{154}{100} = 1\frac{54}{100} = 1.54$$

(number bond: $\frac{154}{100}$ → $\frac{100}{100}$ and $\frac{54}{100}$)

Repeat the process with $\frac{2}{10} + \frac{91}{100}$ and $\frac{45}{100} + \frac{8}{10}$.

Problem Set (10 minutes)

Students should do their personal best to complete the Problem Set within the allotted 10 minutes. For some classes, it may be appropriate to modify the assignment by specifying which problems they work on first. Some problems do not specify a method for solving. Students should solve these problems using the RDW approach used for Application Problems.

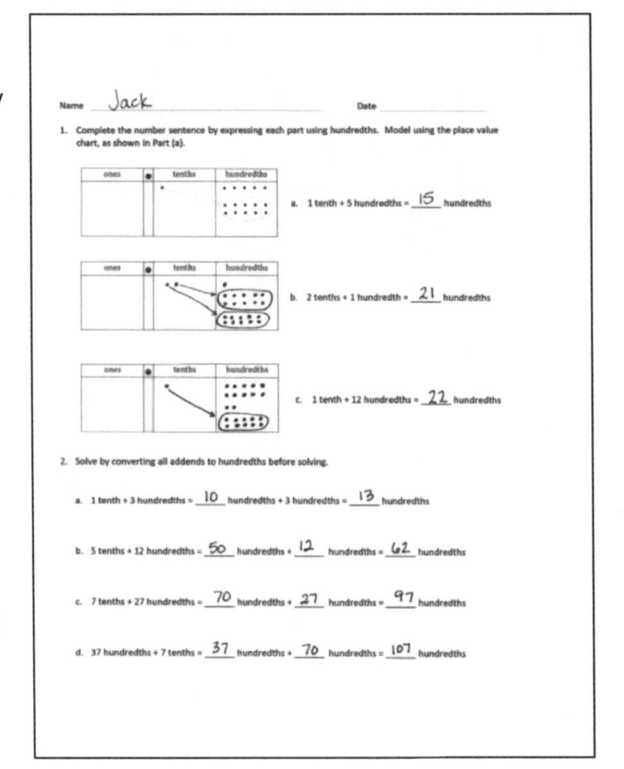

Name Jack Date

1. Complete the number sentence by expressing each part using hundredths. Model using the place value chart, as shown in Part (a).

ones	•	tenths	hundredths

a. 1 tenth + 5 hundredths = 15 hundredths

b. 2 tenths + 1 hundredth = 21 hundredths

c. 1 tenth + 12 hundredths = 22 hundredths

2. Solve by converting all addends to hundredths before solving.

a. 1 tenth + 3 hundredths = 10 hundredths + 3 hundredths = 13 hundredths

b. 5 tenths + 12 hundredths = 50 hundredths + 12 hundredths = 62 hundredths

c. 7 tenths + 27 hundredths = 70 hundredths + 27 hundredths = 97 hundredths

d. 37 hundredths + 7 tenths = 37 hundredths + 70 hundredths = 107 hundredths

Student Debrief (10 minutes)

Lesson Objective: Apply understanding of fraction equivalence to add tenths and hundredths.

The Student Debrief is intended to invite reflection and active processing of the total lesson experience.

Invite students to review their solutions for the Problem Set. They should check work by comparing answers with a partner before going over answers as a class. Look for misconceptions or misunderstandings that can be addressed in the Debrief. Guide students in a conversation to debrief the Problem Set and process the lesson.

EUREKA MATH
© 2015 Great Minds. eureka-math.org
G4-M6-TE-B5-1.3.1-01.2016

Any combination of the questions below may be used to lead the discussion.

- How did the work in Problem 1 help to prepare you to solve Problem 2?
- In Problem 3(d), what do you notice about your answer? Can the answer be written using a unit other than hundredths? Does that apply to any solutions in Problem 4?
- In Problem 5, if the water and iodine are mixed together, can we just measure the amount of iodine in the large beaker? Explain.
- What have we learned before that made converting to like units so easy? What have we learned before that made adding tenths and hundredths so easy?
- How did the Application Problem connect to today's lesson?

3. Find the sum. Convert tenths to hundredths as needed. Write your answer as a decimal.

a. $\frac{2}{10} + \frac{8}{100} = \frac{20}{100} + \frac{8}{100} = \frac{28}{100} = 0.28$

b. $\frac{13}{100} + \frac{4}{10}$

$\frac{13}{100} + \frac{40}{100} = \frac{53}{100} = 0.53$

c. $\frac{6}{10} + \frac{39}{100}$

$\frac{60}{100} + \frac{39}{100} = \frac{99}{100} = 0.99$

d. $\frac{70}{100} + \frac{3}{10}$

$\frac{70}{100} + \frac{30}{100} = \frac{100}{100} = 1$

4. Solve. Write your answer as a decimal.

a. $\frac{9}{10} + \frac{42}{100}$

$\frac{90}{100} + \frac{42}{100} = 1\frac{32}{100} = 1.32$ ($\frac{42}{100}$ decomposed into $\frac{10}{100}$ and $\frac{32}{100}$)

b. $\frac{70}{100} + \frac{5}{10}$

$\frac{70}{100} + \frac{50}{100} = 1\frac{20}{100} = 1\frac{2}{10} = 1.2$ ($\frac{50}{100}$ decomposed into $\frac{30}{100}$ and $\frac{20}{100}$)

c. $\frac{68}{100} + \frac{8}{10}$

$\frac{68}{100} + \frac{80}{100} = 1\frac{48}{100} = 1.48$ ($\frac{68}{100}$ decomposed into $\frac{20}{100}$ and $\frac{48}{100}$)

d. $\frac{7}{10} + \frac{87}{100}$

$\frac{70}{100} + \frac{87}{100} = 1\frac{57}{100} = 1.57$ ($\frac{87}{100}$ decomposed into $\frac{30}{100}$ and $\frac{57}{100}$)

5. Beaker A has $\frac{63}{100}$ liter of iodine. It is filled the rest of the way with water up to 1 liter. Beaker B has $\frac{4}{10}$ liter of iodine. It is filled the rest of the way with water up to 1 liter. If both beakers are emptied into a large beaker, how much iodine will be in the large beaker?

? — $\frac{63}{100}$ L | $\frac{4}{10}$ L

$\frac{63}{100} + \frac{4}{10} = \frac{63}{100} + \frac{40}{100} = \frac{103}{100} = 1\frac{3}{100} = 1.03$ ($\frac{103}{100}$ decomposed into $\frac{100}{100}$ and $\frac{3}{100}$)

The larger beaker will have 1.03 liters of iodine.

Exit Ticket (3 minutes)

After the Student Debrief, instruct students to complete the Exit Ticket. A review of their work will help with assessing students' understanding of the concepts that were presented in today's lesson and planning more effectively for future lessons. The questions may be read aloud to the students.

© 2015 Great Minds. eureka-math.org
G4-M6-TE-B5-1.3.1-01.2016

Name ______________________________ Date ______________

1. Complete the number sentence by expressing each part using hundredths. Model using the place value chart, as shown in part (a).

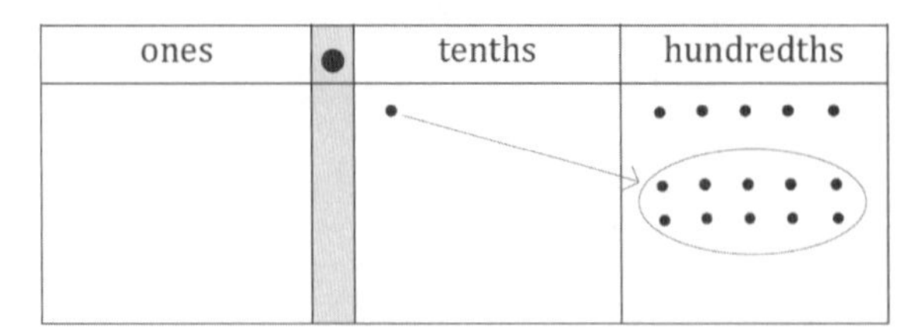

a. 1 tenth + 5 hundredths = ______ hundredths

ones	•	tenths	hundredths

b. 2 tenths + 1 hundredth = ______ hundredths

ones	•	tenths	hundredths

c. 1 tenth + 12 hundredths = ______ hundredths

2. Solve by converting all addends to hundredths before solving.

a. 1 tenth + 3 hundredths = _____ hundredths + 3 hundredths = _____ hundredths

b. 5 tenths + 12 hundredths = _____ hundredths + _____ hundredths = _____ hundredths

c. 7 tenths + 27 hundredths = _____ hundredths + _____ hundredths = _____ hundredths

d. 37 hundredths + 7 tenths = _____ hundredths + _____ hundredths = _____ hundredths

© 2015 Great Minds. eureka-math.org
G4-M6-TE-B5-1.3.1-01.2016

3. Find the sum. Convert tenths to hundredths as needed. Write your answer as a decimal.

   a. $\frac{2}{10}+\frac{8}{100}$

   b. $\frac{13}{100}+\frac{4}{10}$

   c. $\frac{6}{10}+\frac{39}{100}$

   d. $\frac{70}{100}+\frac{3}{10}$

4. Solve. Write your answer as a decimal.

   a. $\frac{9}{10}+\frac{42}{100}$

   b. $\frac{70}{100}+\frac{5}{10}$

   c. $\frac{68}{100}+\frac{8}{10}$

   d. $\frac{7}{10}+\frac{87}{100}$

5. Beaker A has $\frac{63}{100}$ liter of iodine. It is filled the rest of the way with water up to 1 liter. Beaker B has $\frac{4}{10}$ liter of iodine. It is filled the rest of the way with water up to 1 liter. If both beakers are emptied into a large beaker, how much iodine does the large beaker contain?

© 2015 Great Minds. eureka-math.org
G4-M6-TE-B5-1.3.1-01.2016

Name ____________________ Date ____________

1. Complete the number sentence by expressing each part using hundredths. Use the place value chart to model.

ones	•	tenths	hundredths

1 tenth + 9 hundredths = _____ hundredths

2. Find the sum. Write your answer as a decimal.

$$\frac{4}{10} + \frac{73}{100}$$

© 2015 Great Minds. eureka-math.org
G4-M6-TE-B5-1.3.1-01.2016

Name ______________________________ Date ______________

1. Complete the number sentence by expressing each part using hundredths. Model using the place value chart, as shown in part (a).

ones	•	tenths	hundredths
		•	• • • • • • • • (circled: • • • • • • • • • •)

a. 1 tenth + 8 hundredths = _____ hundredths

ones	•	tenths	hundredths

b. 2 tenths + 3 hundredths = _____ hundredths

ones	•	tenths	hundredths

c. 1 tenth + 14 hundredths = _____ hundredths

2. Solve by converting all addends to hundredths before solving.

a. 1 tenth + 2 hundredths = ______ hundredths + 2 hundredths = ______ hundredths

b. 4 tenths + 11 hundredths = ______ hundredths + ______ hundredths = ______ hundredths

c. 8 tenths + 25 hundredths = ______ hundredths + ______ hundredths =______ hundredths

d. 43 hundredths + 6 tenths = ______ hundredths + ______ hundredths = ______ hundredths

© 2015 Great Minds. eureka-math.org
G4-M6-TE-B5-1.3.1-01.2016

3. Find the sum. Convert tenths to hundredths as needed. Write your answer as a decimal.

a. $\frac{3}{10} + \frac{7}{100}$

b. $\frac{16}{100} + \frac{5}{10}$

c. $\frac{5}{10} + \frac{40}{100}$

d. $\frac{20}{100} + \frac{8}{10}$

4. Solve. Write your answer as a decimal.

a. $\frac{5}{10} + \frac{53}{100}$

b. $\frac{27}{100} + \frac{8}{10}$

c. $\frac{4}{10} + \frac{78}{100}$

d. $\frac{98}{100} + \frac{7}{10}$

5. Cameron measured $\frac{65}{100}$ inch of rainwater on the first day of April. On the second day of April, he measured $\frac{83}{100}$ inch of rainwater. How many total inches of rainwater did Cameron measure on the first two days of April?

EUREKA MATH

© 2015 Great Minds. eureka-math.org
G4-M6-TE-B5-1.3.1-01.2016

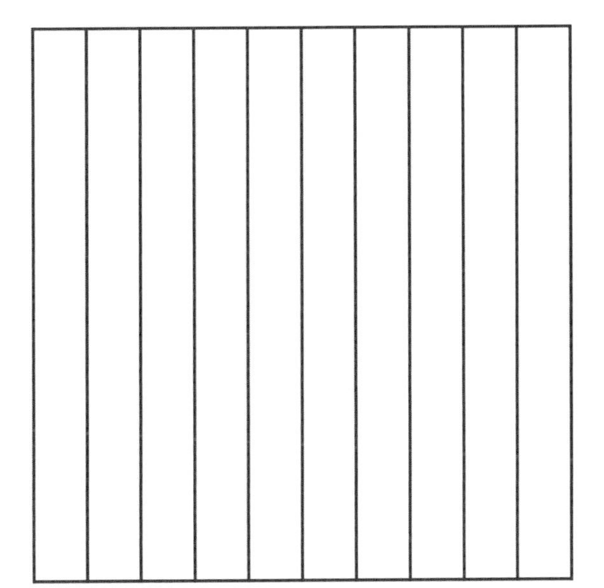

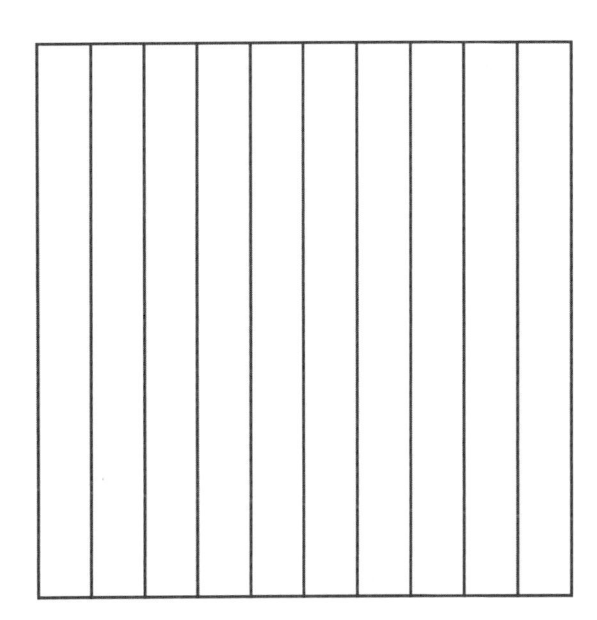

ones	•	tenths	hundredths

area model and place value chart

© 2015 Great Minds. eureka-math.org
G4-M6-TE-B5-1.3.1-01.2016

Lesson 13

Objective: Add decimal numbers by converting to fraction form.

Suggested Lesson Structure

- Fluency Practice (8 minutes)
- Concept Development (42 minutes)
- Student Debrief (10 minutes)

Total Time (60 minutes)

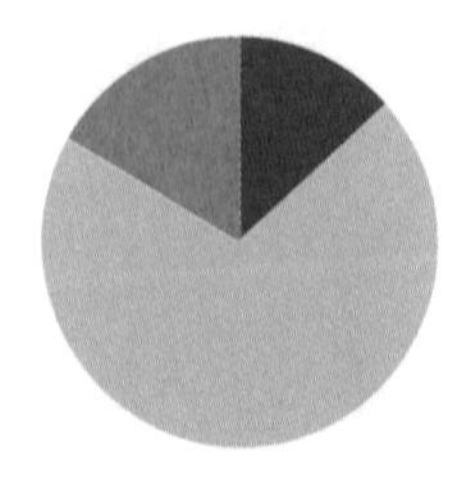

Fluency Practice (8 minutes)

- Order Decimal Numbers **4.NF.7** (4 minutes)
- Write in Decimal and Fraction Notation **4.NF.5** (4 minutes)

Order Decimal Numbers (4 minutes)

Materials: (S) Personal white board

Note: This fluency activity reviews Lesson 11.

T: (Write 0.44, $\frac{1}{10}$, and 0.5.) Arrange the numbers in order from least to greatest.

S: (Write $\frac{1}{10}$, 0.44, and 0.5.)

Continue with the following possible sequence:

- 0.6, 0.55, $\frac{16}{10}$, $\frac{65}{100}$, 0.87, 0.1, 0.77, 0.88
- $\frac{87}{10}$, 6 ones and 8 hundredths, $\frac{68}{100}$, 8 and 6 tenths, $\frac{680}{100}$, 6.86

NOTES ON MULTIPLE MEANS OF ACTION AND EXPRESSION:

Adjust the Order Decimal Numbers fluency activity so that English language learners gain more practice in oral comprehension and transcribing. Rather than writing the numbers on the board, give directions, such as, "Arrange the following numbers in order from least to greatest: 44 hundredths, 1 tenth, 5 tenths." If desired, give an additional direction, such as, "Write some numbers as decimals and some as fractions." Students who are challenged by writing at such a fast pace may enjoy ordering cards (with decimals and fractions) as used in Lesson 11.

Write in Decimal and Fraction Notation (4 minutes)

Materials: (S) Personal white board

Note: This fluency activity reviews Lesson 7.

T: (Write 25.34.) Say the number.

S: 25 and 34 hundredths.

T: Write 25 and 34 hundredths in decimal expanded form without multiplication.

S: (Write 20 + 5 + 0.3 + 0.04.)

© 2015 Great Minds. eureka-math.org
G4-M6-TE-B5-1.3.1-01.2016

T: Write 25 and 34 hundredths in decimal expanded form with multiplication.

S: (Write 25.34 = (2 × 10) + (5 × 1) + (3 × 0.1) + (4 × 0.01).)

T: Write 25 and 34 hundredths in fraction expanded form with multiplication.

S: (Write 25.34 = $(2 \times 10) + (5 \times 1) + (3 \times \frac{1}{10}) + (4 \times \frac{1}{100})$.)

Continue the process for the following possible sequence: 28.07 and 452.70.

Concept Development (42 minutes)

Materials: (S) Personal white board

Problem 1: Add two decimal numbers less than 1 by converting to fraction form.

T: (Write 0.3 + 0.57.) Say the expression.

S: 3 tenths plus 57 hundredths.

T: Let's use what we know to add. Convert 3 tenths + 57 hundredths to fraction form.

S: (Write $\frac{3}{10} + \frac{57}{100}$.)

T: Solve.

S: $\frac{3}{10} = \frac{30}{100}$. So, $\frac{30}{100} + \frac{57}{100} = \frac{87}{100}$.

T: Write your answer as a decimal.

S: 0.87.

T: Write 0.5 + 0.64. Convert to fraction form.

MP.2

S: (Write $\frac{5}{10} + \frac{64}{100}$.)

T: Solve.

S: $\frac{5}{10} = \frac{50}{100}$. So, $\frac{50}{100} + \frac{64}{100} = \frac{114}{100}$. That's more than 1.

T: Convert to a mixed number.

S: $\frac{114}{100} = 1\frac{14}{100}$. → I solved by decomposing an addend to make 1 using a number bond. The answer is $1\frac{14}{100}$.

T: Write your answer as a decimal.

S: 1.14.

T: Add 0.30 to 0.5.

S: $0.30 = \frac{30}{100}$. $0.5 = \frac{5}{10} = \frac{50}{100}$. So, $\frac{30}{100} + \frac{50}{100} = \frac{80}{100}$. $\frac{80}{100}$ is the same as $\frac{8}{10}$, so the answer is 0.80 or 0.8. → I converted hundredths to tenths instead before adding! $\frac{30}{100} = \frac{300 \div 10}{100 \div 10} = \frac{3}{10}$. So, $\frac{3}{10} + \frac{5}{10} = \frac{8}{10} = 0.8$.

Repeat the process with the following possible sequence: 0.2 + 0.31 and 0.29 + 0.8.

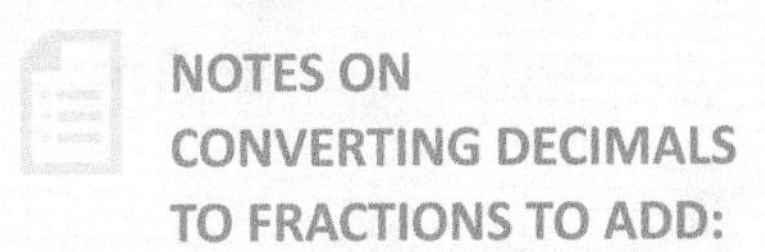

NOTES ON CONVERTING DECIMALS TO FRACTIONS TO ADD:

While converting decimals to fractions before adding may not seem as quick as just adding decimals (e.g., 0.3 and 0.57), doing so strengthens student understanding of the fraction and decimal relationship, increases their ability to think flexibly, and prepares them for greater success with fractions and decimals in Grade 5.

$$0.3 + 0.57 = \frac{3}{10} + \frac{57}{100} = \frac{30}{100} + \frac{57}{100} = \frac{87}{100} = 0.87$$

$$0.5 + 0.64 = \frac{5}{10} + \frac{64}{100} = \frac{50}{100} + \frac{64}{100}$$

$\frac{64}{100}$ → $\frac{50}{100}$ and $\frac{14}{100}$

$$= 1\frac{14}{100} = 1.14$$

© 2015 Great Minds. eureka-math.org
G4-M6-TE-B5-1.3.1-01.2016

Problem 2: Add two decimal numbers involving whole numbers and like fractional units by converting to fractional form.

T: (Write 6.8 + 5.7.) Rewrite this expression as the sum of two mixed numbers.

S: (Write $6\frac{8}{10} + 5\frac{7}{10}$.)

T: What do you know about mixed number addition to help you solve this problem?

S: I can add the whole numbers and then add the tenths. → I can add ones to ones and then add the fractions because they have the same denominator.

T: Solve with your partner.

S: $6\frac{8}{10} + 5\frac{7}{10} = (6 + 5) + \left(\frac{8}{10} + \frac{7}{10}\right) = 11\frac{15}{10} = 12\frac{5}{10}$.
(Another possible solution is shown to the right.)

$6.8 + 5.7 = 6\frac{8}{10} + 5\frac{7}{10}$
$= 11\frac{15}{10}$ ($\frac{15}{10}$ split into 1 and $\frac{5}{10}$)
$= 12\frac{5}{10}$
$6.8 + 5.7 = 12.5$

T: Rewrite your number sentence in decimal form.

S: 6.8 + 5.7 = 12.5.

T: (Write 4.28 + 2.97.) Rewrite this expression as the sum of two mixed numbers.

S: (Write $4\frac{28}{100} + 2\frac{97}{100}$.)

T: Solve with your partner. (One possible solution is shown to the right.)

$4.28 + 2.97 = 4\frac{28}{100} + 2\frac{97}{100}$
$= 6\frac{125}{100} = 7\frac{25}{100}$ ($\frac{125}{100}$ split into 1 and $\frac{25}{100}$)
$4.28 + 2.97 = 7.25$

T: Rewrite your number sentence in decimal form.

S: 4.28 + 2.97 = 7.25.

Problem 3: Add two decimal numbers involving whole numbers, tenths, and hundredths with unlike units by converting to fractional form.

T: (Write 3.5 + 2.49.) Convert this expression to fraction form as the sum of two mixed numbers.

S: (Write $3\frac{5}{100} + 2\frac{49}{100}$.)

T: What do you know about mixed number addition to help you solve this problem?

S: I can add ones to ones and then add the fractions after I change them to like units. → I have to change the tenths to hundredths to add the fractions.

$3.5 + 2.49 = 3\frac{50}{100} + 2\frac{49}{100}$
$= 5\frac{50}{100} + \frac{49}{100}$
$= 5\frac{99}{100}$
$3.5 + 2.49 = 5.99$

T: Solve with your partner.

S: $3\frac{50}{100} + 2\frac{49}{100} = 5\frac{50}{100} + \frac{49}{100} = 5\frac{99}{100}$.

T: Rewrite your number sentence in decimal form.

S: 3.5 + 2.49 = 5.99.

© 2015 Great Minds. eureka-math.org
G4-M6-TE-B5-1.3.1-01.2016

T: (Write 5.6 + 4.53.) Rewrite this expression as the sum of mixed numbers in fraction form.

S: (Write $5\frac{6}{10} + 4\frac{53}{100}$.)

T: Work with a partner to solve. After you have found the sum in fraction form, rewrite the decimal number sentence.

T: (Allow students time to work, and then present two or three alternate solutions as exemplified below.) Analyze and discuss the following solution strategies with your partner.

$$5.6 + 4.53 = 5\frac{6}{10} + 4\frac{53}{100}$$
$$= 5\frac{60}{100} + 4\frac{53}{100}$$
$$= 9\frac{60}{100} + \frac{53}{100}$$
$$= 9\frac{113}{100}$$
[$\frac{113}{100}$ split into 1 and $\frac{13}{100}$]
$$= 10\frac{13}{100}$$
$$5.6 + 4.53 = 10.13$$

$$5.6 + 4.53 = 5\frac{6}{10} + 4\frac{53}{100}$$
[$\frac{53}{100}$ split into $\frac{4}{10}$ and $\frac{13}{100}$]
$$= 9 + 1 + \frac{13}{100}$$
$$= 10\frac{13}{100}$$
$$5.6 + 4.53 = 10.13$$

$$5.6 + 4.53 = 5\frac{60}{100} + 4\frac{53}{100}$$
[$\frac{53}{100}$ split into $\frac{40}{100}$ and $\frac{13}{100}$]
$$= 10\frac{13}{100}$$
$$5.6 + 4.53 = 10.13$$

S: The first solution shows adding like units and decomposing the sum of the hundredths into 1 and 13 hundredths. → The second solution shows decomposing $\frac{53}{100}$ to take out $\frac{4}{10}$ to make 1. They then added 9 ones with the 1 they made from 6 tenths and 4 tenths to get 10 ones and 13 hundredths. → The third solution shows converting tenths to hundredths in one step. Then, they decomposed the hundredths to make 1 from 60 hundredths and 40 hundredths. 6 ones and 4 ones is 10 ones with 13 hundredths. → All of them show the same decimal number sentence.

T: Yes, remember that there are multiple solution strategies that we learned when adding fractions that we can use here when adding decimal fractions.

Repeat with 3.82 + 19.6.

Problem Set (10 minutes)

Students should do their personal best to complete the Problem Set within the allotted 10 minutes. For some classes, it may be appropriate to modify the assignment by specifying which problems they work on first. Some problems do not specify a method for solving. Students should solve these problems using the RDW approach used for Application Problems.

© 2015 Great Minds. eureka-math.org
G4-M6-TE-B5-1.3.1-01.2016

Student Debrief (10 minutes)

Lesson Objective: Add decimal numbers by converting to fraction form.

The Student Debrief is intended to invite reflection and active processing of the total lesson experience.

Invite students to review their solutions for the Problem Set. They should check work by comparing answers with a partner before going over answers as a class. Look for misconceptions or misunderstandings that can be addressed in the Debrief. Guide students in a conversation to debrief the Problem Set and process the lesson.

Any combination of the questions below may be used to lead the discussion.

- Explain to your partner the process of adding two mixed numbers. Why do we need to convert to like units?
- What other conversion could you have used for Problems 2(a) and 2(c)?
- For Problems 2(b) and 2(d), explain how in the solution you could make 1 before adding the hundredths together.
- What was the added complexity of Problem 2 in the Problem Set? How did your prior knowledge of adding mixed numbers from Module 5 help to make this task easier?

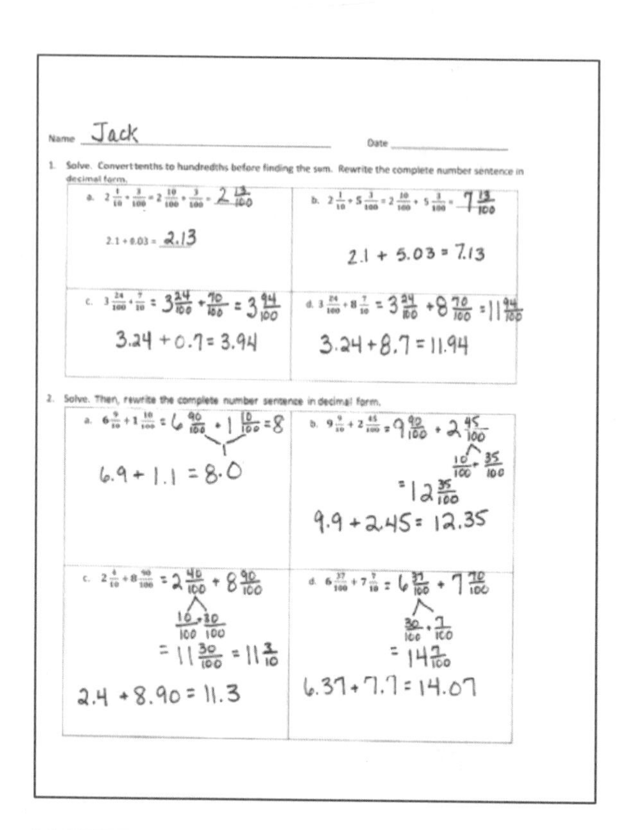
Name Jack Date

1. Solve. Convert tenths to hundredths before finding the sum. Rewrite the complete number sentence in decimal form.

a. $2\frac{1}{10} + \frac{3}{100} = 2\frac{10}{100} + \frac{3}{100} = 2\frac{13}{100}$; $2.1 + 0.03 = 2.13$

b. $2\frac{1}{10} + 5\frac{3}{100} = 2\frac{10}{100} + 5\frac{3}{100} = 7\frac{13}{100}$; $2.1 + 5.03 = 7.13$

c. $3\frac{24}{100} + \frac{7}{10} = 3\frac{24}{100} + \frac{70}{100} = 3\frac{94}{100}$; $3.24 + 0.7 = 3.94$

d. $3\frac{24}{100} + 8\frac{7}{10} = 3\frac{24}{100} + 8\frac{70}{100} = 11\frac{94}{100}$; $3.24 + 8.7 = 11.94$

2. Solve. Then, rewrite the complete number sentence in decimal form.

a. $6\frac{9}{10} + 1\frac{10}{100} = 6\frac{90}{100} + 1\frac{10}{100} = 8$; $6.9 + 1.1 = 8.0$

b. $9\frac{9}{10} + 2\frac{45}{100} = 9\frac{90}{100} + 2\frac{45}{100}$; $\frac{10}{100} + \frac{35}{100}$; $= 12\frac{35}{100}$; $9.9 + 2.45 = 12.35$

c. $2\frac{4}{10} + 8\frac{90}{100} = 2\frac{40}{100} + 8\frac{90}{100}$; $\frac{10}{100} + \frac{30}{100}$; $= 11\frac{30}{100} = 11\frac{3}{10}$; $2.4 + 8.90 = 11.3$

d. $6\frac{37}{100} + 7\frac{7}{10} = 6\frac{37}{100} + 7\frac{70}{100}$; $\frac{30}{100} + \frac{7}{100}$; $= 14\frac{7}{100}$; $6.37 + 7.7 = 14.07$

3. Solve by rewriting the number sentence in fraction form. After solving, rewrite the complete number sentence in decimal form.

a. 6.4 + 5.3: $6\frac{4}{10} + 5\frac{3}{10} = 11\frac{7}{10}$; $6.4 + 5.3 = 11.7$

b. 6.62 + 2.98: $6\frac{62}{100} + 2\frac{98}{100} = 9\frac{60}{100}$; $6.62 + 2.98 = 9.6$

c. 2.1 + 0.94: $2\frac{10}{100} + \frac{94}{100} = 3\frac{4}{100}$; $\frac{6}{100} + \frac{4}{100}$; $2.1 + 0.94 = 3.04$

d. 2.1 + 5.94: $2\frac{10}{100} + 5\frac{94}{100} = 8\frac{4}{100}$; $\frac{6}{100} + \frac{4}{100}$; $2.1 + 5.94 = 8.04$

e. 5.7 + 4.92: $5\frac{70}{100} + 4\frac{92}{100} = 10\frac{62}{100}$; $\frac{62}{100} + \frac{8}{100}$; $5.7 + 4.92 = 10.62$

f. 5.68 + 4.9: $5\frac{68}{100} + 4\frac{90}{100} = 10\frac{58}{100}$; $\frac{58}{100}\ \frac{10}{100}$; $5.68 + 4.9 = 10.58$

g. 4.8 + 3.27: $4\frac{80}{100} + 3\frac{27}{100} = 8\frac{7}{100}$; $\frac{20}{100} + \frac{7}{100}$; $4.8 + 3.27 = 8.07$

h. 17.6 + 3.59: $17\frac{60}{100} + 3\frac{59}{100} = 21\frac{19}{100}$; $\frac{40}{100}\ \frac{19}{100}$; $17.6 + 3.59 = 21.19$

Exit Ticket (3 minutes)

After the Student Debrief, instruct students to complete the Exit Ticket. A review of their work will help with assessing students' understanding of the concepts that were presented in today's lesson and planning more effectively for future lessons. The questions may be read aloud to the students.

© 2015 Great Minds. eureka-math.org
G4-M6-TE-B5-1.3.1-01.2016

Name ______________________________ Date ______________

1. Solve. Convert tenths to hundredths before finding the sum. Rewrite the complete number sentence in decimal form. Problems 1(a) and 1(b) are partially completed for you.

a. $2\frac{1}{10} + \frac{3}{100} = 2\frac{10}{100} + \frac{3}{100} =$ ________ 2.1 + 0.03 = ______	b. $2\frac{1}{10} + 5\frac{3}{100} = 2\frac{10}{100} + 5\frac{3}{100} =$ ________
c. $3\frac{24}{100} + \frac{7}{10}$	d. $3\frac{24}{100} + 8\frac{7}{10}$

2. Solve. Then, rewrite the complete number sentence in decimal form.

a. $6\frac{9}{10} + 1\frac{10}{100}$	b. $9\frac{9}{10} + 2\frac{45}{100}$
c. $2\frac{4}{10} + 8\frac{90}{100}$	d. $6\frac{37}{100} + 7\frac{7}{10}$

© 2015 Great Minds. eureka-math.org
G4-M6-TE-B5-1.3.1-01.2016

3. Solve by rewriting the number sentence in fraction form. After solving, rewrite the complete number sentence in decimal form.

a. 6.4 + 5.3	b. 6.62 + 2.98
c. 2.1 + 0.94	d. 2.1 + 5.94
e. 5.7 + 4.92	f. 5.68 + 4.9
g. 4.8 + 3.27	h. 17.6 + 3.59

© 2015 Great Minds. eureka-math.org
G4-M6-TE-B5-1.3.1-01.2016

Name ______________________________ Date ________________

Solve by rewriting the number sentence in fraction form. After solving, rewrite the complete number sentence in decimal form.

1. 7.3 + 0.95

2. 8.29 + 5.9

© 2015 Great Minds. eureka-math.org
G4-M6-TE-B5-1.3.1-01.2016

Name ______________________________ Date ______________

1. Solve. Convert tenths to hundredths before finding the sum. Rewrite the complete number sentence in decimal form. Problems 1(a) and 1(b) are partially completed for you.

a. $5\frac{2}{10} + \frac{7}{100} = 5\frac{20}{100} + \frac{7}{100} =$ ________ $5.2 + 0.07 =$ ________	b. $5\frac{2}{10} + 3\frac{7}{100} = 8\frac{20}{100} + \frac{7}{100} =$ ________
c. $6\frac{5}{10} + \frac{1}{100}$	d. $6\frac{5}{10} + 7\frac{1}{100}$

2. Solve. Then, rewrite the complete number sentence in decimal form.

a. $4\frac{9}{10} + 5\frac{10}{100}$	b. $8\frac{7}{10} + 2\frac{65}{100}$
c. $7\frac{3}{10} + 6\frac{87}{100}$	d. $5\frac{48}{100} + 7\frac{8}{10}$

© 2015 Great Minds. eureka-math.org
G4-M6-TE-B5-1.3.1-01.2016

3. Solve by rewriting the number sentence in fraction form. After solving, rewrite the complete number sentence in decimal form.

a. $2.1 + 0.87 = 2\frac{1}{10} + \frac{87}{100}$	b. $7.2 + 2.67$
c. $7.3 + 1.8$	d. $7.3 + 1.86$
e. $6.07 + 3.93$	f. $6.87 + 3.9$
g. $8.6 + 4.67$	h. $18.62 + 14.7$

© 2015 Great Minds. eureka-math.org
G4-M6-TE-B5-1.3.1-01.2016

Lesson 14

Objective: Solve word problems involving the addition of measurements in decimal form.

Suggested Lesson Structure

■	Fluency Practice	(12 minutes)
■	Concept Development	(38 minutes)
■	Student Debrief	(10 minutes)
	Total Time	**(60 minutes)**

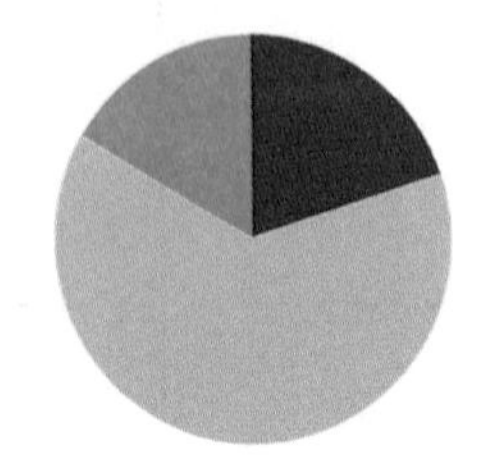

Fluency Practice (12 minutes)

- State the Value of the Coins **4.MD.2** (2 minutes)
- Add Decimals **4.NF.5** (5 minutes)
- Write in Decimal and Fraction Notation **4.NF.5** (5 minutes)

State the Value of the Coins (2 minutes)

Materials: (S) Personal white board

Note: This fluency activity prepares students for Lessons 15–16.

T: (Write 1 dime = __ ¢.) What is the value of 1 dime?
S: 10¢.
T: 2 dimes?
S: 20¢.
T: 3 dimes?
S: 30¢.
T: 8 dimes?
S: 80¢.
T: (Write 10 dimes = ___dollar.) Write the number sentence.
S: (Write 10 dimes = 1 dollar.)
T: (Write 20 dimes = ___dollars.) Write the number sentence.
S: (Write 20 dimes = 2 dollars.)
T: (Write 1 penny = ___¢.) What is the value of 1 penny?
S: 1¢.

© 2015 Great Minds. eureka-math.org
G4-M6-TE-B5-1.3.1-01.2016

T: 2 pennies?
S: 2¢.
T: 3 pennies?
S: 3¢.
T: 9 pennies?
S: 9¢.
T: (Write 7 pennies = __¢.) Write the number sentence.
S: (Write 7 pennies = 7¢.)

Add Decimals (5 minutes)

Materials: (S) Personal white board

Note: This fluency activity reviews Lesson 13.

T: (Write 4 tens + 2 ones.) Say the addition sentence in standard form.
S: 40 + 2 = 42.
T: (Write $\frac{4}{10} + \frac{2}{100} = \frac{\ }{100}$.) Write the number sentence.
S: (Write $\frac{4}{10} + \frac{2}{100} = \frac{42}{100}$.)
T: (Write $\frac{4}{10} + \frac{2}{100} = \frac{42}{100}$.) Write the number sentence in decimal form.
S: (Write 0.4 + 0.02 = 0.42.)

Continue with the following possible sequence: $\frac{8}{10} + \frac{3}{100}$, $\frac{13}{100} + \frac{2}{10}$, $\frac{5}{10} + \frac{30}{100}$, $\frac{40}{100} + \frac{4}{10}$, $\frac{7}{10} + \frac{30}{100}$, and $\frac{8}{10} + \frac{37}{100}$.

NOTES ON MULTIPLE MEANS OF ENGAGEMENT:

English language learners and others may benefit from a reminder, such as a poster, personal dictionary, or word wall, that defines and provides examples of *standard form, fraction form, unit form,* and *decimal form.* Examples may provide clarity for the Add Decimals fluency activity.

Write in Decimal and Fraction Notation (5 minutes)

Materials: (S) Personal white board

Note: This fluency activity reviews Lesson 12.

T: (Write 36.79.) Say the number.
S: 36 and 79 hundredths.
T: Write 36 and 79 hundredths in decimal expanded form without multiplication.
S: (Write 36.79 = 30 + 6 + 0.7 + 0.09.)
T: (Write 36.79 = (_ × 10) + (_ × 1) + (_ × 0.1) + (_ × 0.01).) Complete the number sentence.
S: (Write 36.79 = (3 × 10) + (6 × 1) + (7 × 0.1) + (9 × 0.01).)
T: Write 36 and 79 hundredths in fraction expanded form with multiplication.
S: (Write $36\frac{79}{100} = (3 \times 10) + (6 \times 1) + (7 \times \frac{1}{10}) + (9 \times \frac{1}{100})$.)

Continue with the following possible sequence: 34.09 and 734.80.

© 2015 Great Minds. eureka-math.org
G4-M6-TE-B5-1.3.1-01.2016

Concept Development (38 minutes)

Materials: (S) Personal white board, Problem Set

Suggested Delivery of Instruction for Solving This Lesson's Word Problems

1. Model the problem.

Have two pairs of students model the problem at the board while the others work independently or in pairs at their seats. Review the following questions before beginning the first problem:

- Can you draw something?
- What can you draw?
- What conclusions can you make from your drawing?

As students work, circulate. Reiterate the questions above. After two minutes, have the two pairs of students share only their labeled diagrams. For about one minute, have the demonstrating students receive and respond to feedback and questions from their peers.

2. Calculate to solve and write a statement.

Give students two minutes to finish their work on that question, sharing their work and thinking with a peer. All should then write their equations and statements of the answer.

3. Assess the solution for reasonableness.

Give students one to two minutes to assess and explain the reasonableness of their solutions.

NOTES ON MULTIPLE MEANS OF REPRESENTATION:

In today's lesson, students apply their skill with adding decimals by first converting them to fraction form. The first two problems are single-step problems. Encourage students to use the RDW process because, in doing so, they again realize that part–whole relationships are the same whether the parts are whole numbers, fractions, or mixed numbers.

Problem 1

Barrel A contains 2.7 liters of water. Barrel B contains 3.09 liters of water. Together, how much water do the two barrels contain?

W

2.7 L	3.09 L

$2.7 = 2\frac{7}{10} = 2\frac{70}{100}$

$3.09 = 3\frac{9}{100}$

Solution A

$W = 2.7\text{ L} + 3.09\text{ L}$

$= 2\frac{70}{100}\text{ L} + 3\frac{9}{100}\text{ L}$

$= 5\frac{70}{100}\text{ L} + \frac{9}{100}\text{ L}$

$= 5\frac{79}{100}\text{ L}$

$W = 5.79\text{ L}$

Solution B

$2\frac{70}{100} \xrightarrow{+3} 5\frac{70}{100} \xrightarrow{+\frac{9}{100}} 5\frac{79}{100}$

$W = 5.79\text{ L}$

The 2 barrels contain 5.79 Liters of water.

The first problem of the day starts at a simple level to give students the opportunity to simply apply their skill with converting decimal numbers to fraction form to solve a word problem. Students solve this problem by converting 2.7 liters and 3.09 liters to fractional form, converting tenths to hundredths, and adding the mixed numbers. Remind students to convert their answers to decimal form when writing their statements.

© 2015 Great Minds. eureka-math.org
G4-M6-TE-B5-1.3.1-01.2016

Problem 2

Alissa ran a distance of 15.8 kilometers one week and 17.34 kilometers the following week. How far did she run in the two weeks?

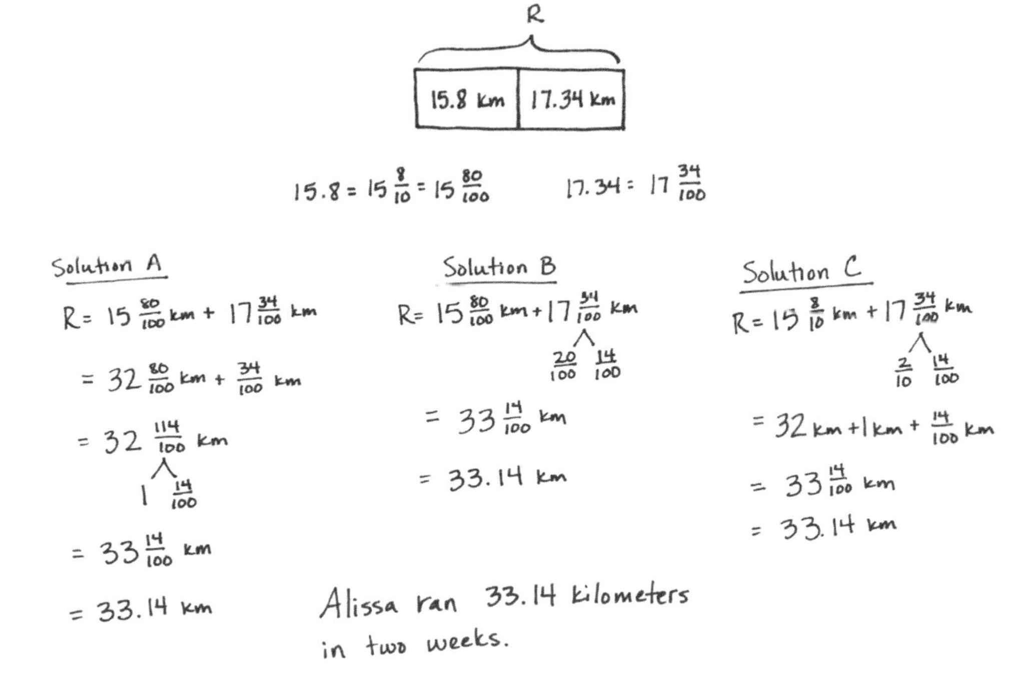

Problem 2 invites various solution strategies because the sum of the fractions is greater than 1, and the whole numbers are larger. In Solution A, students add like units and decompose by drawing a number bond to show $\frac{114}{100}$ as $1 + \frac{14}{100}$ and then adding 32. In Solutions B and C, students use different methods of breaking apart $\frac{34}{100}$ to add up to make 1.

© 2015 Great Minds. eureka-math.org
G4-M6-TE-B5-1.3.1-01.2016

Problem 3

An apple orchard sold 140.5 kilograms of apples in the morning and 15.85 kilograms more apples in the afternoon than in the morning. How many total kilograms of apples were sold that day?

M [140.5 kg]
A [140.5 kg | 15.85 kg] } ?

Solution A

$140\frac{5}{10} + 15\frac{85}{100} = 155\frac{50}{100} + \frac{85}{100}$

$= 155\frac{135}{100}$

$= 156\frac{35}{100}$

$140\frac{5}{10} + 156\frac{35}{100} = 296\frac{50}{100} + \frac{35}{100}$

$= 296\frac{85}{100}$

Solution B

$\left(2 \times 140\frac{5}{10}\right) + 15.85 = 280\frac{10}{10} + 15\frac{85}{100}$

$= 296\frac{85}{100}$

The apple orchard sold 296.85 kilograms of apples.

This problem brings the additional complexity of two steps. Students solve this problem by converting 140.5 kilograms and 15.85 kilograms to fractional form, converting tenths to hundredths, and then adding the mixed numbers. Remind students to convert their answers to decimal form and to include the labeled units in their answers. Solution A shows solving for the number of kilograms sold in the afternoon and then solving for the total number of kilograms sold in the day by adding the kilograms of apples from the morning with those from the afternoon. In Solution B, the number of kilograms sold in the morning is multiplied by 2, and then the additional kilograms sold in the afternoon are added.

EUREKA MATH

© 2015 Great Minds. eureka-math.org
G4-M6-TE-B5-1.3.1-01.2016

Problem 4

A team of three ran a relay race. The final runner's time was the fastest, measuring 29.2 seconds. The middle runner's time was 1.89 seconds slower than the final runner's. The starting runner's time was 0.9 seconds slower than the middle runner's. What was the team's total time for the race?

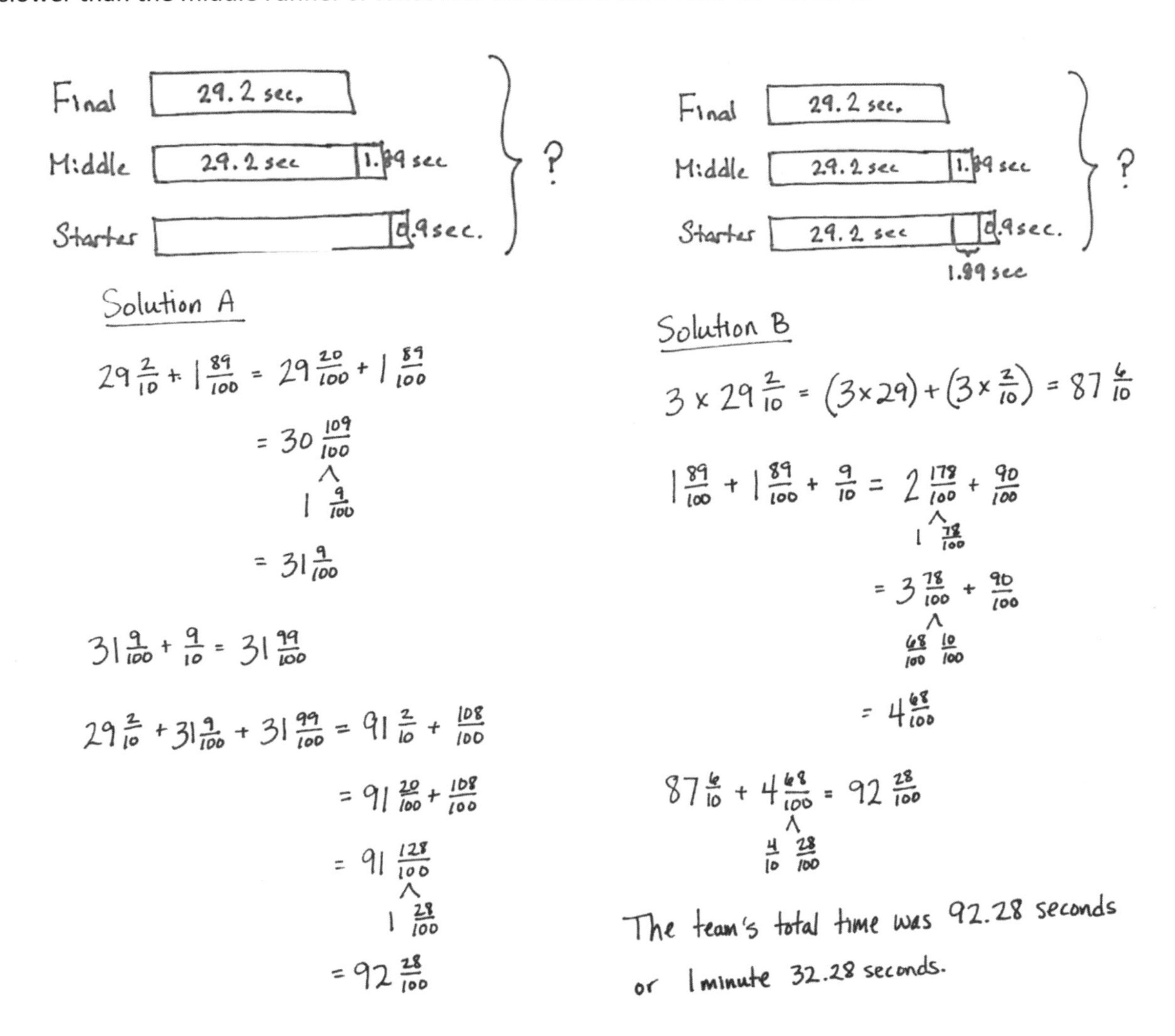

This problem involves two additional challenges. First, students must realize that when a runner goes slower, there is more time added on. Second, to find the starting runner's time, students must add the 9 tenths second to the middle runner's time. Notice the difference in Solution A's and Solution B's models. In Solution A, the student finds the time of each individual runner, first adding 1.89 seconds to 29.2 seconds and then adding 0.9 seconds to that sum to find the time of the starting runner. On the other hand, Solution B shows how a student solves by thinking of the starting runner in relationship to the final runner. As a result, she is able to discern the 3 units of 29.2 seconds, multiplies 29.2 by 3, adds $1\frac{89}{100} + 1\frac{89}{100} + \frac{9}{10}$, and adds the two sums together.

© 2015 Great Minds. eureka-math.org
G4-M6-TE-B5-1.3.1-01.2016

Student Debrief (10 minutes)

Lesson Objective: Solve word problems involving the addition of measurements in decimal form.

The Student Debrief is intended to invite reflection and active processing of the total lesson experience.

Invite students to review their solutions for the Problem Set. They should check work by comparing answers with a partner before going over answers as a class. Look for misconceptions or misunderstandings that can be addressed in the Debrief. Guide students in a conversation to debrief the Problem Set and process the lesson.

Any combination of the questions below may be used to lead the discussion.

- What was the added complexity of Problem 3? What about Problem 4?
- Explain the strategies that you used to solve Problems 3 and 4.

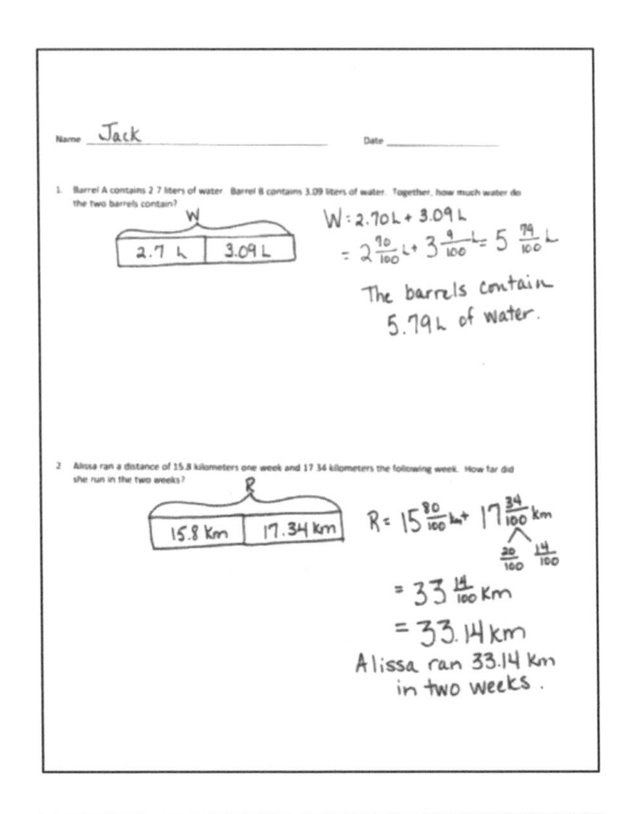

Exit Ticket (3 minutes)

After the Student Debrief, instruct students to complete the Exit Ticket. A review of their work will help with assessing students' understanding of the concepts that were presented in today's lesson and planning more effectively for future lessons. The questions may be read aloud to the students.

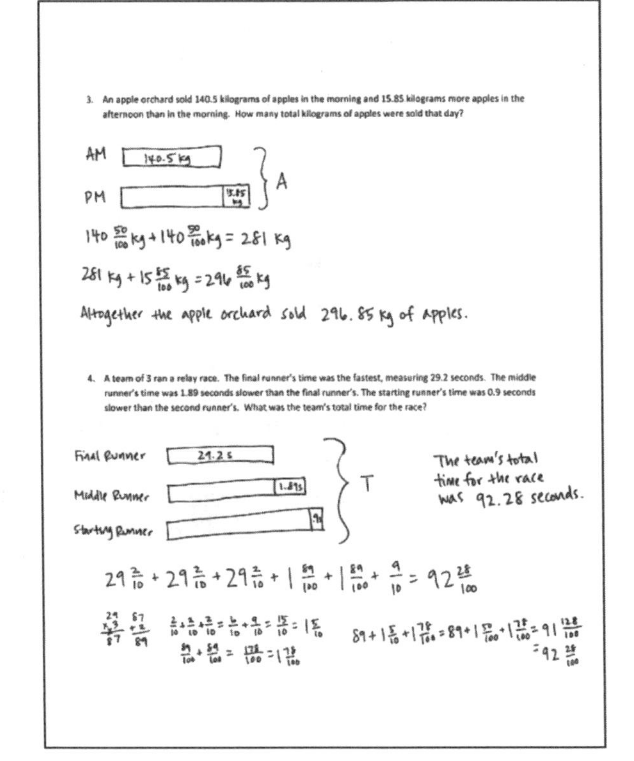

EUREKA MATH
© 2015 Great Minds. eureka-math.org
G4-M6-TE-B5-1.3.1-01.2016

Name ______________________________ Date ________________

1. Barrel A contains 2.7 liters of water. Barrel B contains 3.09 liters of water. Together, how much water do the two barrels contain?

2. Alissa ran a distance of 15.8 kilometers one week and 17.34 kilometers the following week. How far did she run in the two weeks?

© 2015 Great Minds. eureka-math.org
G4-M6-TE-B5-1.3.1-01.2016

3. An apple orchard sold 140.5 kilograms of apples in the morning and 15.85 kilograms more apples in the afternoon than in the morning. How many total kilograms of apples were sold that day?

4. A team of three ran a relay race. The final runner's time was the fastest, measuring 29.2 seconds. The middle runner's time was 1.89 seconds slower than the final runner's. The starting runner's time was 0.9 seconds slower than the middle runner's. What was the team's total time for the race?

© 2015 Great Minds. eureka-math.org
G4-M6-TE-B5-1.3.1-01.2016

EUREKA MATH

Name ______________________________ Date ______________

Elise ran 6.43 kilometers on Saturday and 5.6 kilometers on Sunday. How many total kilometers did she run on Saturday and Sunday?

© 2015 Great Minds. eureka-math.org
G4-M6-TE-B5-1.3.1-01.2016

Name ______________________________ Date ________________

1. The snowfall in Year 1 was 2.03 meters. The snowfall in Year 2 was 1.6 meters. How many total meters of snow fell in Years 1 and 2?

2. A deli sliced 22.6 kilograms of roast beef one week and 13.54 kilograms the next. How many total kilograms of roast beef did the deli slice in the two weeks?

© 2015 Great Minds. eureka-math.org
G4-M6-TE-B5-1.3.1-01.2016

3. The school cafeteria served 125.6 liters of milk on Monday and 5.34 more liters of milk on Tuesday than on Monday. How many total liters of milk were served on Monday and Tuesday?

4. Max, Maria, and Armen were a team in a relay race. Max ran his part in 17.3 seconds. Maria was 0.7 seconds slower than Max. Armen was 1.5 seconds slower than Maria. What was the total time for the team?

© 2015 Great Minds. eureka-math.org
G4-M6-TE-B5-1.3.1-01.2016

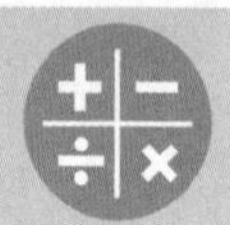

Topic E

Money Amounts as Decimal Numbers

4.MD.2, 4.NF.5, 4.NF.6

Focus Standard:		4.MD.2	Use the four operations to solve word problems involving distances, intervals of time, liquid volumes, masses of objects, and money, including problems involving simple fractions or decimals, and problems that require expressing measurements given in a larger unit in terms of a smaller unit. Represent measurement quantities using diagrams such as number line diagrams that feature a measurement scale.
Instructional Days:		2	
Coherence	**-Links from:**	G2–M7	Problem Solving with Length, Money, and Data
		G3–M5	Fractions as Numbers on the Number Line
	-Links to:	G5–M2	Multi-Digit Whole Number and Decimal Fraction Operations

In Topic E, students work with money amounts as decimal numbers, applying what they have come to understand about decimals.

Students recognize 1 penny as $\frac{1}{100}$ dollar, 1 dime as $\frac{1}{10}$ dollar, and 1 quarter as $\frac{25}{100}$ dollar in Lesson 15. They apply their understanding of tenths and hundredths to express money amounts in both fraction and decimal forms. Students use this understanding to decompose varying configurations and forms of dollars, quarters, dimes, and pennies and express each as a decimal fraction and decimal number. They then expand this skill to include money amounts greater than a dollar in decimal form.

In Lesson 16, students continue their work with money and apply their understanding that only like units can be added. They solve word problems involving money using all four operations (**4.MD.2**). Addition and subtraction word problems are computed using dollars and cents in unit form. Multiplication and division word problems are computed using cents in unit form. All answers are converted from unit form into decimal form, using the dollar symbol as the unit.

2 dollars, 1 quarter, 3 dimes, 7 pennies

= 2 dollars 62 cents

= $2\frac{62}{100}$ dollars

= 2.62 dollars

= $2.62

EUREKA MATH

© 2015 Great Minds. eureka-math.org
G4-M6-TE-B5-1.3.1-01.2016

Jack has 2 quarters and 7 dimes. Jim has 1 dollar, 3 quarters, and 6 pennies. How much money do they have together? Write your answer as a decimal.

Jack | 50¢ | 70¢ |

Jim | $1 | 75¢ | 6¢ |

They have $3.01 together.

Solution A

1 dollar 20 cents + 1 dollar 81 cents

= 2 dollars 101 cents (100, 1)

= 3 dollars 1 cent

= $3.01

Solution B

1 dollar 20 cents + 1 dollar 81 cents (80, 1)

= 3 dollars 1 cent

= $3.01

A Teaching Sequence Toward Mastery of Money Amounts as Decimal Numbers	
Objective 1:	**Express money amounts given in various forms as decimal numbers. (Lesson 15)**
Objective 2:	**Solve word problems involving money. (Lesson 16)**

© 2015 Great Minds. eureka-math.org
G4-M6-TE-B5-1.3.1-01.2016

Lesson 15

Objective: Express money amounts given in various forms as decimal numbers.

Suggested Lesson Structure

- Fluency Practice (10 minutes)
- Application Problem (4 minutes)
- Concept Development (36 minutes)
- Student Debrief (10 minutes)

Total Time **(60 minutes)**

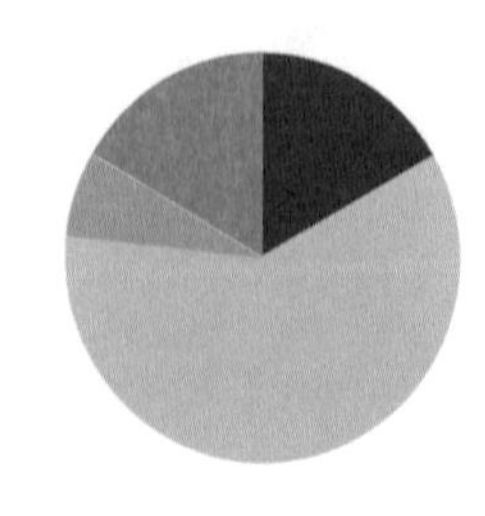

Fluency Practice (10 minutes)

- Add Fractions **4.NF.5** (5 minutes)
- State the Value of the Coins **4.MD.2** (5 minutes)

Add Fractions (5 minutes)

Note: This fluency activity reviews Lesson 13.

T: (Write 90 + 7 = ___.) Say the addition sentence in unit form.
S: 9 tens + 7 ones = 97 ones.
T: (Write $\frac{9}{10} + \frac{7}{100} = \frac{}{100}$.) Say the addition sentence in unit form.
S: 9 tenths + 7 hundredths = 97 hundredths.

Continue with the following possible sequence: 40 + 8 and $\frac{4}{10} + \frac{8}{100}$; 20 + 9 and $\frac{2}{10} + \frac{9}{100}$.

T: (Write 70 + 18 = ___.) Say the addition sentence in unit form.
S: 7 tens + 18 ones = 88 ones.
T: (Write $\frac{7}{10} + \frac{18}{100} = \frac{}{100}$.) Say the addition sentence in unit form.
S: 7 tenths + 18 hundredths = 88 hundredths.

Continue with the following possible sequence: 60 + 13 and $\frac{6}{10} + \frac{13}{100}$; 30 + 29 and $\frac{3}{10} + \frac{29}{100}$.

© 2015 Great Minds. eureka-math.org
G4-M6-TE-B5-1.3.1-01.2016

State the Value of the Coins (5 minutes)

Note: This fluency activity prepares students for Lessons 15–16.

T: (Write 10¢ = 1 ________.) What coin has a value of 10 cents?
T: 1 dime.
T: 90¢ is the same as how many dimes?
T: 9 dimes.
T: (Write 25¢ = 1 ________.) What coin has a value of 25 cents?
T: 1 quarter.
T: 50¢ is the same as how many quarters?
T: 2 quarters.
T: 75¢ is the same as how many quarters?
T: 3 quarters.
T: 100¢ is the same as how many quarters?
T: 4 quarters.
T: What is the value of 2 quarters?
T: 50 cents.
T: What is the total value of 2 quarters and 2 dimes?
T: 70 cents.
T: What is the total value of 2 quarters and 6 dimes?
T: 110 cents.

Continue with the following possible sequence: 1 quarter 5 dimes, 3 quarters 2 dimes, 2 quarters 7 dimes, and 3 quarters 2 dimes 1 penny.

Application Problem (4 minutes)

At the end of the day, Cameron counted the money in his pockets. He counted 7 pennies, 2 dimes, and 2 quarters. Tell the amount of money, in cents, that was in Cameron's pockets.

Solution A

7 + 20 + 50 = 77

Cameron has 77¢.

Solution B

7 pennies: 7¢
2 dimes: 20¢
2 quarters: 50¢

50
20
+ 7
77

Cameron has 77 cents.

Note: This Application Problem builds on the previous knowledge of money from Grade 2 Module 7, where students solved word problems involving money. In the last two lessons of this module, students extend their prior work with money amounts to think of the number of dollars and cents units and record money amounts using decimals.

© 2015 Great Minds. eureka-math.org
G4-M6-TE-B5-1.3.1-01.2016

Concept Development (36 minutes)

Materials: (S) Personal white board

Problem 1: Express pennies, dimes, and quarters as fractional parts of a dollar.

T: How many pennies are in 1 dollar?
S: 100 pennies.
T: $\frac{1}{100}$ dollar is equal to how many cents?
S: 1 cent.
T: (Write 1¢ = $\frac{1}{100}$ dollar.)
T: We can write 1 hundredth dollar using a decimal. Write $\frac{1}{100}$ in decimal form.
S: (Write 0.01.)
T: Place the dollar sign before the ones. (Write 1¢ = $\frac{1}{100}$ dollar = $0.01.) (Point to the number sentence.) We can read $0.01 as 1 cent.
T: (Show 7 pennies.) 7 pennies are how many cents?
S: 7 cents.
T: What fraction of a dollar is 7 cents?
S: $\frac{7}{100}$ dollar.
T: Write a number sentence to show the value of 7 pennies as cents, as a fraction of a dollar, and in decimal form.
S: (Write 7¢ = $\frac{7}{100}$ dollar = $0.07.)

MP.2

NOTES ON MULTIPLE MEANS FOR ACTION AND EXPRESSION:

Depending on the needs of English language learners and students working below grade level, try to couple the language at the beginning of this vignette with a visual model, such as the array of pennies on the Problem Set or an area model.

NOTES ON MULTIPLE MEANS OF ACTION AND EXPRESSION:

To support students working below grade level in writing equivalent number sentences, offer a sentence frame such as the following:

___¢ = $\frac{\_\_}{100}$ dollar = $___.___ ___

Repeat writing equivalent number sentences for 31, 80, and 100 pennies.

T: A dime also represents a fractional part of a dollar. How many dimes are in a dollar?
S: 10 dimes.
T: Draw a tape diagram to show how many dimes are needed to make 1 dollar.
S: (Draw.)
T: What fraction of a dollar is 1 dime?
S: $\frac{1}{10}$ dollar.
T: $\frac{1}{10}$ dollar is equal to how many cents?
S: 10 cents.

EUREKA MATH
© 2015 Great Minds. eureka-math.org
G4-M6-TE-B5-1.3.1-01.2016

T: (Write 10¢ = $\frac{1}{10}$ dollar.) Write $\frac{1}{10}$ dollar as an equivalent decimal using the dollar sign to tell the unit.

S: (Write 10¢ = $\frac{1}{10}$ dollar = $0.10.)

Repeat writing equivalent number sentences for 8 dimes and 10 dimes.

T: With your partner, draw a tape diagram to show how many quarters equal 1 dollar. Write a number sentence to show the equivalence of the value of 1 quarter written as cents, as a fraction of a dollar, and as a decimal.

Expect many students to write $\frac{1}{4}$ dollar, which is correct. To write the value of 1 quarter as a decimal, remind students to write an equivalent fraction using 100 as the denominator so that students show 25¢ = $\frac{25}{100}$ dollar = $0.25.

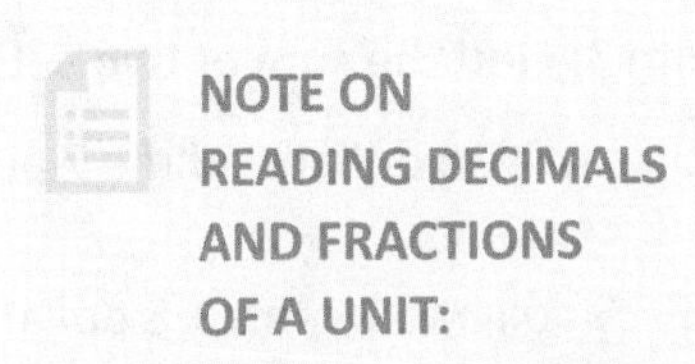

NOTE ON READING DECIMALS AND FRACTIONS OF A UNIT:

How do people read fractions and decimals? Make sure to offer English language learners and others valuable practice reading fractions and decimals correctly. To make close connections between decimals, fractions and units, read numbers such as 0.33 meter as "thirty-three hundredths meter" and $\frac{1}{100}$ dollar as "one hundredth dollar." Also, share common ways in which decimals and fractions are read daily, such as "zero point thirty-three meters" or "one hundredth of a dollar." Model for and guide students toward the preferred method of reading decimals and fractions based on the situation.

Problem 2: Express the total value of combinations of pennies, dimes, and quarters in fraction and decimal form.

T: (Write 7 dimes 2 pennies.) What is the value of 7 dimes 2 pennies expressed in cents?

S: 72 cents.

T: What number sentence did you use to find that value?

S: 70 + 2 = 72. → (7 × 10¢) + 2¢ = 72¢.

T: What fraction of a dollar is 72 cents?

S: $\frac{72}{100}$ dollar.

T: On your personal white board, express $\frac{72}{100}$ dollar in decimal form, using the dollar sign.

S: $0.72.

Repeat with 2 quarters 3 dimes 6 pennies.

T: (Write 3 quarters 4 dimes.) What is the value of 3 quarters 4 dimes expressed in cents? (Allow students time to work.)

S: 115 cents.

T: How did you find that value?

S: I counted by 25 three times and then counted up by 10 four times. → (3 × 25) + (4 × 10) = 115. → 75¢ + 40¢ = 115¢.

T: Do we have more or less than a dollar?

S: More.

T: What fraction of a dollar is 115¢?

S: $\frac{115}{100}$ dollars. → $1\frac{15}{100}$ dollars.

© 2015 Great Minds. eureka-math.org
G4-M6-TE-B5-1.3.1-01.2016

T: Express $1\frac{15}{100}$ dollars as a decimal, using the dollar sign to express the unit.

S: $1.15.

Repeat the process with 5 quarters 7 pennies.

T: What did we do when finding the value of a set of coins?

S: We multiplied by 25 to find the value of the quarters and by 10 to find the value of the dimes. → We just used multiplication and addition with whole numbers, and then we expressed our answer as a fraction of a dollar and in decimal form with the dollar sign.

Problem 3: Find the sum of two sets of bills and cents using whole number calculations and unit form

T: (Write 6 dollars 1 dime 7 pennies + 8 dollars 1 quarter.) Let's rewrite each addend as dollars and cents.

S: 6 dollars 17 cents + 8 dollars 25 cents.

T: Let's add like units to find the sum. 6 dollars + 8 dollars is ...?

S: 14 dollars.

T: 17 cents + 25 cents is ...?

S: 42 cents.

T: Write the complete number sentence on your board.

S: 6 dollars 17 cents + 8 dollars 25 cents = 14 dollars 42 cents.

T: Write your sum in decimal form using the dollar sign to designate the unit.

S: $14.42.

T: (Write 5 dollars 3 dimes 17 pennies + 4 dollars 3 quarters 2 dimes.) Work with a partner to write an expression showing each addend in unit form as dollars and cents.

S: 5 dollars 47 cents + 4 dollars 95 cents.

T: Add dollars with dollars and cents with cents to find the sum.

S: 9 dollars 142 cents. → 10 dollars 42 cents.

T: Why do these two different solutions show the same answer? Talk to your partner.

S: 142 cents is the same as 1 dollar 42 cents. We changed 9 dollars to 10 dollars (Solution A). → We completed the dollar. 95 cents + 47 cents is the same as 95 + 5 + 42 or 100 + 42, which is 1 dollar and 42 cents (Solution B). → We added to get 142 cents and then decomposed the cents into 1 dollar and 42 cents (Solution A).

(3×10) + 17 = 47
(3×25) + 20 = 95

5 dollars 3 dimes 17 pennies + 4 dollars 3 quarters 2 dimes

Solution A

5 dollars 47 cents + 4 dollars 95 cents
= 9 dollars 142 cents
(142 → 100, 42)
= 10 dollars 42 cents
= $10.42

Solution B

5 dollars 47 cents + 4 dollars 95 cents
= 9 dollars 47 cents + 95 cents
(47 → 42, 5)
= 10 dollars 42 cents
= $10.42

EUREKA MATH

© 2015 Great Minds. eureka-math.org
G4-M6-TE-B5-1.3.1-01.2016

Give students additional practice as necessary. This final component is directly applied in Lesson 16 to word problems.

- 10 dollars 1 quarter 3 dimes + 3 dollars 5 dimes 14 pennies
- 15 dollars 7 dimes 6 pennies + 2 quarters 23 pennies

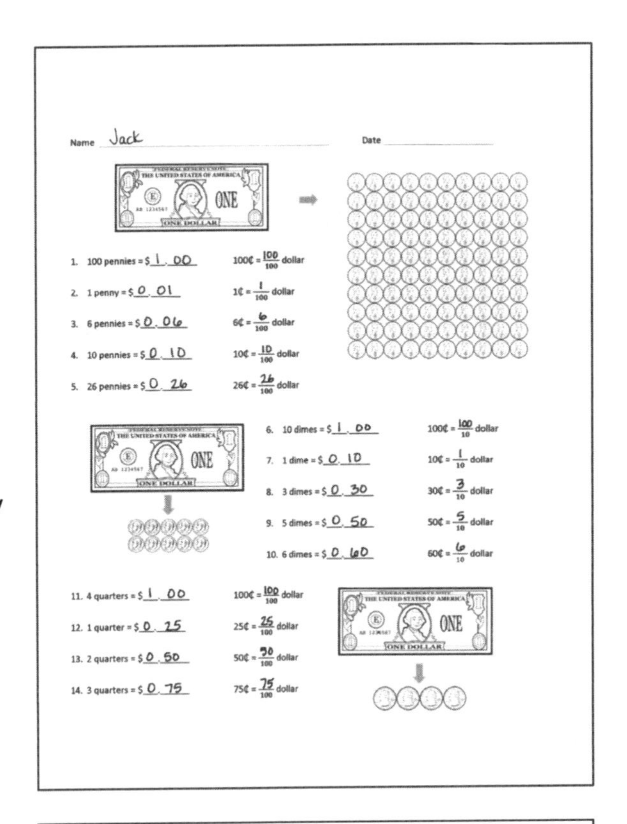
Name Jack Date

1. 100 pennies = $1.00 100¢ = $\frac{100}{100}$ dollar
2. 1 penny = $0.01 1¢ = $\frac{1}{100}$ dollar
3. 6 pennies = $0.06 6¢ = $\frac{6}{100}$ dollar
4. 10 pennies = $0.10 10¢ = $\frac{10}{100}$ dollar
5. 26 pennies = $0.26 26¢ = $\frac{26}{100}$ dollar
6. 10 dimes = $1.00 100¢ = $\frac{10}{10}$ dollar
7. 1 dime = $0.10 10¢ = $\frac{1}{10}$ dollar
8. 3 dimes = $0.30 30¢ = $\frac{3}{10}$ dollar
9. 5 dimes = $0.50 50¢ = $\frac{5}{10}$ dollar
10. 6 dimes = $0.60 60¢ = $\frac{6}{10}$ dollar
11. 4 quarters = $1.00 100¢ = $\frac{100}{100}$ dollar
12. 1 quarter = $0.25 25¢ = $\frac{25}{100}$ dollar
13. 2 quarters = $0.50 50¢ = $\frac{50}{100}$ dollar
14. 3 quarters = $0.75 75¢ = $\frac{75}{100}$ dollar

Problem Set (10 minutes)

Students should do their personal best to complete the Problem Set within the allotted 10 minutes. For some classes, it may be appropriate to modify the assignment by specifying which problems they work on first. Some problems do not specify a method for solving. Students should solve these problems using the RDW approach used for Application Problems.

Solve. Give the total amount of money in fraction and decimal form.

15. 3 dimes and 8 pennies $\frac{38}{100}$ dollar $0.38
16. 8 dimes and 23 pennies $\frac{103}{100}$ dollars $1.03
17. 3 quarters, 3 dimes, and 5 pennies $\frac{110}{100}$ dollars $1.10
18. 236 cents is what fraction of a dollar? $\frac{236}{100}$ dollars $2.36

Solve. Express the answer as a decimal.

19. 2 dollars 17 pennies + 4 dollars 2 quarters = 2 dollars 17 cents + 4 dollars 50 cents
= 6 dollars 67 cents
= $6.67
20. 3 dollars 8 dimes + 1 dollar 2 quarters 5 pennies = 3 dollars 80 cents + 1 dollar 55 cents (20 35)
= 5 dollars 35 cents
= $5.35
21. 9 dollars 9 dimes + 4 dollars 3 quarters 16 pennies = 9 dollars 90 cents + 4 dollars 91 cents (10 81)
= 14 dollars 81 cents
= $14.81

Student Debrief (10 minutes)

Lesson Objective: Express money amounts given in various forms as decimal numbers.

The Student Debrief is intended to invite reflection and active processing of the total lesson experience.

Invite students to review their solutions for the Problem Set. They should check work by comparing answers with a partner before going over answers as a class. Look for misconceptions or misunderstandings that can be addressed in the Debrief. Guide students in a conversation to debrief the Problem Set and process the lesson.

Any combination of the questions below may be used to lead the discussion.

- How is money related to decimals and fractions? How is it different? Think about why we would write money in expanded form.
- I have $\frac{2}{5}$ dollar in my pocket. Use what you know about equivalent fractions to determine how many cents I have. What are some possible combinations of coins that may be in my pocket? Do not forget about nickels!

© 2015 Great Minds. eureka-math.org
G4-M6-TE-B5-1.3.1-01.2016

- Are $1 and $1.00 equal? Are $0.1 and $0.10 equal? Are all these forms correct? Which form may not be used frequently and why?
- How did the Application Problem prepare you for today's lesson?
- How might dimes be expressed as fractions differently than as tenths of a dollar? Use an example from Problems 6–10.
- How can the fraction of a dollar for Problem 13 be simplified?
- When adding fractions and whole numbers, we sometimes complete the next whole or the next hundred to simplify the addition. How, in Problem 20, could you decompose 8 dimes to simplify the addition?

Exit Ticket (3 minutes)

After the Student Debrief, instruct students to complete the Exit Ticket. A review of their work will help with assessing students' understanding of the concepts that were presented in today's lesson and planning more effectively for future lessons. The questions may be read aloud to the students.

© 2015 Great Minds. eureka-math.org
G4-M6-TE-B5-1.3.1-01.2016

Name ______________________________ Date ________________

1. 100 pennies = $___.______ 100¢ = $\frac{\quad}{100}$ dollar

2. 1 penny = $___.______ 1¢ = $\frac{\quad}{100}$ dollar

3. 6 pennies = $___.______ 6¢ = $\frac{\quad}{100}$ dollar

4. 10 pennies = $___.______ 10¢ = $\frac{\quad}{100}$ dollar

5. 26 pennies = $___.______ 26¢ = $\frac{\quad}{100}$ dollar

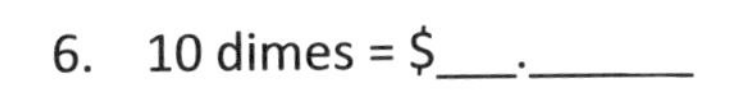

6. 10 dimes = $___.______ 100¢ = $\frac{\quad}{10}$ dollar

7. 1 dime = $___.______ 10¢ = $\frac{\quad}{10}$ dollar

8. 3 dimes = $___.______ 30¢ = $\frac{\quad}{10}$ dollar

9. 5 dimes = $___.______ 50¢ = $\frac{\quad}{10}$ dollar

10. 6 dimes = $___.______ 60¢ = $\frac{\quad}{10}$ dollar

11. 4 quarters = $___.______ 100¢ = $\frac{\quad}{100}$ dollar

12. 1 quarter = $___.______ 25¢ = $\frac{\quad}{100}$ dollar

13. 2 quarters = $___.______ 50¢ = $\frac{\quad}{100}$ dollar

14. 3 quarters = $___.______ 75¢ = $\frac{\quad}{100}$ dollar

© 2015 Great Minds. eureka-math.org
G4-M6-TE-B5-1.3.1-01.2016

Solve. Give the total amount of money in fraction and decimal form.

15. 3 dimes and 8 pennies

16. 8 dimes and 23 pennies

17. 3 quarters 3 dimes and 5 pennies

18. 236 cents is what fraction of a dollar?

Solve. Express the answer as a decimal.

19. 2 dollars 17 pennies + 4 dollars 2 quarters

20. 3 dollars 8 dimes + 1 dollar 2 quarters 5 pennies

21. 9 dollars 9 dimes + 4 dollars 3 quarters 16 pennies

© 2015 Great Minds. eureka-math.org
G4-M6-TE-B5-1.3.1-01.2016

Name ______________________________ Date ______________

Solve. Give the total amount of money in fraction and decimal form.

1. 2 quarters and 3 dimes

2. 1 quarter 7 dimes and 23 pennies

Solve. Express the answer as a decimal.

3. 2 dollars 1 quarter 14 pennies + 3 dollars 2 quarters 3 dimes

© 2015 Great Minds. eureka-math.org
G4-M6-TE-B5-1.3.1-01.2016

Name ______________________________ Date ______________

1. 100 pennies = $___.______ $100¢ = \frac{\quad}{100}$ dollar

2. 1 penny = $___.______ $1¢ = \frac{\quad}{100}$ dollar

3. 3 pennies = $___.______ $3¢ = \frac{\quad}{100}$ dollar

4. 20 pennies = $___.______ $20¢ = \frac{\quad}{100}$ dollar

5. 37 pennies = $___.______ $37¢ = \frac{\quad}{100}$ dollar

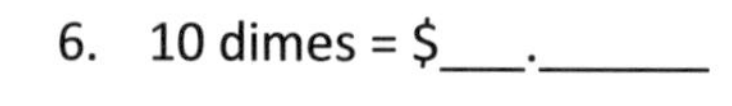

6. 10 dimes = $___.______ $100¢ = \frac{\quad}{10}$ dollar

7. 2 dimes = $___.______ $20¢ = \frac{\quad}{10}$ dollar

8. 4 dimes = $___.______ $40¢ = \frac{\quad}{10}$ dollar

9. 6 dimes = $___.______ $60¢ = \frac{\quad}{10}$ dollar

10. 9 dimes = $___.______ $90¢ = \frac{\quad}{10}$ dollar

11. 3 quarters = $___.______ $75¢ = \frac{\quad}{100}$ dollar

12. 2 quarters = $___.______ $50¢ = \frac{\quad}{100}$ dollar

13. 4 quarters = $___.______ $100¢ = \frac{\quad}{100}$ dollar

14. 1 quarter = $___.______ $25¢ = \frac{\quad}{100}$ dollar

© 2015 Great Minds. eureka-math.org
G4-M6-TE-B5-1.3.1-01.2016

Solve. Give the total amount of money in fraction and decimal form.

15. 5 dimes and 8 pennies

16. 3 quarters and 13 pennies

17. 3 quarters 7 dimes and 16 pennies

18. 187 cents is what fraction of a dollar?

Solve. Express the answer in decimal form.

19. 1 dollar 2 dimes 13 pennies + 2 dollars 3 quarters

20. 2 dollars 6 dimes + 2 dollars 2 quarters 16 pennies

21. 8 dollars 8 dimes + 7 dollars 1 quarter 8 dimes

© 2015 Great Minds. eureka-math.org
G4-M6-TE-B5-1.3.1-01.2016

Lesson 16

Objective: Solve word problems involving money.

Suggested Lesson Structure

■ Fluency Practice	(12 minutes)
■ Concept Development	(38 minutes)
■ Student Debrief	(10 minutes)
Total Time	**(60 minutes)**

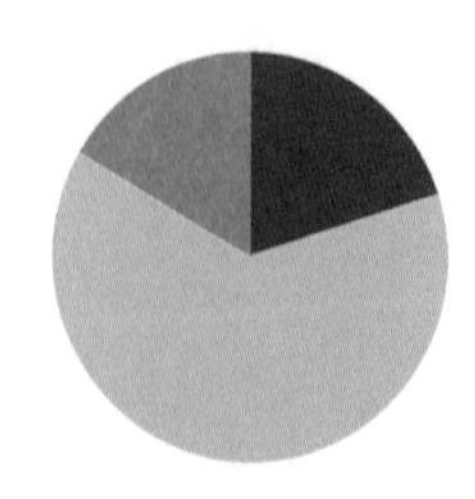

Fluency Practice (12 minutes)

- Sprint: Add Decimal Fractions **4.NF.5** (9 minutes)
- State the Value of a Set of Coins **4.MD.2** (3 minutes)

Sprint: Add Decimal Fractions (9 minutes)

Materials: (S) Add Decimal Fractions Sprint

Note: This Sprint reviews Lesson 13.

State the Value of a Set of Coins (3 minutes)

Materials: (S) Personal white board

Note: This fluency activity reviews Lesson 15.

T: (Write 2 quarters 4 dimes.) What is the value of 2 quarters and 4 dimes?
S: 90¢.
T: Write 90 cents as a fraction of a dollar.
S: (Write $\frac{90}{100}$ dollar.)
T: Write 90 cents in decimal form using the dollar symbol.
S: (Write \$0.90.)
T: Write 130 cents in decimal form using the dollar symbol.
S: (Write \$1.30.)
T: What is the value in cents of 3 quarters and 7 dimes?
S: 145¢.

EUREKA MATH
© 2015 Great Minds. eureka-math.org
G4-M6-TE-B5-1.3.1-01.2016

T: Write 145 cents as a fraction of a dollar.

S: (Write $\frac{145}{100}$ dollar.)

T: Write 145 cents in decimal form using the dollar symbol.

S: (Write $1.45.)

Continue with the following possible sequence: 1 quarter 9 dimes 12 pennies, 3 quarters 5 dimes 20 pennies.

Concept Development (38 minutes)

Materials: (S) Problem Set

Suggested Delivery of Instruction for Solving This Lesson's Word Problems

Note: Lesson 15 closed with students finding sums of dollar and cents amounts in unit form. If necessary, begin this lesson with a short segment revisiting that process.

1. Model the problem.

Have two pairs of students model the problem at the board while the others work independently or in pairs at their seats. Review the following questions before beginning the first problem:

- Can you draw something?
- What can you draw?
- What conclusions can you make from your drawing?

As students work, circulate. Reiterate the questions above. After two minutes, have the two pairs of students share only their labeled diagrams. For about one minute, have the demonstrating students receive and respond to feedback and questions from their peers.

2. Calculate to solve and write a statement.

Give students two minutes to finish their work on that question, sharing their work and thinking with a peer. All should then write their equations and statements of the answer.

3. Assess the solution for reasonableness.

Give students one to two minutes to assess and explain the reasonableness of their solution.

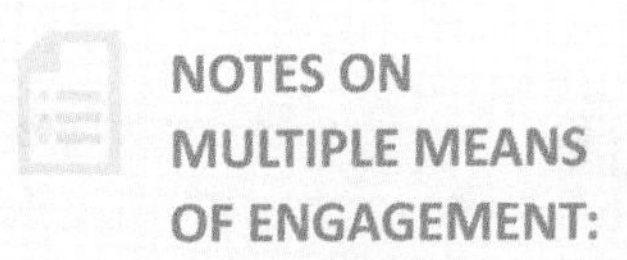

Give everyone a fair chance to be successful by providing appropriate scaffolds. Demonstrating students may use translators, interpreters, or sentence frames to present and respond to feedback. Models shared may include concrete manipulatives, computer software, or other adaptive materials.

If the pace of the lesson is a consideration, prepare presenters beforehand. The first problem may be most approachable for students working below grade level.

© 2015 Great Minds. eureka-math.org
G4-M6-TE-B5-1.3.1-01.2016

Problem 1

Miguel has 1 dollar bill, 2 dimes, and 7 pennies. John has 2 dollar bills, 3 quarters, and 9 pennies. How much money do the two boys have in all?

M | $1 | 20¢ | 7¢
J | $2 | 75¢ | 9¢

Solution A

1 dollar 27 cents + 2 dollars 84 cents

= 3 dollars 111 cents (100, 11)

= 4 dollars 11 cents

= $4.11

Solution B

1 dollar 27 cents + 2 dollars 84 cents (11, 16)

= 1 dollar 11 cents + 2 dollars 100 cents

= 4 dollars 11 cents

= $4.11

Miguel and John have $4.11 in all.

Students use their knowledge of mixed metric unit addition from Module 2 to add amounts of money. Each amount is expressed using the units of dollars and cents. Students know that 100 cents is equal to 1 dollar. Solution A shows a student decomposing 111 cents after finding the sum of the dollars and cents. Solution B shows a student decomposing Miguel's 27 cents to make 1 dollar before finding the total sum.

Problem 2

Suilin needs 7 dollars 13 cents to buy a book. In her wallet, she finds 3 dollar bills, 4 dimes, and 14 pennies. How much more money does Suilin need to buy the book?

$7.13
| $3.54 | B |

Solution A

7 dollars 13 cents – 3 dollars 54 cents

= 6 dollars 113 cents – 3 dollars 54 cents

= 3 dollars 59 cents

= $3.59

Solution B

7 dollars 13 cents – 3 dollars 54 cents (13, 41)

= 4 dollars – 41 cents ($3, 100¢)

= 3 dollars 59 cents

= $3.59

EUREKA MATH

© 2015 Great Minds. eureka-math.org
G4-M6-TE-B5-1.3.1-01.2016

Solution C

3 dollars 54 cents $\xrightarrow{+46¢}$ 4 dollars $\xrightarrow{+\$3}$ 7 dollars $\xrightarrow{+13¢}$ 7 dollars 13 cents

$3 + 46¢ + 13¢

59¢

= $3.59

Suilin needs $3.59 more to buy the book.

Students solve using unit form because they do not learn addition and subtraction of decimals until Grade 5. Solution A shows unbundling 1 dollar as 100 cents, making 113 cents to subtract 54 cents from. Solution B decomposed the cents in the subtrahend to more easily subtract from 1 dollar or 100 cents. Solution C adds up using the arrow way. Each solution shows conversion of the mixed unit into a decimal for dollars and cents.

Problem 3

Vanessa has 6 dimes and 2 pennies. Joachim has 1 dollar, 3 dimes, and 5 pennies. Jimmy has 5 dollars and 7 pennies. They want to put their money to gether to buy a game that costs $8.00. Do they have enough money to buy the game? If not, how much more money do they need ?

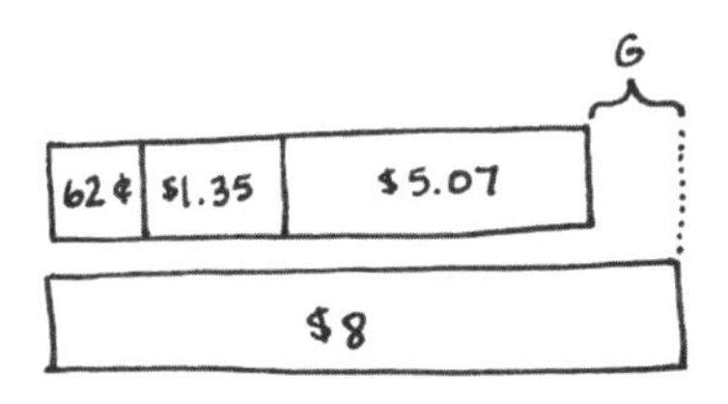

Solution A

62 cents + 1 dollar 35 cents + 5 dollars 7 cents

= 6 dollars 104 cents (100, 4)

= 7 dollars 4 cents

= $7.04

8 dollars − 7 dollars 4 cents ($7, 100¢)

= 96 cents

G = $0.96

Solution B

8 dollars $\xrightarrow{-\$5}$ 3 dollars $\xrightarrow{-7¢}$ 2 dollars 93 cents

2 dollars 93 cents $\xrightarrow{-\$1}$ 1 dollar 93 cents $\xrightarrow{-35¢}$ 1 dollar 58 cents

158 cents $\xrightarrow{-62¢}$ 96 cents G = $0.96

They don't have enough money. They need $0.96 more to buy the game.

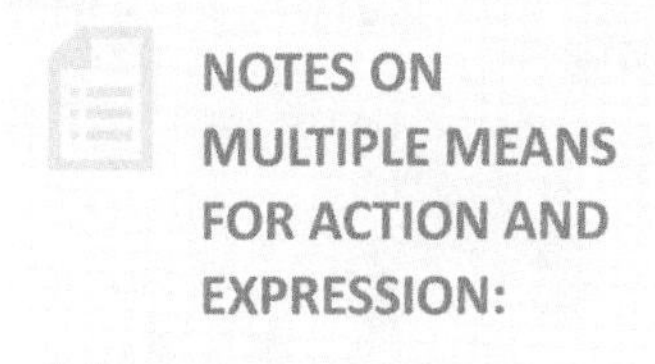

NOTES ON MULTIPLE MEANS FOR ACTION AND EXPRESSION:

Scaffold solving Problem 3 for students working below grade level by facilitating their management of information from the word problem. A labeled tape diagram, table, place value chart, or another organizational aid may help learners with cognitive disabilities keep information organized.

© 2015 Great Minds. eureka-math.org
G4-M6-TE-B5-1.3.1-01.2016

In this multi-step problem, students may first find the sum of three money amounts and then subtract to find out how much more money they need, as shown in Solution A. Solution B shows the arrow way, subtracting each person's money one at a time.

Problem 4

A pen costs $2.29. A calculator costs 3 times as much as a pen. How much do a pen and a calculator cost together?

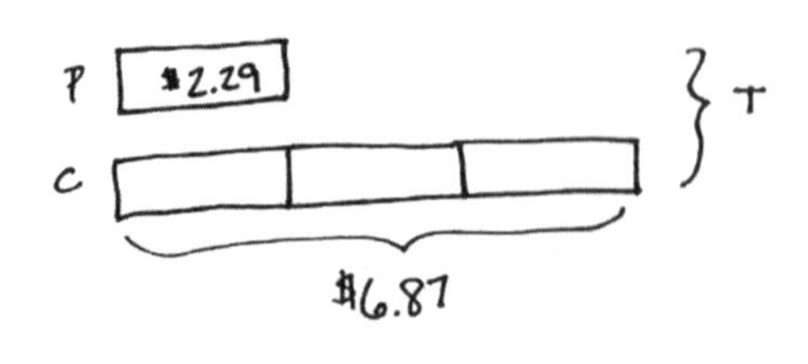

Solution A

$2.29 = 229 cents

229 cents
× 3
687 cents

6 dollars 87 cents + 2 dollars 29 cents

= 8 dollars 116 cents
100 16

= 9 dollars 16 cents

T = $9.16

Solution B

$2.29 = 229 cents

229
× 4
916

916¢ = $9.16

T = $9.16

Solution C

230 cents
× 4
920 cents

T = $9.16

920 cents − 4 cents = 916 cents

A pen and a calculator cost $9.16 together.

In this multiplicative comparison word problem, students have to contemplate how to multiply money when they have not learned how to multiply with decimals. Solution A shows a student first solving for the cost of the calculator, then multiplying to find the total number of cents, and finally adding the cost of the pen after expressing the amount of each item as dollars and cents. Solution B is a more efficient method, solving for both items concurrently using cents. Solution C uses a compensation strategy to simplify the multiplication. Instead of a unit size of $2.29, the student adds 1 penny to each of the 4 units in the problem, finds 4 groups of $2.30, and then subtracts the 4 pennies that were added.

EUREKA MATH
© 2015 Great Minds. eureka-math.org
G4-M6-TE-B5-1.3.1-01.2016

Problem 5

Krista has 7 dollars and 32 cents. Malory has 2 dollars and 4 cents. How much money does Krista need to give Malory so that each of them has the same amount of money?

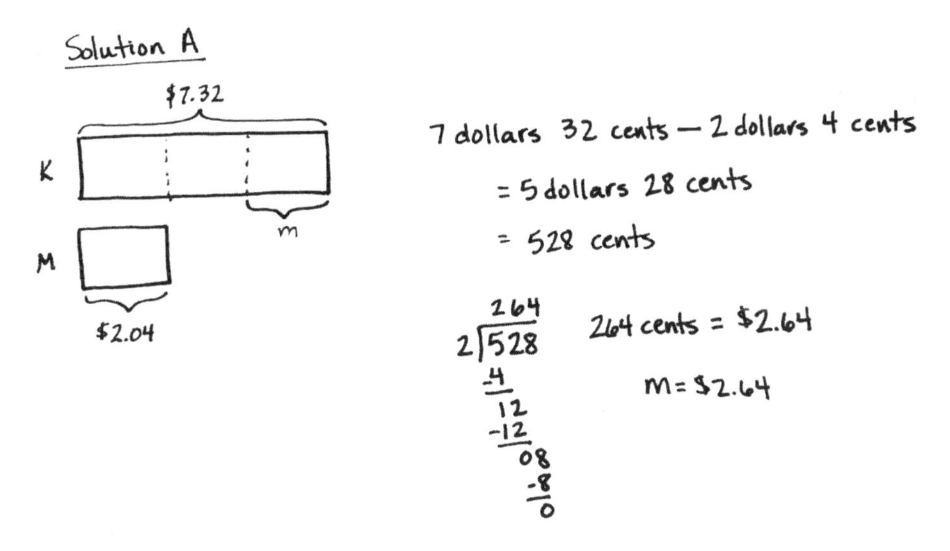

Solution B

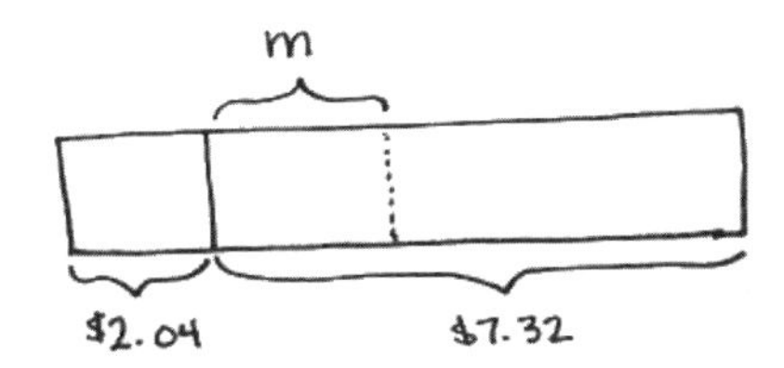

7 dollars 32 cents + 2 dollars 4 cents

= 9 dollars 36 cents

= 936 cents

468
2 ⟌936
-8
13
-12
16
-16
0

468 cents = $4.68

2 dollars 4 cents $\xrightarrow{+64¢}$ 2 dollars 68 cents $\xrightarrow{+\$2}$ 4 dollars 68 cents

m = $2.64

Malory needs $2.64 from Krista.

This challenging multi-step word problem requires students to divide money, similarly to Problem 4 with multiplication, by finding the total amount of cents since decimal division is a Grade 5 standard. Solution A divides the difference of money the girls have. Solution B divides the total amount of money, requiring an additional step either by finding how much more money Malory needs or subtracting from Krista's money.

© 2015 Great Minds. eureka-math.org
G4-M6-TE-B5-1.3.1-01.2016

Student Debrief (10 minutes)

Lesson Objective: Solve word problems involving money.

The Student Debrief is intended to invite reflection and active processing of the total lesson experience.

Invite students to review their solutions for the Problem Set. They should check work by comparing answers with a partner before going over answers as a class. Look for misconceptions or misunderstandings that can be addressed in the Debrief. Guide students in a conversation to debrief the Problem Set and process the lesson.

Any combination of the questions below may be used to lead the discussion.

- Why does money relate so closely to our study of fractions and decimals?
- How could you use rounding to find the reasonableness of your answer to Problem 4? With your partner, estimate the cost of a pen and a calculator. Are your answers reasonable?
- In Problem 5, we saw two different tape diagrams drawn. How can the way you draw affect which strategy you choose to solve?
- Problem 5 can be challenging at first read. Think of an alternative scenario that may help a younger student solve a similar problem. (Consider using smaller numbers like 9 and 5 and a context like pieces of candy.)

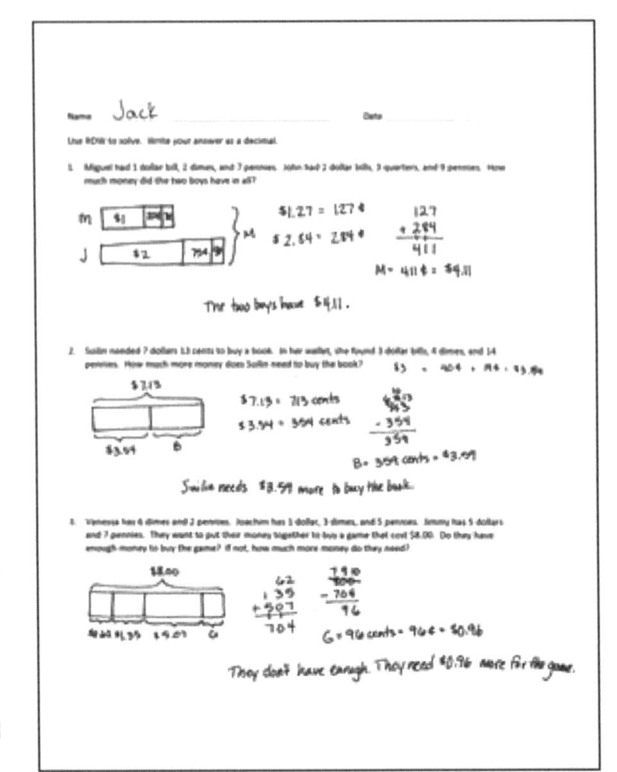
Name Jack Date

Use RDW to solve. Write your answer as a decimal.

1. Miguel had 1 dollar bill, 2 dimes, and 7 pennies. John had 2 dollar bills, 3 quarters, and 9 pennies. How much money did the two boys have in all?

The two boys have $4.11.

2. Sailin needed 7 dollars 13 cents to buy a book. In her wallet, she found 3 dollar bills, 4 dimes, and 14 pennies. How much more money does Sailin need to buy the book?

Sailin needs $3.59 more to buy the book.

3. Vanessa has 6 dimes and 2 pennies. Joachim has 1 dollar, 3 dimes, and 5 pennies. Jimmy has 5 dollars and 7 pennies. They want to put their money together to buy a game that cost $8.00. Do they have enough money to buy the game? If not, how much more money do they need?

They don't have enough. They need $0.96 more for the game.

Exit Ticket (3 minutes)

After the Student Debrief, instruct students to complete the Exit Ticket. A review of their work will help with assessing students' understanding of the concepts that were presented in today's lesson and planning more effectively for future lessons. The questions may be read aloud to the students.

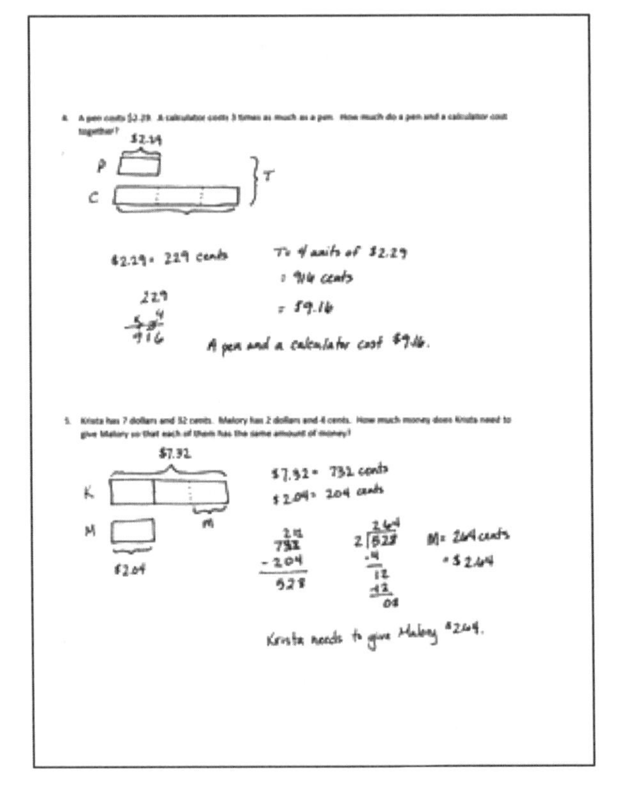
4. A pen costs $2.29. A calculator costs 3 times as much as a pen. How much do a pen and a calculator cost together?

A pen and a calculator cost $9.16.

5. Krista has 7 dollars and 32 cents. Malory has 2 dollars and 4 cents. How much money does Krista need to give Malory so that each of them has the same amount of money?

Krista needs to give Malory $2.64.

© 2015 Great Minds. eureka-math.org
G4-M6-TE-B5-1.3.1-01.2016

Number Correct: ______

A

Add Decimal Fractions

1.	$\frac{1}{10} =$	.
2.	$\frac{1}{100} =$	.
3.	$\frac{1}{10} + \frac{1}{100} =$	.
4.	$\frac{3}{10} =$	.
5.	$\frac{3}{100} =$	.
6.	$\frac{3}{10} + \frac{3}{100} =$	.
7.	$\frac{5}{10} =$	.
8.	$\frac{5}{100} =$	.
9.	$\frac{5}{10} + \frac{5}{100} =$	.
10.	$\frac{7}{10} =$	.
11.	$\frac{9}{100} =$	.
12.	$\frac{7}{10} + \frac{9}{100} =$	.
13.	$\frac{9}{100} + \frac{7}{10} =$	.
14.	$\frac{4}{10} =$	.
15.	$\frac{6}{100} =$	.
16.	$\frac{4}{10} + \frac{6}{100} =$	.
17.	$\frac{4}{100} + \frac{6}{10} =$	.
18.	$\frac{8}{10} + \frac{5}{100} =$	.
19.	$\frac{9}{10} + \frac{2}{100} =$	.
20.	$\frac{1}{100} + \frac{8}{10} =$	.
21.	$\frac{4}{100} + \frac{1}{10} =$	.
22.	$\frac{7}{100} + \frac{4}{10} =$	.

23.	$\frac{2}{10} =$	.
24.	$\frac{20}{100} =$	.
25.	$\frac{2}{10} + \frac{20}{100} =$	.
26.	$\frac{3}{10} =$	.
27.	$\frac{30}{100} =$	.
28.	$\frac{3}{10} + \frac{30}{100} =$	.
29.	$\frac{5}{10} + \frac{20}{100} =$	.
30.	$\frac{8}{10} + \frac{10}{100} =$	.
31.	$\frac{8}{10} + \frac{20}{100} =$	.
32.	$\frac{8}{10} + \frac{30}{100} =$	.
33.	$\frac{8}{10} + \frac{50}{100} =$	.
34.	$\frac{9}{10} + \frac{40}{100} =$	.
35.	$\frac{9}{10} + \frac{47}{100} =$	.
36.	$\frac{7}{10} + \frac{50}{100} =$	.
37.	$\frac{7}{10} + \frac{59}{100} =$	.
38.	$\frac{6}{10} + \frac{60}{100} =$	.
39.	$\frac{6}{10} + \frac{64}{100} =$	.
40.	$\frac{65}{100} + \frac{6}{10} =$	.
41.	$\frac{91}{100} + \frac{7}{10} =$	.
42.	$\frac{8}{10} + \frac{73}{100} =$	.
43.	$\frac{9}{10} + \frac{82}{100} =$	.
44.	$\frac{98}{100} + \frac{9}{10} =$	.

© 2015 Great Minds. eureka-math.org
G4-M6-TE-B5-1.3.1-01.2016

B

Number Correct: ______

Improvement: ______

Add Decimal Fractions

1.	$\frac{2}{10} =$	.	23.	$\frac{1}{10} =$	.
2.	$\frac{2}{100} =$	.	24.	$\frac{10}{100} =$	.
3.	$\frac{2}{10} + \frac{2}{100} =$	.	25.	$\frac{1}{10} + \frac{10}{100} =$	.
4.	$\frac{4}{10} =$	.	26.	$\frac{4}{10} =$	.
5.	$\frac{4}{100} =$	.	27.	$\frac{40}{100} =$	.
6.	$\frac{4}{10} + \frac{4}{100} =$	.	28.	$\frac{4}{10} + \frac{40}{100} =$	.
7.	$\frac{6}{10} =$	.	29.	$\frac{5}{10} + \frac{30}{100} =$	.
8.	$\frac{6}{100} =$	.	30.	$\frac{7}{10} + \frac{20}{100} =$	.
9.	$\frac{6}{10} + \frac{6}{100} =$	.	31.	$\frac{7}{10} + \frac{30}{100} =$	.
10.	$\frac{4}{10} =$	.	32.	$\frac{7}{10} + \frac{40}{100} =$	.
11.	$\frac{8}{100} =$	.	33.	$\frac{7}{10} + \frac{60}{100} =$	.
12.	$\frac{4}{10} + \frac{8}{100} =$	.	34.	$\frac{9}{10} + \frac{30}{100} =$	.
13.	$\frac{8}{100} + \frac{4}{10} =$	.	35.	$\frac{9}{10} + \frac{37}{100} =$	.
14.	$\frac{5}{10} =$	.	36.	$\frac{8}{10} + \frac{40}{100} =$	.
15.	$\frac{7}{100} =$	.	37.	$\frac{8}{10} + \frac{49}{100} =$	.
16.	$\frac{5}{10} + \frac{7}{100} =$	.	38.	$\frac{7}{10} + \frac{70}{100} =$	.
17.	$\frac{7}{100} + \frac{5}{10} =$	.	39.	$\frac{7}{10} + \frac{76}{100} =$	.
18.	$\frac{9}{10} + \frac{6}{100} =$	.	40.	$\frac{78}{100} + \frac{7}{10} =$	.
19.	$\frac{8}{10} + \frac{3}{100} =$	.	41.	$\frac{81}{100} + \frac{7}{10} =$	.
20.	$\frac{1}{100} + \frac{7}{10} =$	.	42.	$\frac{9}{10} + \frac{73}{100} =$	.
21.	$\frac{3}{100} + \frac{1}{10} =$	.	43.	$\frac{9}{10} + \frac{84}{100} =$	.
22.	$\frac{8}{100} + \frac{3}{10} =$	.	44.	$\frac{84}{100} + \frac{8}{10} =$	.

© 2015 Great Minds. eureka-math.org
G4-M6-TE-B5-1.3.1-01.2016

Name ______________________________ Date ________________

Use the RDW process to solve. Write your answer as a decimal.

1. Miguel has 1 dollar bill, 2 dimes, and 7 pennies. John has 2 dollar bills, 3 quarters, and 9 pennies. How much money do the two boys have in all?

2. Suilin needs 7 dollars 13 cents to buy a book. In her wallet, she finds 3 dollar bills, 4 dimes, and 14 pennies. How much more money does Suilin need to buy the book?

3. Vanessa has 6 dimes and 2 pennies. Joachim has 1 dollar, 3 dimes, and 5 pennies. Jimmy has 5 dollars and 7 pennies. They want to put their money together to buy a game that costs $8.00. Do they have enough money to buy the game? If not, how much more money do they need?

© 2015 Great Minds. eureka-math.org
G4-M6-TE-B5-1.3.1-01.2016

4. A pen costs $2.29. A calculator costs 3 times as much as a pen. How much do a pen and a calculator cost together?

5. Krista has 7 dollars and 32 cents. Malory has 2 dollars and 4 cents. How much money does Krista need to give Malory so that each of them has the same amount of money?

© 2015 Great Minds. eureka-math.org
G4-M6-TE-B5-1.3.1-01.2016

Name ______________________________ Date ________________

Use the RDW process to solve. Write your answer as a decimal.

David's mother told him that he could keep all the money he finds under the sofa cushions in their house. David finds 6 quarters, 4 dimes, and 26 pennies. How much money does David find altogether?

© 2015 Great Minds. eureka-math.org
G4-M6-TE-B5-1.3.1-01.2016

Name ______________________________ Date ______________

Use the RDW process to solve. Write your answer as a decimal.

1. Maria has 2 dollars, 3 dimes, and 4 pennies. Lisa has 1 dollar and 5 quarters. How much money do the two girls have in all?

2. Meiling needs 5 dollars 35 cents to buy a ticket to a show. In her wallet, she finds 2 dollar bills, 11 dimes, and 5 pennies. How much more money does Meiling need to buy the ticket?

3. Joe has 5 dimes and 4 pennies. Jamal has 2 dollars, 4 dimes, and 5 pennies. Jimmy has 6 dollars and 4 dimes. They want to put their money together to buy a book that costs $10.00. Do they have enough? If not, how much more do they need?

EUREKA MATH

© 2015 Great Minds. eureka-math.org
G4-M6-TE-B5-1.3.1-01.2016

4. A package of mechanical pencils costs $4.99. A package of pens costs twice as much as a package of pencils. How much do a package of pens and a package of pencils cost together?

5. Carlos has 8 dollars and 48 cents. Alissa has 4 dollars and 14 cents. How much money does Carlos need to give Alissa so that each of them has the same amount of money?

© 2015 Great Minds. eureka-math.org
G4-M6-TE-B5-1.3.1-01.2016

Name ______________________________ Date ______________

1. Decompose each fraction into hundredths using area models. Then, write the equivalent number sentence using decimals.

a. $\frac{8}{10} = \frac{\quad}{\quad}$

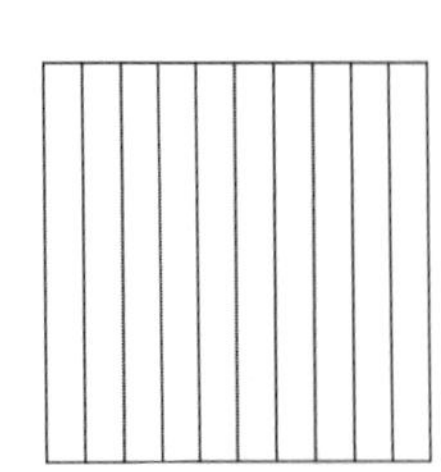
=
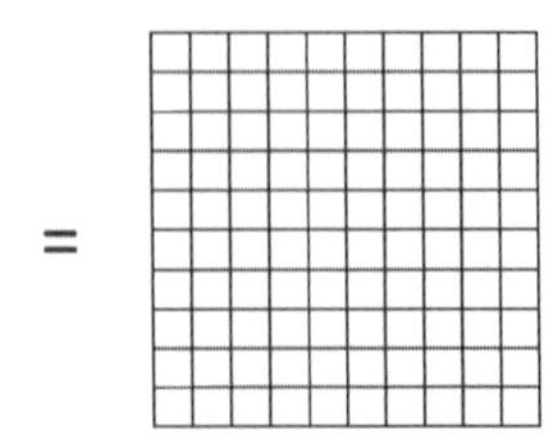

b. $\frac{18}{10} = \frac{\quad}{\quad}$

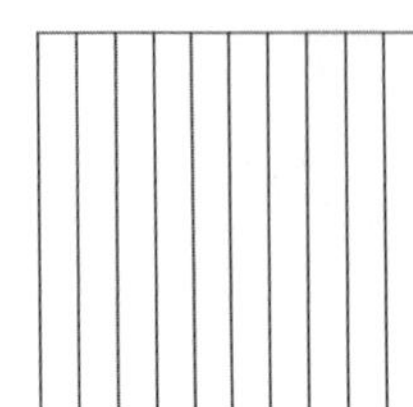
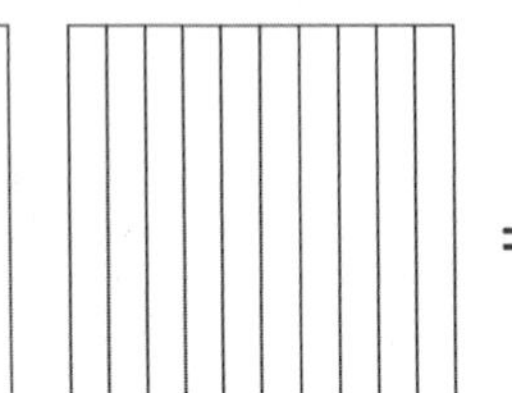
=
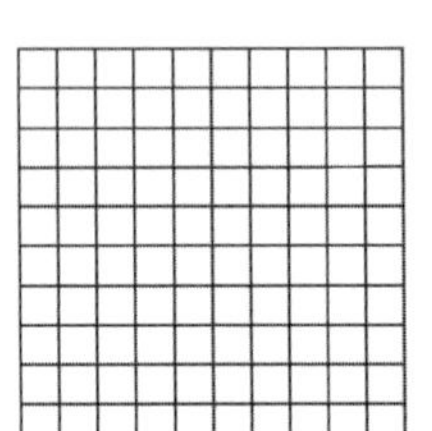
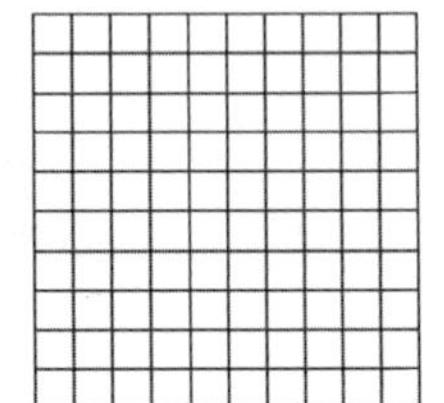

Decompose each fraction into hundredths. Then, write the equivalent number sentence for each part using decimals.

c. $\frac{2}{10} = \frac{\quad}{\quad}$

d. $\frac{5}{10} = \frac{\quad}{\quad}$

2. Several points are plotted on the number lines below. Identify the decimal number associated with each point.

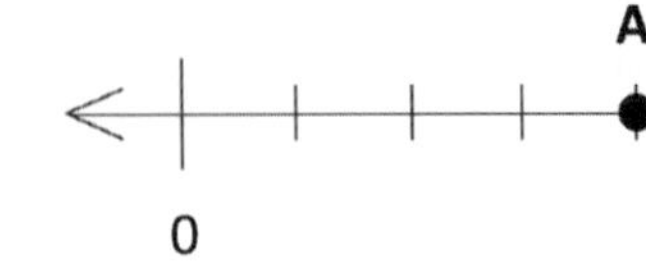
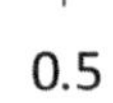
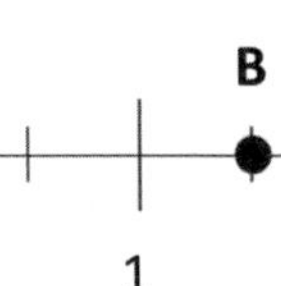
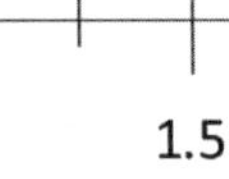
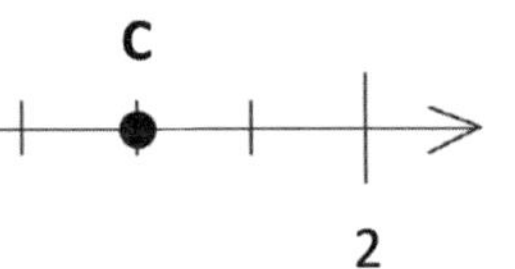

A. ______ B. ______ C. ______

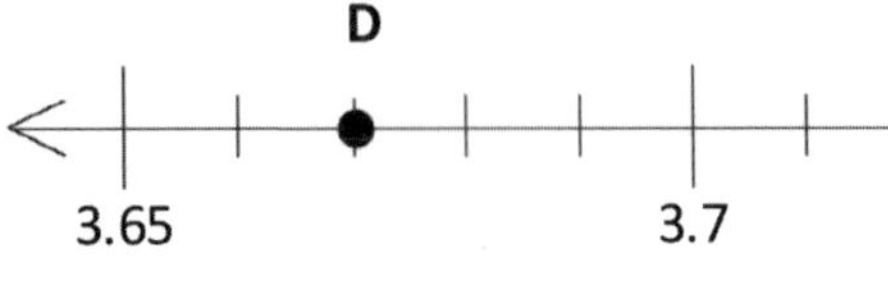
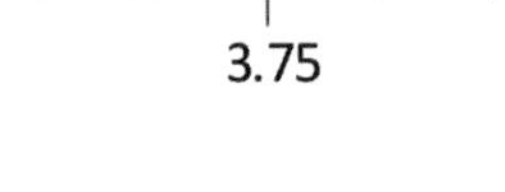
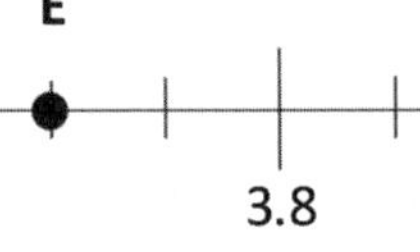
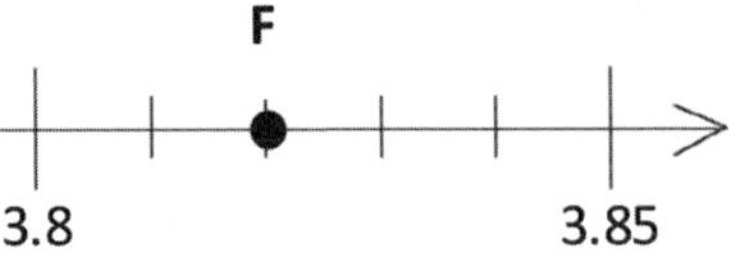

D. ______ E. ______ F. ______

© 2015 Great Minds. eureka-math.org
G4-M6-TE-B5-1.3.1-01.2016
EUREKA MATH

3. Use the symbols >, =, or < to compare the following. Justify your conclusions using pictures, numbers, or words.

a. 0.02 ◯ 0.22

b. 0.6 ◯ 0.60

c. 17 tenths ◯ 1.7

d. 1.04 ◯ $1\frac{4}{10}$

e. 0.38 ◯ $\frac{38}{10}$

f. 4.05 ◯ $4\frac{5}{100}$

g. 3 tenths + 2 hundredths ◯ 1 tenth + 13 hundredths

h. 8 hundredths + 7 tenths ◯ 6 tenths + 17 hundredths

© 2015 Great Minds. eureka-math.org
G4-M6-TE-B5-1.3.1-01.2016

4. Solve.

   a. Express your solution as a fraction of a meter. 0.3 m + 1.45 m

   b. Express your solution as a fraction of a liter. 1.7 L + 0.82 L

   c. Express your solution as a fraction of a dollar. 4 dimes 1 penny + 77 pennies

5. Solve.

   a. $\frac{7}{10} + \frac{8}{100}$

   b. $\frac{4}{10} + \frac{51}{100}$

   c. $\frac{5}{10} + \frac{68}{100}$

   d. $\frac{98}{100} + \frac{2}{10}$

   e. $\frac{12}{100} + \frac{12}{10}$

   f. $\frac{1}{10} + \frac{13}{100} + \frac{8}{10}$

© 2015 Great Minds. eureka-math.org
G4-M6-TE-B5-1.3.1-01.2016

6. Answer the following questions about a track meet.

   a. Jim and Joe ran in a relay race. Jim had a time of 9.8 seconds. Joe had a time of 10.32 seconds. Together, how long did it take them to complete the race? Record your answer as a decimal.

   b. The times of the 5 fastest runners were 7.11 seconds, 7.06 seconds, 7.6 seconds, 7.90 seconds, and 7.75 seconds. Locate these times on the number line. Record the times as decimals and fractions. One has been completed for you.

   c. Natalie threw a discus 32.04 meters. She threw 3.8 meters farther on her next throw. Write a statement to compare the two distances that Natalie threw the discus using >, <, or =.

© 2015 Great Minds. eureka-math.org
G4-M6-TE-B5-1.3.1-01.2016

d. At the concession stand, Marta spent 89 cents on a bottle of water and 5 dimes on a bag of chips. Shade the area models to represent the cost of each item.

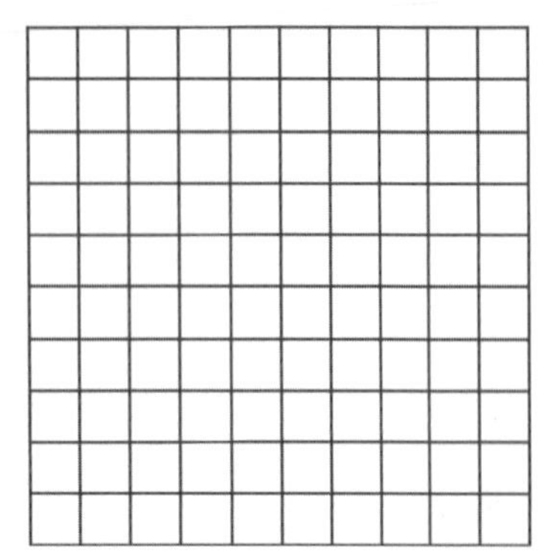

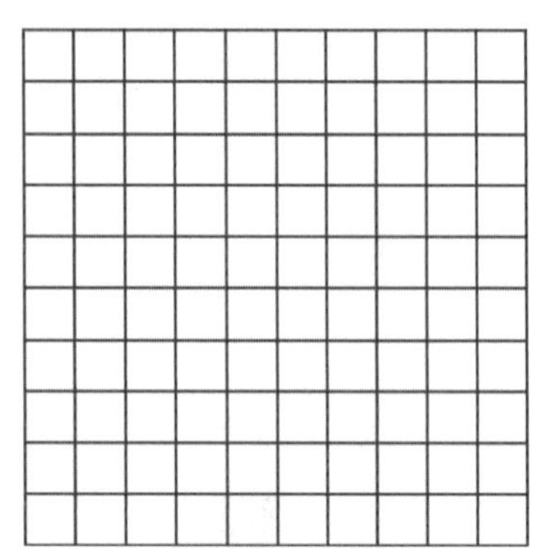

e. Write a number sentence in fraction form to find the total cost of a water bottle and a bag of chips. After solving, write the complete number sentence in decimal form.

f. Brian and Sonya each have a container. They mark their containers to show tenths. Brian and Sonya both fill their containers with 0.7 units of juice. However, Brian has more juice in his container. Explain how this is possible.

EUREKA MATH

© 2015 Great Minds. eureka-math.org
G4-M6-TE-B5-1.3.1-01.2016

End-of-Module Assessment Task Standards Addressed		Topics A–E
Understand decimal notation for fractions, and compare decimal fractions.		
4.NF.5	Express a fraction with denominator 10 as an equivalent fraction with denominator 100, and use this technique to add two fractions with respective denominators 10 and 100. *For example, express 3/10 as 30/100, and add 3/10 + 4/100 = 34/100.* (Students who can generate equivalent fractions can develop strategies for adding fractions with unlike denominators in general. But addition and subtraction with unlike denominators in general is not a requirement at this grade.)	
4.NF.6	Use decimal notation for fractions with denominators 10 or 100. *For example, rewrite 0.62 as 62/100; describe a length as 0.62 meters; locate 0.62 on a number line diagram.*	
4.NF.7	Compare two decimals to hundredths by reasoning about their size. Recognize that comparisons are valid only when the two decimals refer to the same whole. Record the results of comparisons with the symbols >, =, or <, and justify the conclusions, e.g., by using a visual model.	
Solve problems involving measurement and conversion of measurements from a larger unit to a smaller unit.		
4.MD.2	Use the four operations to solve word problems involving distances, intervals of time, liquid volumes, masses of objects, and money, including problems involving simple fractions or decimals, and problems that require expressing measurements given in a Larger unit in terms of a smaller unit. Represent measurement quantities using diagrams such as number line diagrams that feature a measurement scale.	

Evaluating Student Learning Outcomes

A Progression Toward Mastery is provided to describe steps that illuminate the gradually increasing understandings that students develop *on their way to proficiency.* In this chart, this progress is presented from left (Step 1) to right (Step 4). The learning goal for students is to achieve Step 4 mastery. These steps are meant to help teachers and students identify and celebrate what the students CAN do now and what they need to work on next.

© 2015 Great Minds. eureka-math.org
G4-M6-TE-B5-1.3.1-01.2016

A Progression Toward Mastery				
Assessment Task Item and Standards Assessed	**STEP 1 Little evidence of reasoning without a correct answer. (1 Point)**	**STEP 2 Evidence of some reasoning without a correct answer. (2 Points)**	**STEP 3 Evidence of some reasoning with a correct answer or evidence of solid reasoning with an incorrect answer. (3 Points)**	**STEP 4 Evidence of solid reasoning with a correct answer. (4 Points)**
1 **4.NF.5** **4.NF.6**	Student answers fewer than two parts correctly.	Student answers two parts correctly.	Student correctly answers three of the four parts of the question, showing solid reasoning. OR Student answers all parts correctly without correctly modeling on the place value charts	Student correctly uses the area models to represent: a. $\frac{8}{10} = \frac{80}{100}; 0.8 = 0.80$ b. $\frac{18}{10} = \frac{180}{100}; 1.8 = 1.80$ c. $\frac{2}{10} = \frac{20}{100}; 0.2 = 0.20$ d. $\frac{5}{10} = \frac{50}{100}; 0.5 = 0.50$
2 **4.NF.6**	Student correctly answers two or fewer parts of the question.	Student correctly answers three parts of the question.	Student correctly answers four or five parts of the question.	Student correctly answers: a. 0.4 b. 1.1 c. 1.8 d. 3.67 e. 3.78 f. 3.82
3 **4.NF.6** **4.NF.7**	Student answers four or fewer parts of the question correctly with little to no reasoning.	Student correctly answers four or five parts of the question, providing evidence of some reasoning	Student correctly answers six or seven parts of the question, with solid reasoning for each part correct. OR Student correctly solves all parts but does not provide solid reasoning for one or two parts.	Student correctly answers and reasons correctly using pictures, numbers, or words for each part: a. $<$ b. $=$ c. $=$ d. $<$ e. $<$ f. $=$ g. $>$ h. $>$

© 2015 Great Minds. eureka-math.org
G4-M6-TE-B5-1.3.1-01.2016

A Progression Toward Mastery

4 **4.NF.5**	Student correctly answers one or no parts.	Student correctly answers two parts of the question but does not include the units or provide ample evidence of reasoning.	Student correctly answers two of the three parts of the question, providing solid evidence or reasoning. OR Student solves all three parts correctly, providing only some or partially correct reasoning.	Student correctly answers: a. $1\frac{75}{100}$ meters b. $2\frac{52}{100}$ liters c. $1\frac{18}{100}$ dollars
5 **4.NF.5**	Student correctly answers two or fewer parts of the question.	Student correctly answers three or four of the six parts of the question.	Student correctly answers five of the six parts of the question.	Student correctly answers: a. $\frac{78}{100}$ b. $\frac{91}{100}$ c. $\frac{118}{100}$ or $1\frac{18}{100}$ d. $\frac{118}{100}$ or $1\frac{18}{100}$ e. $\frac{132}{100}$ or $1\frac{32}{100}$ f. $\frac{103}{100}$ or $1\frac{3}{100}$
6 **4.NF.5** **4.NF.6** **4.NF.7** **4.MD.2**	Student correctly answers fewer than three problems, providing little to no reasoning.	Student correctly answers three or four of the six problems, providing some reasoning.	Student correctly answers five of the six problems with solid reasoning. OR Student answers all six parts correctly but provides less than solid evidence in no more than two parts.	Student correctly: a. Answers 20.12 seconds. b. Plots the times on the number line and records each time as a decimal and fraction. c. Answers $32\frac{4}{100}$ m < $35\frac{84}{100}$ m; or 32.04 m < 35.84 m. d. Shades each area model representing each item.

© 2015 Great Minds. eureka-math.org
G4-M6-TE-B5-1.3.1-01.2016

A Progression Toward Mastery

				e. $\frac{89}{100} + \frac{50}{100} + \frac{139}{100} =$ $1\frac{39}{100}$; $0.89 + $0.50 = $1.39 f. Reasons that Brian's container of juice is larger, and, therefore, each tenth unit fills more juice than Sonya's container. Comparing is only valid when the unit whole is the same. The containers' unit wholes were of different sizes.

© 2015 Great Minds. eureka-math.org
G4-M6-TE-B5-1.3.1-01.2016

Name Jack Date ____________

1. Decompose each fraction into hundredths using area models. Then, write the equivalent number sentence using decimals.

a. $\frac{8}{10} = \frac{80}{100}$

0.8 = 0.80

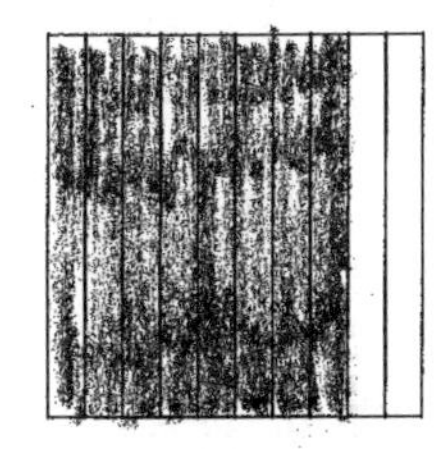

=

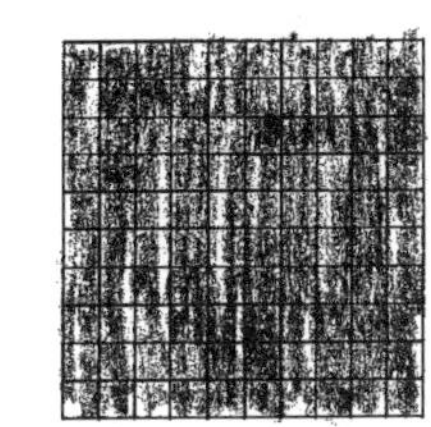

b. $\frac{18}{10} = \frac{180}{100}$

1.8 = 1.80

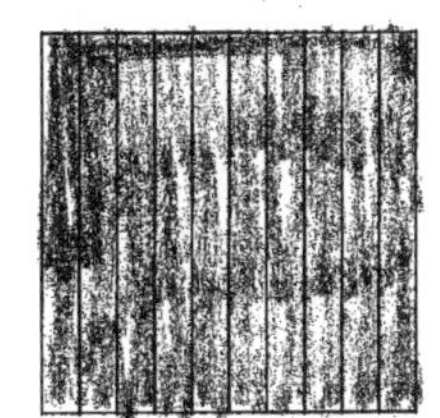

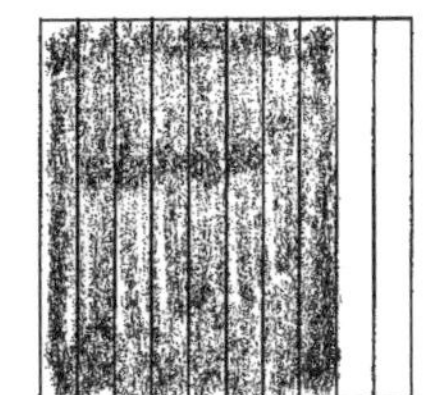

=

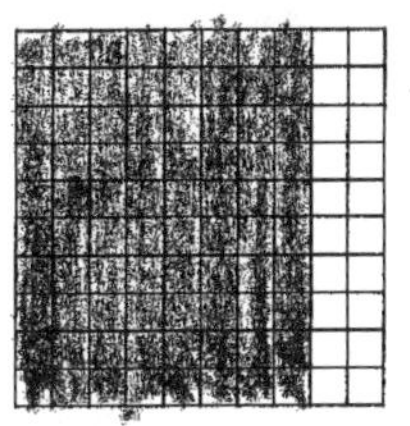

Decompose each fraction into hundredths. Then, write the equivalent statement for each part using decimals.

c. $\frac{2}{10} = \frac{20}{100}$ 0.2 = 0.20

d. $\frac{5}{10} = \frac{50}{100}$ 0.5 = 0.50

2. Several points are plotted on the number lines below. Identify the decimal number associated with each point.

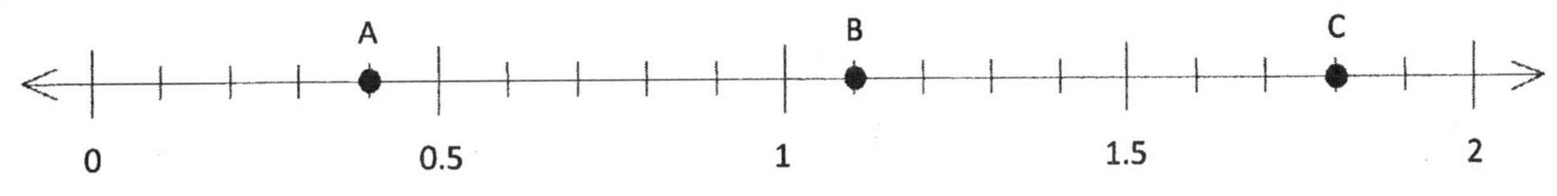

A. 0.4 B. 1.1 C. 1.8

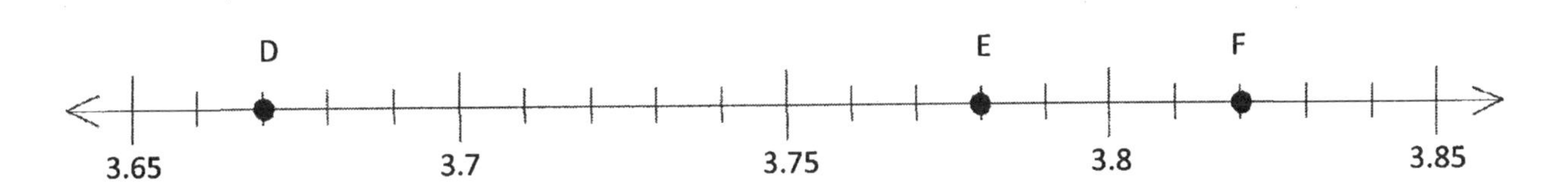

D. 3.67 E. 3.78 F. 3.82

© 2015 Great Minds. eureka-math.org
G4-M6-TE-B5-1.3.1-01.2016

3. Use the symbols >, =, or < to compare the following. Justify your conclusions using pictures, numbers, or words.

a. 0.02 (<) 0.22

2 hundredths is less than 22 hundredths

b. 0.6 (=) 0.60

$0.6 = \frac{6}{10}$ and $\frac{6}{10} = \frac{6 \times 10}{10 \times 10} = \frac{60}{100}$

$0.60 = \frac{60}{100}$ They are equal.

c. 17 tenths (=) 1.7

$\frac{17}{10} = \frac{10}{10} + \frac{7}{10} = 1\frac{7}{10} = 1.7$

d. 1.04 (<) $1\frac{4}{10}$

Hundredths are smaller than tenths, so 4 hundredths is less than 4 tenths. Since they both have one whole, $1.04 < 1\frac{4}{10}$.

e. 0.38 (<) $\frac{38}{10}$

$\frac{38}{10} = 3\frac{8}{10}$ ($\frac{38}{10}$ decomposed into $\frac{30}{10}$ and $\frac{8}{10}$)

38 hundredths is less than 1. 38 tenths is greater than 1.

f. 4.05 (=) $4\frac{5}{100}$

4.05 is 4 and 5 hundredths. That is the same as $4\frac{5}{100}$.

g. 3 tenths + 2 hundredths (>) 1 tenth + 13 hundredths

$\frac{3}{10} + \frac{2}{100} = \frac{30}{100} + \frac{2}{100} = \frac{32}{100}$ $\frac{1}{10} + \frac{13}{100} = \frac{10}{100} + \frac{13}{100} = \frac{23}{100}$

32 hundredths is greater than 23 hundredths.

h. 8 hundredths + 7 tenths (>) 6 tenths + 17 hundredths

$\frac{8}{100} + \frac{7}{10} = \frac{8}{100} + \frac{70}{100} = \frac{78}{100}$ $\frac{6}{10} + \frac{17}{100} = \frac{60}{100} + \frac{17}{100} = \frac{77}{100}$

78 hundredths is greater than 77 hundredths.

EUREKA MATH

© 2015 Great Minds. eureka-math.org
G4-M6-TE-B5-1.3.1-01.2016

4. Solve.

   a. Express your solution as a fraction of a meter. $0.3\text{ m} + 1.45\text{ m}$

   $\frac{3}{10}\text{m} + 1\frac{45}{100}\text{m} = \frac{30}{100}\text{m} + 1\frac{45}{100}\text{m} = 1\frac{75}{100}\text{m}$

   b. Express your solution as a fraction of a liter. $1.7\text{ L} + 0.82\text{ L}$

   $1\frac{7}{10}\text{L} + \frac{82}{100}\text{L} = 1\frac{70}{100}\text{L} + \frac{82}{100}\text{L} = 1\frac{152}{100}\text{L} = 2\frac{52}{100}\text{L}$

   $\frac{100}{100}$ $\frac{52}{100}$

   c. Express your solution as a fraction of a dollar. 4 dimes 1 penny + 77 pennies

   $\frac{4}{10}$ dollar $+ \frac{1}{100}$ dollar $+ \frac{77}{100}$ dollar $= \frac{40}{100}$ dollar $+ \frac{1}{100}$ dollar $+ \frac{77}{100}$ dollar

   $= \frac{118}{100}$ dollars $= 1\frac{18}{100}$ dollars

5. Solve.

   a. $\frac{7}{10} + \frac{8}{100}$

   $\frac{70}{100} + \frac{8}{100} = \frac{78}{100}$

   b. $\frac{4}{10} + \frac{51}{100}$

   $\frac{40}{100} + \frac{51}{100} = \frac{91}{100}$

   c. $\frac{5}{10} + \frac{68}{100}$

   $\frac{50}{100} + \frac{68}{100} = \frac{118}{100} = 1\frac{18}{100}$

   $\frac{100}{100}$ $\frac{18}{100}$

   d. $\frac{98}{100} + \frac{2}{10}$

   $\frac{98}{100} + \frac{20}{100} = \frac{118}{100} = 1\frac{18}{100}$

   $\frac{100}{100}$ $\frac{18}{100}$

   e. $\frac{12}{100} + \frac{12}{10}$

   $\frac{12}{100} + \frac{120}{100} = \frac{132}{100} = 1\frac{32}{100}$

   $\frac{100}{100}$ $\frac{32}{100}$

   f. $\frac{1}{10} + \frac{13}{100} + \frac{8}{10}$

   $\frac{10}{100} + \frac{13}{100} + \frac{80}{100} = \frac{103}{100} = 1\frac{3}{100}$

   $\frac{100}{100}$ $\frac{3}{100}$

© 2015 Great Minds. eureka-math.org
G4-M6-TE-B5-1.3.1-01.2016

6. Answer the following questions about a track meet.

   a. Jim and Joe ran in a relay race. Jim had a time of 9.8 seconds. Joe had a time of 10.32 seconds. Together, how long did it take them to complete the race? Record your answer as a decimal.

$9.8 = 9\frac{8}{10} = 9\frac{80}{100}$

$10.32 = 10\frac{32}{100}$

$9\frac{80}{100} + 10\frac{32}{100} = 19\frac{112}{100} = 20\frac{12}{100} = 20.12$

$\frac{112}{100} = \frac{100}{100} + \frac{12}{100}$

It took them 20.12 seconds to complete the race.

   b. The times of the 5 fastest runners were 7.11 seconds, 7.06 seconds, 7.6 seconds, 7.90 seconds, and 7.75 seconds. Locate these times on the number line. Record the times as decimals and fractions. One has been completed for you.

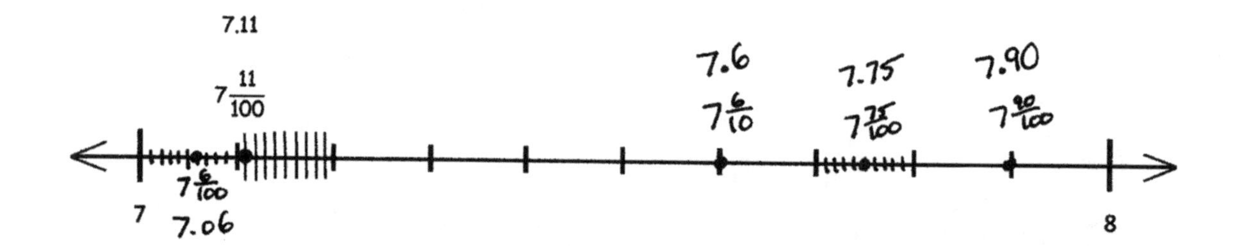

   c. Natalie threw a discus 32.04 meters. She threw 3.8 meters farther on her next throw. Write a statement to compare the two distances that Natalie threw the discus using >, <, or =.

$32.04 = 32\frac{4}{100}$

$3.8 = 3\frac{80}{100}$

$32\frac{4}{100} + 3\frac{80}{100} = 35\frac{84}{100} = 35.84$

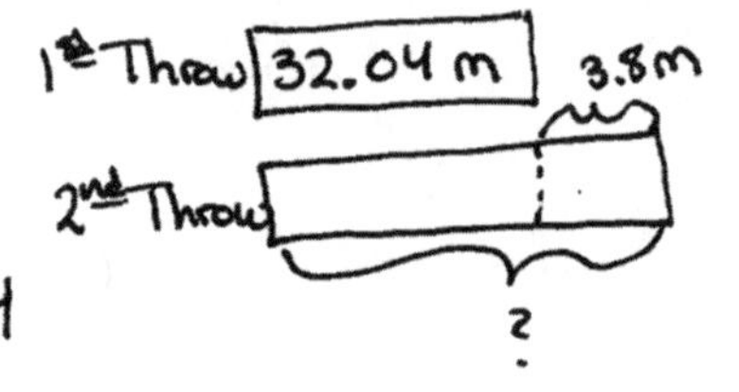

$32.04\text{m} < 35.84\text{m}$

© 2015 Great Minds. eureka-math.org
G4-M6-TE-B5-1.3.1-01.2016

d. At the concession stand, Marta spent 89 cents on a bottle of water and 5 dimes on a bag of chips. Shade the area models to represent the cost of each item.

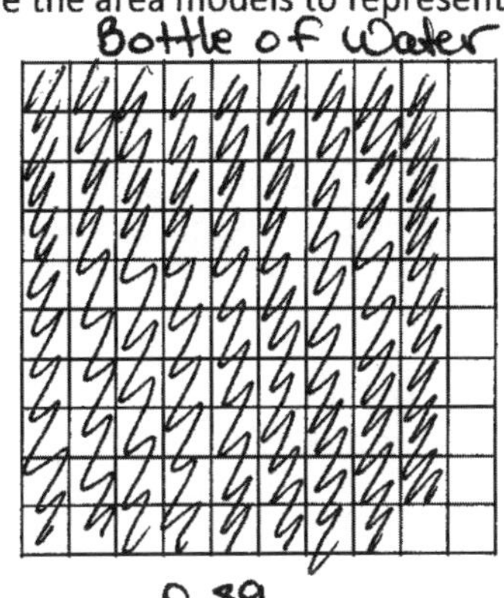

Bag of Chips

0.50

e. Write a number sentence in fraction form to find the total cost of a water bottle and a bag of chips. After solving, write the complete number sentence in decimal form.

$$\frac{89}{100} + \frac{50}{100} = \frac{139}{100} = 1\frac{39}{100}$$

$$\frac{139}{100} \rightarrow \frac{100}{100} \quad \frac{39}{100}$$

$0.89 + 0.50 = 1.39$

$\$0.89 + \$0.50 = \$1.39$

f. Brian and Sonya each have a container. They mark their containers to show tenths. Brian and Sonya each fill their containers with 0.7 units of juice. However, Brian has more juice in his container. Explain how this is possible.

It is possible that Brian has more juice in his container because we don't know that Brian and Sonya's containers are the same size. If Brian's container is larger than Sonya's, his tenths of a unit will be larger than Sonya's and, therefore, he will have more juice.

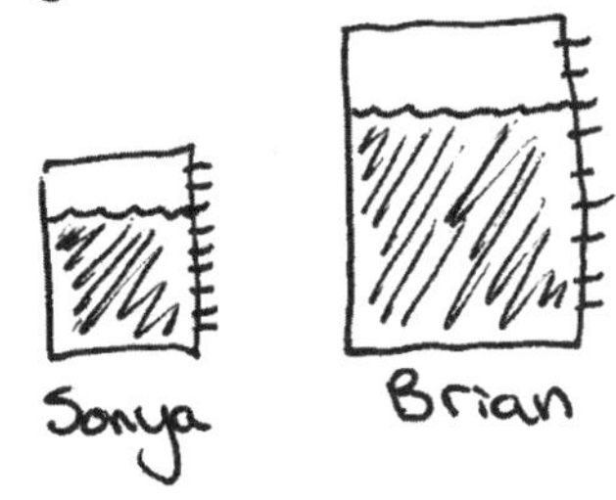

© 2015 Great Minds. eureka-math.org
G4-M6-TE-B5-1.3.1-01.2016

Answer Key

Eureka Math®
Grade 4
Module 6

Special thanks go to the Gordon A. Cain Center and to the Department of Mathematics at Louisiana State University for their support in the development of *Eureka Math*.

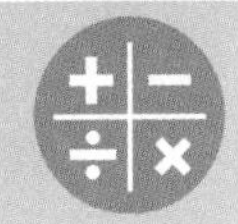

Answer Key

GRADE 4 • MODULE 6

Decimal Fractions

© 2015 Great Minds. eureka-math.org
G4-M6-TE-B5-1.3.1-01.2016

Lesson 1

Sprint

Side A

1. 2	12. 12	23. 5	34. 200
2. 3	13. 5	24. 85	35. 24
3. 4	14. 15	25. 185	36. 240
4. 8	15. 8	26. 7	37. 400
5. 5	16. 18	27. 27	38. 69
6. 9	17. 28	28. 427	39. 690
7. 7	18. 38	29. 9	40. 900
8. 6	19. 68	30. 59	41. 94
9. 1	20. 64	31. 759	42. 528
10. 10	21. 87	32. 12	43. 670
11. 2	22. 43	33. 120	44. 700

Side B

1. 1	12. 13	23. 4	34. 300
2. 2	13. 6	24. 84	35. 25
3. 3	14. 16	25. 184	36. 250
4. 7	15. 9	26. 8	37. 500
5. 4	16. 19	27. 28	38. 74
6. 8	17. 29	28. 428	39. 740
7. 6	18. 39	29. 6	40. 400
8. 5	19. 69	30. 56	41. 91
9. 9	20. 65	31. 756	42. 582
10. 10	21. 86	32. 13	43. 760
11. 3	22. 42	33. 130	44. 600

© 2015 Great Minds. eureka-math.org
G4-M6-TE-B5-1.3.1-01.2016

Problem Set

1. First 7 units shaded; 0.2, 0.3, ..., 0.9;
   $\frac{0}{10}, \frac{2}{10}, \frac{3}{10}, \dots, \frac{10}{10}$; 0.7 circled
2. third container $\frac{9}{10}$ shaded
   $\frac{6}{10}$ = 0.6; $\frac{8}{10}$ = 0.8; $\frac{9}{10}$
3. $\frac{4}{10}$; 0.8; $\frac{2}{10}$ or 0.2
4. $\frac{5}{10}$; 0.5; 0.5 or $\frac{5}{10}$
5. a. $\frac{2}{10}$; 0.2
   b. $\frac{8}{10}$; 0.8
   c. $\frac{4}{10}$; 0.4
6. Lines drawn to matching values

Exit Ticket

1. a. $\frac{1}{10}$; 0.1
   b. $\frac{6}{10}$; 0.6
2. Lines drawn to matching values

Homework

1. First 4 units shaded; 0.2, 0.3, ..., 0.9;
   $\frac{0}{10}, \frac{2}{10}, \frac{3}{10}, \dots, \frac{10}{10}$; 0.4 circled
2. $\frac{7}{10}$ = 0.7; $\frac{8}{10}$ = 0.8; $\frac{3}{10}$;
   third container $\frac{3}{10}$ shaded
3. $\frac{7}{10}$; 0.6
4. $\frac{5}{10}$; 0.5; 1
5. a. $\frac{6}{10}$; 0.6
   b. $\frac{7}{10}$; 0.7
   c. $\frac{2}{10}$; 0.2
6. Lines drawn to matching values

© 2015 Great Minds. eureka-math.org
G4-M6-TE-B5-1.3.1-01.2016

Lesson 2

Problem Set

1. Line segments drawn to given lengths
   a. 2.6 cm = $2\frac{6}{10}$ cm
   b. 3.4 cm = $3\frac{4}{10}$ cm
   c. 3.7 cm = $3\frac{7}{10}$ cm
   d. 4.2 cm = $4\frac{2}{10}$ cm
   e. 2.5 cm = $2\frac{5}{10}$ cm

2. Models shaded appropriately
   a. 2.6
   b. 4.2; $4 + \frac{2}{10} = 4 + 0.2 = 4.2$
   c. 3.4; $3 + \frac{4}{10} = 3 + 0.4 = 3.4$
   d. 2.5; $2 + \frac{5}{10} = 2 + 0.5 = 2.5$; 2.5
   e. 3.7; $3 + \frac{7}{10} = 3 + 0.7 = 3.7$; 1.3

Exit Ticket

1. Line segment drawn to given length; $4\frac{8}{10}$ cm
2. a. 3.7, $3\frac{7}{10}$; models shaded appropriately
   b. 2.4, $2\frac{4}{10}$; models shaded appropriately; 2.6

Homework

1. Line segments drawn to given lengths
   a. $2\frac{6}{10}$ cm
   b. $3\frac{5}{10}$ cm
   c. $1\frac{7}{10}$ cm
   d. $4\frac{3}{10}$ cm
   e. $2\frac{2}{10}$ cm

2. Models shaded appropriately
   a. 2.4
   b. 3.8; $3 + \frac{8}{10} = 3 + 0.8 = 3.8$
   c. 4.1; $4 + \frac{1}{10} = 4 + 0.1 = 4.1$
   d. 1.4; $1 + \frac{4}{10} = 1 + 0.4 = 1.4$; 3.6
   e. 3.3; $3 + \frac{3}{10} = 3 + 0.3 = 3.3$; 1.7

© 2015 Great Minds. eureka-math.org
G4-M6-TE-B5-1.3.1-01.2016
EUREKA MATH

Lesson 3

Problem Set

1. a. 28; 2 ones and 8 tenths disks drawn; 2.8; 0.2

   b. 33; 3 ones and 3 tenths disks drawn; 3.3; 0.7

2. a. Answer provided

   b. Disks drawn appropriately

   $(1 \times 10) + (7 \times 1) + (5 \times \frac{1}{10}) = 17\frac{5}{10}$

   $(1 \times 10) + (7 \times 1) + (5 \times 0.1) = 17.5$

   c. Disks drawn appropriately

   $(2 \times 10) + (3 \times 1) + (2 \times \frac{1}{10}) = 23\frac{2}{10}$

   $(2 \times 10) + (3 \times 1) + (2 \times 0.1) = 23.2$

   d. Disks drawn appropriately

   $(7 \times 10) + (4 \times 1) + (7 \times \frac{1}{10}) = 74\frac{7}{10}$

   $(7 \times 10) + (4 \times 1) + (7 \times 0.1) = 74.7$

3. a. 3.9 plotted with endpoints 3 and 4; 3.9; $(3 \times 1) + (9 \times 0.1)$ or $(3 \times 1) + (9 \times \frac{1}{10})$

   b. 17.5; $17\frac{5}{10}$; $(1 \times 10) + (7 \times 1) + (5 \times \frac{1}{10})$ or $(1 \times 10) + (7 \times 1) + (5 \times 0.1)$; 0.5

   c. 74.7 plotted with endpoints 74 and 75; 74.7; $74\frac{7}{10}$; 0.3

   d. 22.2 plotted with endpoints 22 and 23; 22.2; $(2 \times 10) + (2 \times 1) + (2 \times 0.1)$ or $(2 \times 10) + (2 \times 1) + (2 \times \frac{1}{10})$; 0.8

   e. 80.8 plotted with endpoints 80 and 81; 80.8; $80\frac{8}{10}$; 0.2

Exit Ticket

1. 18; 1 one and 8 tenths disks drawn; 1.8; 0.2

2. a. 12.9 plotted with endpoints 12 and 13; 12.9; $(1 \times 10) + (2 \times 1) + (9 \times \frac{1}{10})$ or $(1 \times 10) + (2 \times 1) + (9 \times 0.1)$; 0.1

   b. 70.7 plotted with endpoints 70 and 71; $70\frac{7}{10}$; $(7 \times 10) + (7 \times \frac{1}{10})$ or $(7 \times 10) + (7 \times 0.1)$; 0.3

© 2015 Great Minds. eureka-math.org
G4-M6-TE-B5-1.3.1-01.2016

Homework

1. a. 14; 1 one and 4 tenths disks drawn; 1.4; 0.6

   b. 25; 2 ones and 5 tenths disks drawn; 2.5; 0.5

2. a. Answer provided

   b. Disks drawn appropriately

   $(5 \times 10) + (3 \times 1) + (7 \times \frac{1}{10}) = 53\frac{7}{10}$

   $(5 \times 10) + (3 \times 1) + (7 \times 0.1) = 53.7$

   c. Disks drawn appropriately

   $(3 \times 10) + (2 \times 1) + (3 \times \frac{1}{10}) = 32\frac{3}{10}$

   $(3 \times 10) + (2 \times 1) + (3 \times 0.1) = 32.3$

   d. Disks drawn appropriately

   $(8 \times 10) + (4 \times 1) + (8 \times \frac{1}{10}) = 84\frac{8}{10}$

   $(8 \times 10) + (4 \times 1) + (8 \times 0.1) = 84.8$

3. a. 4.6 plotted with endpoints 4 and 5; 4.6; $(4 \times 1) + (6 \times \frac{1}{10})$ or $(4 \times 1) + (6 \times 0.1)$; 0.4

   b. 24.5, $24\frac{5}{10}$; $(2 \times 10) + (4 \times 1) + (5 \times \frac{1}{10})$ or $(2 \times 10) + (4 \times 1) + (5 \times 0.1)$; 0.5

   c. 63.6 plotted with endpoints 63 and 64; 63.6; $63\frac{6}{10}$; 0.4

   d. 71.3 plotted with endpoints 71 and 72; 71.3; $(7 \times 10) + (1 \times 1) + (3 \times \frac{1}{10})$ or $(7 \times 10) + (1 \times 1) + (3 \times 0.1)$; 0.7

   e. 90.9 plotted with endpoints 90 and 91; 90.9; $90\frac{9}{10}$; 0.1

© 2015 Great Minds. eureka-math.org
G4-M6-TE-B5-1.3.1-01.2016

Lesson 4

Sprint

Side A

1. 0.2
2. 0.3
3. 0.4
4. 0.8
5. 0.6
6. 1
7. 2
8. 3
9. 7
10. 5
11. 0.5
12. 8
13. 0.7
14. 4
15. 0.9
16. 1.0
17. 1.1
18. 1.2
19. 1.5
20. 2.5
21. 4.5
22. 3.8
23. 10
24. 20
25. 50
26. 40
27. 41
28. 42
29. 46
30. 26
31. 36
32. 34
33. 23
34. 4.3
35. 2.0
36. 18
37. 3.4
38. 5.0
39. 47
40. 2.8
41. 3.0
42. 32
43. 2.0
44. 21

Side B

1. 0.1
2. 0.2
3. 0.3
4. 0.7
5. 0.5
6. 2
7. 3
8. 4
9. 8
10. 6
11. 0.4
12. 9
13. 0.6
14. 5
15. 0.9
16. 1.0
17. 1.1
18. 1.2
19. 1.7
20. 2.7
21. 4.7
22. 3.4
23. 10
24. 20
25. 40
26. 30
27. 31
28. 32
29. 36
30. 16
31. 26
32. 42
33. 25
34. 3.4
35. 5.0
36. 17
37. 4.3
38. 2.0
39. 46
40. 2.4
41. 4.0
42. 23
43. 3.0
44. 41

© 2015 Great Minds. eureka-math.org
G4-M6-TE-B5-1.3.1-01.2016

Problem Set

1. a. 10 cm

   b. $\frac{1}{100}$ m

   c. $\frac{1}{10}$ m or $\frac{10}{100}$ m

   d. 0.1 m or 0.10 m

   e. $\frac{1}{10}$ m or $\frac{10}{100}$ m

2. a. 10

   b. 10

   c. 100

3. a. Answer provided

   b. $\frac{2}{10}$ m + $\frac{4}{100}$ m = $\frac{24}{100}$ m = 0.24 m; number bond showing $\frac{2}{10}$ m and $\frac{4}{100}$ m is 0.24 m

   c. $\frac{3}{10}$ m + $\frac{8}{100}$ m = $\frac{38}{100}$ m = 0.38 m; number bond showing $\frac{3}{10}$ m and $\frac{8}{100}$ m is 0.38 m

4. a. Shaded appropriately; 0.8 m

   b. Shaded appropriately; 0.07 m

   c. Shaded appropriately; 0.19 m

5. a. Number bond showing $\frac{1}{10}$ m and $\frac{9}{100}$ m is 0.19 m

   b. Number bond showing $\frac{2}{10}$ m and $\frac{8}{100}$ m is 0.28 m

   c. Number bond showing $\frac{7}{10}$ and $\frac{7}{100}$ is 0.77

   d. Number bond showing $\frac{9}{10}$ and $\frac{4}{100}$ is 0.94

Exit Ticket

1. Shaded appropriately; 0.6 m

2. a. Number bond showing $\frac{6}{10}$ m and $\frac{2}{100}$ m is 0.62 m

   b. Number bond showing $\frac{2}{10}$ and $\frac{7}{100}$ is 0.27

© 2015 Great Minds. eureka-math.org
G4-M6-TE-B5-1.3.1-01.2016

Homework

1. a. 30 cm
   b. $\frac{3}{100}$ m
   c. $\frac{3}{10}$ m or $\frac{30}{100}$ m
   d. 0.3 m or 0.30 m
   e. $\frac{3}{10}$ m or $\frac{30}{100}$ m
2. a. 50
   b. 50
   c. 100
3. a. Answer provided
   b. $\frac{3}{10}$ m + $\frac{8}{100}$ m = $\frac{38}{100}$ m = 0.38 m; number bond showing $\frac{3}{10}$ m and $\frac{8}{100}$ m is 0.38 m
   c. $\frac{4}{10}$ m + $\frac{6}{100}$ m = $\frac{46}{100}$ m = 0.46 m; number bond showing $\frac{4}{10}$ m and $\frac{6}{100}$ m is 0.46 m
4. a. Shaded appropriately; 0.9 m
   b. Shaded appropriately; 0.15 m
   c. Shaded appropriately; 0.41 m
5. a. Number bond showing $\frac{2}{10}$ m and $\frac{3}{100}$ m is 0.23 m
   b. Number bond showing $\frac{3}{10}$ m and $\frac{8}{100}$ m is 0.38 m
   c. Number bond showing $\frac{8}{10}$ and $\frac{2}{100}$ is 0.82
   d. Number bond showing $\frac{7}{10}$ and $\frac{6}{100}$ is 0.76

© 2015 Great Minds. eureka-math.org
G4-M6-TE-B5-1.3.1-01.2016

Lesson 5

Problem Set

1. a. 10, 10, 30; models shaded appropriately; 0.30
   b. 10, 10, 5; models shaded appropriately; 0.5
2. a. 3, 7; $\frac{37}{100}$; 0.37; model shaded appropriately
   b. 7, 5; $\frac{75}{100}$; 0.75; model shaded appropriately
3. a. 10 disks circled; 12, 1, 2; number bond showing $\frac{1}{10}$ and $\frac{2}{100}$ is 0.12
   b. 2 groups of 10 disks circled; 27, 2, 7; number bond showing $\frac{2}{10}$ and $\frac{7}{100}$ is 0.27
4. a. 03; 3; 3 (0.01) disks drawn
   b. 15; 1, 5; 1 (0.1) disk and 5 (0.01) disks drawn
   c. $\frac{72}{100}$; 72; 7 (0.1) disks and 2 (0.01) disks drawn
   d. $\frac{8}{10}$; 8; 8 (0.1) disks drawn
   e. $\frac{72}{100}$; 72; 7 (0.1) disks and 2 (0.01) disks drawn
   f. $\frac{80}{100}$; 80; 8 (0.1) disks drawn

Exit Ticket

1. 07; 7; 7 (0.01) disks drawn
2. 34; 3, 4; 3 (0.1) disks and 4 (0.01) disks drawn

© 2015 Great Minds. eureka-math.org
G4-M6-TE-B5-1.3.1-01.2016

Homework

1. a. 10, 10, 40; model shaded appropriately; 0.4 or 0.40
   b. 10, 10, 6; model shaded appropriately; 0.6
2. a. 3, 6; 0.36; $\frac{36}{100}$; model shaded appropriately
   b. 8, 2; 0.82; $\frac{82}{100}$; model shaded appropriately
3. a. 1 group of 10 disks circled; 14, 1, 4; number bond showing $\frac{1}{10}$ and $\frac{4}{100}$ is 0.14
   b. 2 groups of 10 disks circled; 24, 2, 4; number bond showing $\frac{2}{10}$ and $\frac{4}{100}$ is 0.24
4. a. 04; 4; 4 (0.01) disks drawn
   b. 13; 1, 3; 1 (0.1) disk and 3 (0.01) disks drawn
   c. $\frac{41}{100}$; 41; 4 (0.1) disks and 1 (0.01) disk drawn
   d. $\frac{9}{10}$; 9; 9 (0.1) disks drawn
   e. $\frac{63}{100}$; 63; 6 (0.1) disks and 3 (0.01) disks drawn
   f. $\frac{90}{100}$; 90; 9 (0.1) disks drawn

© 2015 Great Minds. eureka-math.org
G4-M6-TE-B5-1.3.1-01.2016

Lesson 6

Problem Set

1. a. 1.15, model shaded appropriately; point plotted accurately on number line
   b. 2.47, model shaded appropriately; point plotted accurately on number line
2. a. Point plotted accurately on number line
   b. Point plotted accurately on number line
3. a. $1\frac{2}{100}$; 1.02
   b. $1\frac{17}{100}$; 1.17
   c. $2\frac{8}{100}$; 2.08
   d. $2\frac{27}{100}$; 2.27
   e. $4\frac{58}{100}$; 4.58
   f. $7\frac{70}{100}$; 7.70
4. Lines drawn to matching values

Exit Ticket

1. a. 7.20 plotted accurately on number line
   b. 1.75 plotted accurately on number line
2. a. $8\frac{24}{100}$; 8.24
   b. $2\frac{6}{100}$; 2.06

Homework

1. a. 2.35; model shaded appropriately; point plotted accurately on number line
   b. 3.17; model shaded appropriately; point plotted accurately on number line
2. a. 5.9 plotted accurately on number line
   b. 3.25 plotted accurately on number line
3. a. $2\frac{2}{100}$; 2.02
   b. $2\frac{16}{100}$; 2.16
   c. $3\frac{7}{100}$; 3.07
   d. $1\frac{18}{100}$; 1.18
   e. $9\frac{62}{100}$; 9.62
   f. $6\frac{20}{100}$; 6.20
4. Lines drawn to matching values

EUREKA MATH
© 2015 Great Minds. eureka-math.org
G4-M6-TE-B5-1.3.1-01.2016

Lesson 7

Problem Set

1. a. 20 + 0.5 + 0.03 = 20.53

   b. 500 + 0.04 = 500.04

2. a. 4; 4 hundreds
   b. 1; 1 ten
   c. 8; 8 tenths
   d. 3; 3 hundredths
   e. 5; 5 hundreds
   f. 3; 3 tens
   g. 1; 1 tenth
   h. 6; 6 hundredths

3.

$21\frac{4}{10}$	$(2 \times 10) + (1 \times 1) + (4 \times \frac{1}{10})$ $20 + 1 + \frac{4}{10}$	$(2 \times 10) + (1 \times 1) + (4 \times 0.1)$ $20 + 1 + 0.4$
$38\frac{9}{100}$	$(3 \times 10) + (8 \times 1) + (9 \times \frac{1}{100})$ $30 + 8 + \frac{9}{100}$	$(3 \times 10) + (8 \times 1) + (9 \times 0.01)$ $30 + 8 + 0.09$
$50\frac{2}{10}$	$(5 \times 10) + (2 \times \frac{1}{10})$ $50 + \frac{2}{10}$	$(5 \times 10) + (2 \times 0.1)$ $50 + 0.2$
$301\frac{7}{100}$	$(3 \times 100) + (1 \times 1) + (7 \times \frac{1}{100})$ $300 + 1 + \frac{7}{100}$	$(3 \times 100) + (1 \times 1) + (7 \times 0.01)$ $300 + 1 + 0.07$
$620\frac{80}{100}$	$(6 \times 100) + (2 \times 10) + (80 \times \frac{1}{100})$ $600 + 20 + \frac{80}{100}$	$(6 \times 100) + (2 \times 10) + (80 \times 0.01)$ $600 + 20 + 0.80$
$800\frac{8}{100}$	$(8 \times 100) + (8 \times \frac{1}{100})$ $800 + \frac{8}{100}$	$(8 \times 100) + (8 \times 0.01)$ $800 + 0.08$

© 2015 Great Minds. eureka-math.org
G4-M6-TE-B5-1.3.1-01.2016

Exit Ticket

1. a. 8; 8 hundreds
   b. 2; 2 tens
   c. 6; 6 tenths
   b. 4; 4 hundredths

2.

	$(4 \times 100) + (2 \times 10) + (2 \times 1) + (8 \times \frac{1}{100})$	$(4 \times 100) + (2 \times 10) + (2 \times 1) + (8 \times 0.01)$	422.08
$300\frac{92}{100}$		$(3 \times 100) + (9 \times 0.1) + (2 \times 0.01)$	300.92

Homework

1. a. $30 + 0.4 + 0.02 = 30.42$
   b. $400 + 0.03 = 400.03$

2. a. 8, 8 hundreds
   b. 2, 2 tens
   c. 6, 6 tenths
   d. 4, 4 hundredths
   e. 3, 3 hundreds
   f. 4, 4 tens
   g. 1, 1 tenth
   h. 9, 9 hundredths

3.

$25\frac{3}{10}$	$(2 \times 10) + (5 \times 1) + (3 \times \frac{1}{10})$ $20 + 5 + \frac{3}{10}$	$(2 \times 10) + (5 \times 1) + (3 \times 0.1)$ $20 + 5 + 0.3$
$39\frac{7}{100}$	$(3 \times 10) + (9 \times 1) + (7 \times \frac{1}{100})$ $30 + 9 + \frac{7}{100}$	$(3 \times 10) + (9 \times 1) + (7 \times 0.01)$ $30 + 9 + 0.07$
$40\frac{6}{10}$	$(4 \times 10) + (6 \times \frac{1}{10})$ $40 + \frac{6}{10}$	$(4 \times 10) + (6 \times 0.1)$ $40 + 0.6$
$208\frac{90}{100}$	$(2 \times 100) + (8 \times 1) + (90 \times \frac{1}{100})$ $200 + 8 + \frac{90}{100}$	$(2 \times 100) + (8 \times 1) + (9 \times 0.1)$ $200 + 8 + 0.9$
$510\frac{7}{100}$	$(5 \times 100) + (1 \times 10) + (7 \times \frac{1}{100})$ $500 + 10 + \frac{7}{100}$	$(5 \times 100) + (1 \times 10) + (7 \times 0.01)$ $500 + 10 + 0.07$
$900\frac{9}{100}$	$(9 \times 100) + (9 \times \frac{1}{100})$ $900 + \frac{9}{100}$	$(9 \times 100) + (9 \times 0.01)$ $900 + 0.09$

EUREKA MATH
© 2015 Great Minds. eureka-math.org
G4-M6-TE-B5-1.3.1-01.2016

Lesson 8

Sprint

Side A

1. 0.3
2. 0.03
3. 0.23
4. 1.23
5. 4.23
6. $\frac{7}{100}$
7. $1\frac{7}{100}$
8. $\frac{7}{10}$
9. $1\frac{7}{10}$
10. $1\frac{74}{100}$
11. 0.04
12. $\frac{6}{10}$
13. 0.07
14. $\frac{2}{100}$
15. 0.09
16. 0.10
17. 0.12
18. 0.12
19. 0.13
20. 0.14
21. 0.19
22. 3.19
23. 2.16
24. 2.16
25. 3.16
26. 3.14
27. 3.54
28. 2.38
29. 2.08
30. 1.3
31. 10.3
32. 1.46
33. 10.46
34. 30.72
35. 2.35
36. 4.53
37. 4.53
38. 4.53
39. 20.81
40. 4.29
41. 2.74
42. 8.62
43. 8.95
44. 10.94

Side B

1. 0.1
2. 0.2
3. 0.3
4. 0.7
5. 0.5
6. $\frac{2}{10}$
7. $\frac{3}{10}$
8. $\frac{4}{10}$
9. $\frac{8}{10}$
10. $\frac{6}{10}$
11. 0.4
12. $\frac{9}{10}$
13. 0.6
14. $\frac{5}{10}$
15. 0.9
16. 1.0
17. 1.1
18. 1.2
19. 1.7
20. 2.7
21. 4.7
22. 3.4
23. 2.14
24. 2.14
25. 3.14
26. 3.16
27. 3.56
28. 2.49
29. 2.06
30. 1.5
31. 10.5
32. 1.24
33. 10.24
34. 30.96
35. 2.57
36. 4.75
37. 4.75
38. 4.75
39. 20.61
40. 6.47
41. 2.96
42. 6.84
43. 8.73
44. 10.76

© 2015 Great Minds. eureka-math.org
G4-M6-TE-B5-1.3.1-01.2016

Problem Set

1. a. Area model accurately shaded;
   25, 2, 5, 2.5
   b. Explanations will vary.
2. 20; disks drawn to model number
   20; disks drawn to model number
   13; disks drawn to model number
   23; disks drawn to model number
3. a. 10
   b. 20
   c. 17
   d. 29
   e. 107
   f. 209
4. a. 100
   b. 200
   c. 170
   d. 290
   e. 1070
   f. 2090
5. $4\frac{2}{10}$; 42 tenths, $\frac{42}{10}$; 420 hundredths, $\frac{420}{100}$
   $8\frac{4}{10}$; 84 tenths, $\frac{84}{10}$; 840 hundredths, $\frac{840}{100}$
   $10\frac{2}{10}$; 102 tenths, $\frac{102}{10}$; 1020 hundredths, $\frac{1020}{100}$
   $75\frac{5}{10}$; 755 tenths, $\frac{755}{10}$; 7550 hundredths, $\frac{7550}{100}$

Exit Ticket

1. a. 32; disks drawn to model number
   b. 320
2. a. 26
   b. 610

© 2015 Great Minds. eureka-math.org
G4-M6-TE-B5-1.3.1-01.2016

Homework

1. a. Area model accurately shaded;
   22, 2, 2, 2.2
   b. Explanations will vary.
2. 30; disks drawn to model number
   30; disks drawn to model number
   23; disks drawn to model number
   33; disks drawn to model number
3. a. 10
   b. 20
   c. 13
   d. 26
   e. 103
   f. 206
4. a. 100
   b. 200
   c. 130
   d. 260
   e. 1030
   f. 2060
5. $5\frac{3}{10}$; 53 tenths, $\frac{53}{10}$; 530 hundredths, $\frac{530}{100}$
   $9\frac{7}{10}$; 97 tenths, $\frac{97}{10}$; 970 hundredths, $\frac{970}{100}$
   $10\frac{9}{10}$; 109 tenths, $\frac{109}{10}$; 1090 hundredths, $\frac{1090}{100}$
   $68\frac{5}{10}$; 685 tenths, $\frac{685}{10}$; 6850 hundredths, $\frac{6850}{100}$

© 2015 Great Minds. eureka-math.org
G4-M6-TE-B5-1.3.1-01.2016

Lesson 9

Problem Set

1. a. 0.3 m, 0.27 m; 0.3 meters is longer than 0.27 meters, or 0.27 meters is shorter than 0.3 meters.
   b. 0.35 m, 0.4 m; 0.4 meters is longer than 0.35 meters, or 0.35 meters is shorter than 0.4 meters.
   c. 0.27 m, 0.3 m, 0.35 m, 0.4 m
2. a. Bananas and grapes (0.6 kg and 0.61 kg) crossed off
   b. 0.2; 0.12; 0.6; 0.61
   c. Heavier than; lighter than
3. 0.6; 0.3; 0.9; 0.97; 0.19; 0.48
   a. >
   b. <
   c. >
   d. 0.19 L, 0.3 L, 0.48 L, 0.6 L, 0.9 L, 0.97 L

Exit Ticket

1. a. 0.54 m; 0.5 m; 0.47 m
   b. 0.54 m, 0.5 m, 0.47 m
2. a. >
   b. <
   c. <

Homework

1. a. 0.68 m, 0.7 m; 0.7 meters is longer than 0.68 meters, or 0.68 meters is shorter than 0.7 meters.
   b. 0.5 m, 0.44 m; 0.5 meters is longer than 0.44 meters, or 0.44 meters is shorter than 0.5 meters.
   c. 0.44 m, 0.5 m, 0.68 m, 0.7 m
2. a. Basketball and soccer ball (0.62 kg and 0.43 kg) crossed off
   b. 0.15; 0.25; 0.62; 0.43
   c. Heavier than; lighter than
3. 0.7; 0.62; 0.28; 0.4; 0.85; 0.2
   a. >
   b. <
   c. <
   d. 0.2 L, 0.28 L, 0.4 L, 0.62 L, 0.7 L, 0.85 L

© 2015 Great Minds. eureka-math.org
G4-M6-TE-B5-1.3.1-01.2016

Lesson 10

Problem Set

1. a. <; models shaded appropriately
   b. >; models shaded appropriately
   c. <; models shaded appropriately
   d. =; models shaded appropriately
2. a. <; points plotted and labeled accurately
   b. <; points plotted and labeled accurately
3. a. <
   b. >
   c. <
   d. <
   e. =
   f. >
4. a. =
   b. <
   c. <
   d. <
   e. <
   f. <

Exit Ticket

1. =; Ryan and Jessie are wrong, answers may vary; models shaded appropriately
2. a. >
   b. >
   c. =

Homework

1. a. <; models shaded appropriately
   b. >; models shaded appropriately
   c. >; models shaded appropriately
   d. <; models shaded appropriately
2. a. >; points plotted and labeled accurately
   b. <; points plotted and labeled accurately
3. a. >
   b. <
   c. >
   d. <
   e. =
   f. <
4. a. =
   b. >
   c. >
   d. <
   e. =
   f. >

© 2015 Great Minds. eureka-math.org
G4-M6-TE-B5-1.3.1-01.2016

Lesson 11

Problem Set

1. a. Points plotted accurately in following order: $\frac{1}{10}$, $\frac{12}{100}$, 0.2, 0.21, $\frac{32}{100}$, 0.33
   b. Points plotted accurately in following order: 3.62, $\frac{364}{100}$, 3.7, $\frac{38}{10}$, $3\frac{85}{100}$
   c. Points plotted accurately in following order: $\frac{62}{10}$, $\frac{628}{100}$, $6\frac{3}{10}$, 6.31, 6.40, 6.43
2. a. 2.72 > 2.71 > 2.7 > 2.27 > 2.07 > 0.27
   b. 13.2 > 13.02 > 12.3 > 12.2 > 1.34
   c. 75 > 7.5 > 7.4 > 7.34 > 7.3 > 7.2
3. Rhonda
4. December; March

Exit Ticket

1. Points plotted accurately in following order: 1.02, 1.1, 1.11, 1.20, 1.29, 1.3
2. 6.56 > 6.5 > 6.15 > 6.05 > 5.6 > 5.16

Homework

1. a. Points plotted accurately in following order: 0.5, 0.53, 0.6, 0.67, 0.76, 0.79
   b. Points plotted accurately in following order: 8.1, 8.15, 8.2, 8.27, 8.32
   c. Points plotted accurately in following order: 13, 13.03, 13.12, 13.21, 13.3
2. a. 4.43 > 4.33 > 4.31 > 4.30 > 4.03 > 0.34
   b. 17.55 > 17.5 > 17.05 > 15.75 > 15.71 > 15.7
   c. 81 > 9.8 > 8.9 > 8.19 > 8.1 > 8.09
3. Jenna
4. Monday; Wednesday

© 2015 Great Minds. eureka-math.org
G4-M6-TE-B5-1.3.1-01.2016

Lesson 12

Problem Set

1. a. 15
   b. 21; disks modeled appropriately in chart
   c. 22; disks modeled appropriately in chart
2. a. 10, 13
   b. 50, 12, 62
   c. 70, 27, 97
   d. 37, 70, 107
3. a. 0.28
   b. 0.53
   c. 0.99
   d. 1.0 or 1
4. a. 1.32
   b. 1.2
   c. 1.48
   d. 1.57
5. 1.03 L

Exit Ticket

1. 19; disks modeled appropriately in chart
2. 1.13

Homework

1. a. 18
   b. 23; disks modeled appropriately in chart
   c. 24; disks modeled appropriately in chart
2. a. 10, 12
   b. 40, 11, 51
   c. 80, 25, 105
   d. 43, 60, 103
3. a. 0.37
   b. 0.66
   c. 0.90 or 0.9
   d. 1.0 or 1
4. a. 1.03
   b. 1.07
   c. 1.18
   d. 1.68
5. 1.48 inches

© 2015 Great Minds. eureka-math.org
G4-M6-TE-B5-1.3.1-01.2016

Lesson 13

Problem Set

1. a. $2\frac{13}{100}$; 2.13
   b. $7\frac{13}{100}$; 2.1 + 5.03 = 7.13
   c. $3\frac{24}{100} + \frac{70}{100} = 3\frac{94}{100}$; 3.24 + 0.7 = 3.94
   d. $3\frac{24}{100} + 8\frac{70}{100} = 11\frac{94}{100}$; 3.24 + 8.7 = 11.94
2. a. 8; 6.9 + 1.1 = 8.0 or 8
   b. $12\frac{35}{100}$; 9.9 + 2.45 = 12.35
   c. $11\frac{30}{100}$; 2.4 + 8.90 = 11.3
   d. $14\frac{7}{100}$; 6.37 + 7.7 = 14.07
3. a. $6\frac{4}{10} + 5\frac{3}{10} = 11\frac{7}{10}$; 6.4 + 5.3 = 11.7
   b. $6\frac{62}{100} + 2\frac{98}{100} = 9\frac{60}{100}$; 6.62 + 2.98 = 9.6
   c. $2\frac{10}{100} + \frac{94}{100} = 3\frac{4}{100}$; 2.10 + 0.94 = 3.04
   d. $2\frac{10}{100} + 5\frac{94}{100} = 8\frac{4}{100}$; 2.10 + 5.94 = 8.04
   e. $5\frac{70}{100} + 4\frac{92}{100} = 10\frac{62}{100}$; 5.70 + 4.92 = 10.62
   f. $5\frac{68}{100} + 4\frac{90}{100} = 10\frac{58}{100}$; 5.68 + 4.90 = 10.58
   g. $4\frac{80}{100} + 3\frac{27}{100} = 8\frac{7}{100}$; 4.8 + 3.27 = 8.07
   h. $17\frac{60}{100} + 3\frac{59}{100} = 21\frac{19}{100}$; 17.6 + 3.59 = 21.19

Exit Ticket

1. $7\frac{30}{100} + \frac{95}{100} = 8\frac{25}{100}$; 7.3 + 0.95 = 8.25
2. $8\frac{29}{100} + 5\frac{90}{100} = 14\frac{19}{100}$; 8.29 + 5.9 = 14.19

Homework

1. a. $5\frac{27}{100}$; 5.27
   b. $8\frac{27}{100}$; 5.2 + 3.07 = 8.27
   c. $6\frac{50}{100} + \frac{1}{100} = 6\frac{51}{100}$; 6.5 + 0.01 = 6.51
   d. $6\frac{50}{100} + 7\frac{1}{100} = 13\frac{51}{100}$; 6.5 + 7.01 = 13.51
2. a. 10; 4.9 + 5.1 = 10.0 or 10
   b. $11\frac{35}{100}$; 8.7 + 2.65 = 11.35
   c. $14\frac{17}{100}$; 7.3 + 6.87 = 14.17
   d. $13\frac{28}{100}$; 5.48 + 7.8 = 13.28
3. a. $2\frac{97}{100}$; 2.1 + 0.87 = 2.97
   b. $7\frac{20}{100} + 2\frac{67}{100} = 9\frac{87}{100}$; 7.2 + 2.67 = 9.87
   c. $7\frac{3}{10} + 1\frac{8}{10} = 9\frac{1}{10}$; 7.3 + 1.8 = 9.1
   d. $7\frac{30}{100} + 1\frac{86}{100} = 9\frac{16}{100}$; 7.3 + 1.86 = 9.16
   e. $6\frac{7}{100} + 3\frac{93}{100} = 10$; 6.07 + 3.93 = 10.0 or 10
   f. $6\frac{87}{100} + 3\frac{90}{100} = 10\frac{77}{100}$; 6.87 + 3.9 = 10.77
   g. $8\frac{60}{100} + 4\frac{67}{100} = 13\frac{27}{100}$; 8.6 + 4.67 = 13.27
   h. $18\frac{62}{100} + 14\frac{70}{100} = 33\frac{32}{100}$; 18.62 + 14.7 = 33.32

© 2015 Great Minds. eureka-math.org
G4-M6-TE-B5-1.3.1-01.2016

Lesson 14

Problem Set

1. 5.79 liters
2. 33.14 kilometers
3. 296.85 kilograms
4. 92.28 seconds

Exit Ticket

12.03 kilometers

Homework

1. 3.63 meters
2. 36.14 kilograms
3. 256.54 liters
4. 54.8 seconds

© 2015 Great Minds. eureka-math.org
G4-M6-TE-B5-1.3.1-01.2016

Lesson 15

Problem Set

1. $1.00; 100
2. $0.01; 1
3. $0.06; 6
4. $0.10; 10
5. $0.26; 26
6. $1.00; 10
7. $0.10; 1
8. $0.30; 3
9. $0.50; 5
10. $0.60; 6
11. $1.00; 100
12. $0.25; 25
13. $0.50; 50
14. $0.75; 75
15. $\frac{38}{100}$ dollar; $0.38
16. $\frac{103}{100}$ or $1\frac{3}{100}$ dollars; $1.03
17. $\frac{110}{100}$ or $1\frac{10}{100}$ dollar; $1.10
18. $\frac{236}{100}$ or $2\frac{36}{100}$ dollar; $2.36
19. $6.67
20. $5.35
21. $14.81

Exit Ticket

1. $\frac{80}{100}$ dollar; $0.80
2. $\frac{118}{100}$ or $1\frac{18}{100}$ dollars; $1.18
3. $6.19

EUREKA MATH
© 2015 Great Minds. eureka-math.org
G4-M6-TE-B5-1.3.1-01.2016

Homework

1. $1.00; 100
2. $0.01; 1
3. $0.03; 3
4. $0.20; 20
5. $0.37; 37
6. $1.00; 10
7. $0.20; 2
8. $0.40; 4
9. $0.60; 6
10. $0.90; 9
11. $0.75; 75
12. $0.50; 50
13. $1.00; 100
14. $0.25; 25
15. $\frac{58}{100}$ dollar; $0.58
16. $\frac{88}{100}$ dollar; $0.88
17. $\frac{161}{100}$ or $1\frac{61}{100}$ dollar; $1.61
18. $\frac{187}{100}$ or $1\frac{87}{100}$ dollar
19. $4.08
20. $5.26
21. $16.85

© 2015 Great Minds. eureka-math.org
G4-M6-TE-B5-1.3.1-01.2016

Lesson 16

Sprint

Side A

1.	0.1	12.	0.79	23.	0.2	34.	1.3
2.	0.01	13.	0.79	24.	0.20	35.	1.37
3.	0.11	14.	0.4	25.	0.40	36.	1.2
4.	0.3	15.	0.06	26.	0.3	37.	1.29
5.	0.03	16.	0.46	27.	0.30	38.	1.2
6.	0.33	17.	0.64	28.	0.60	39.	1.24
7.	0.5	18.	0.85	29.	0.70	40.	1.25
8.	0.05	19.	0.92	30.	0.90	41.	1.61
9.	0.55	20.	0.81	31.	1.0	42.	1.53
10.	0.7	21.	0.14	32.	1.1	43.	172
11.	0.09	22.	0.47	33.	1.3	44.	1.88

Side B

1.	0.2	12.	0.48	23.	0.1	34.	1.20
2.	0.02	13.	0.48	24.	0.10	35.	1.27
3.	0.22	14.	0.5	25.	0.2	36.	1.2
4.	0.4	15.	0.07	26.	0.4	37.	1.29
5.	0.04	16.	0.57	27.	0.40	38.	1.4
6.	0.44	17.	0.57	28.	0.8	39.	1.46
7.	0.6	18.	0.96	29.	0.8	40.	1.48
8.	0.06	19.	0.83	30.	0.9	41.	1.51
9.	0.66	20.	0.71	31.	1.0	42.	1.63
10.	0.4	21.	0.13	32.	1.1	43.	1.74
11.	0.08	22.	0.38	33.	1.3	44.	1.64

© 2015 Great Minds. eureka-math.org
G4-M6-TE-B5-1.3.1-01.2016

Problem Set

1. $4.11
2. $3.59
3. No; $0.96
4. $9.16
5. $2.64

Exit Ticket

$2.16

Homework

1. $4.59
2. $2.20
3. No; $0.61
4. $14.97
5. $2.17

© 2015 Great Minds. eureka-math.org
G4-M6-TE-B5-1.3.1-01.2016